W9-AFB-065

# PSYCHIATRY AND
# THE DILEMMAS OF CRIME

# PSYCHIATRY
## *and the Dilemmas of*
# CRIME

Seymour L. Halleck, M.D.

*University of Wisconsin*

# *A Study of Causes, Punishment and Treatment*

HARPER AND ROW, PUBLISHERS

NEW YORK, EVANSTON, AND LONDON

*with*

HOEBER MEDICAL BOOKS

NEW YORK

HV6080
H18

95072

PSYCHIATRY AND THE DILEMMAS OF CRIME. *Copyright © 1967 by Hoeber Medical Division, Harper & Row, Publishers, Incorporated. Printed in the United States of America. All rights reserved. No part of this book may be used or reproduced in any manner whatsoever without written permission except in the case of brief quotations embodied in critical articles and reviews.* *For information address Harper & Row, Publishers, Incorporated, 49 East 33rd Street, New York, N.Y. 10016.*

FIRST EDITION

LIBRARY OF CONGRESS CATALOG CARD NUMBER: 67-13714

C-R

To My Mother and Father

# CONTENTS

# ACKNOWLEDGMENTS

Those psychiatrists who are deeply concerned with the criminal are a dedicated but small group, and it has been my good fortune to have known many of these men as teachers and colleagues. My interest in criminology could not have been sustained without the opportunity to work with such outstanding teachers as Edward Rinck, Charles Smith, Stanley Kemler, Norman Graff, Edward Greenwood and Melvin Muroff. I am especially indebted to Dr. Karl Menninger, whose life-long dedication to improvement of the plight of the criminal has served as an inspiration to me as well as to so many other psychiatric criminologists.

Many people representing a variety of disciplines have given generously of their time to read, criticize and suggest changes in earlier drafts of this book. I am grateful to Professor Donald Newman, Professor Frank Remington, Dr. Asher Pacht, Dr. Norman S. Greenfield, Dr. Milton H. Miller and Dr. Paul Miller. I am especially indebted to Dr. William C. Lewis who spent countless hours reading and rereading each chapter.

Miss Phyllis Fedie was extraordinarily helpful in the laborious task of typing the many drafts of this book. Finally, I would like to express my deep appreciation to my wife, Helen, and to my daughters, Nancy, Judy and Betsy, whose patience, understanding and encouragement were indispensable to completing my task.

S. L. H.

# FOREWORD

by
Karl Menninger, M.D.

The first man born on earth killed his brother and became a criminal. His punishment, he said, was greater than he could bear. But he was not executed and his descendants became great musicians, artisans and herdsmen. How would it have turned out if Cain had killed Abel in West Virginia last month?

The criminal tendencies of mankind have been one of our compelling interests since that day in the Euphrates Valley (or the Olduvai Gorge) so many centuries ago. We still don't know how to protect Abel and we still don't know what to do with Cain; whatever we do seems to be wrong. Crimes increase, but most of those who commit them are never caught. Those who are caught seem to get caught over and over again, and are given the same unprofitable treatment.

Television screens and paperbacks are full of exciting and shocking accounts of crimes committed and criminals captured—fascinating fantasies at best. Now comes a book about crime and criminals, which is more fascinating, because it is not fantasy. *Psychiatry and the Dilemmas of Crime* is a scientific treatise written by a psychiatrist who knows and has lived with hundreds of true cases more interesting and gripping than any fiction.

It is a comprehensive, scholarly study, but written so clearly and so delightfully that any reader may enjoy it. Something about the unpretentious yet elegant style of the author, his respect for the subject, and his equal respect for the reader's intelligence make it a pleasure to go through these pages. This book ought surely to head the list of books on crime and criminals.

Dr. Halleck describes what crime is and how many are the factors and determinants that enter into its causation; he describes the people who commit crime, people who are, of course, various versions of ourselves, modified by an enormous number of stresses, exigencies, misapprehensions, provocations, needs, fears, hopes and mistakes. The book deals, too, with the way these offenders are treated by us, the things we do to them in the hope of making them better, but with the result, too often, of making them worse.

I hope every warden reads this book, every prison guard and every lawyer, and especially every judge. I hope every doctor reads it, including psychiatrists. I hope every law student, indeed every college freshman, will read it. For here discussed is one of the great problems of the day, one which all our modern science and civilization and culture haven't solved, *in part just because college freshmen and law students*—even some psychiatrists—don't know anything really about crime.

None of us knows enough about it. And it is certain that we can't make any change in our wretched penal system until people do know about it. We, the public, cannot forever turn our eyes from the ugly sights of our world, especially those of our own making. The public must know the facts and their explanation. It must know how dishonest and untrue are statements such as this typical one that appeared in the newspaper this morning: "The weepers and breast beaters have but one obsessive concern in this field of the Law; they are concerned with the criminal, his civil liberties, his precious rights. Isn't it high time that someone spoke up for the victims?"

This book speaks up for the victims and without any breast beating or sneering or name calling. It says we are going to have more and more victims unless and until we replace our ignorance, hate and fear with an intelligent, scientific revision of our whole wretched system.

This is a modern book, a book with windows to the future, but supplied with a good, sound library of facts from the past. Reading it gives one the wistful feeling that after these centuries of vengeful handling of offenders, of impotent fumbling reforms and futile, hypocritical gestures, we might soon see the beginnings of a better system. Here, at least, is a sensible, practical blueprint for one. In this book, Mr. Halleck emerges as a national authority on this topic of world concern. The author's large experience in this field is backed by sound psychiatric knowledge and proficiency.

Readers will find themselves revising opinions and attitudes which they have held all their lives. I scan or read carefully scores of books on this subject (I am even trying to write one), but on page after page of this book I came across things I hadn't known or hadn't thought about in just this way. Especially regarding youth did I get some new insights.

Once I taught Dr. Halleck, if I may boast a little; now he is teaching me. Nothings thrills an old teacher more than this.

# PREFACE

Psychiatry holds an unstable position in the field of criminology. For every zealot who heralds psychiatric concepts and treatment as the only answer to the crime problem, there is a critic who believes that psychiatric contributions to criminology are unscientific and misleading. A realistic assessment of the value of psychiatric criminology must lie somewhere between these two extremes. Throughout the first part of this book I shall attempt to demonstrate how psychiatric concepts can clarify our understanding of much of the behavior that society defines as crime; I feel that modern psychiatry can offer conceptual models of maladaptation which integrate biological, psychological and sociological perspectives of the criminal.

It is not easy for the criminologist to search for the causes of crime in an objective manner, whatever approach is taken. Criminal behavior has such serious consequences that society's demand for immediate solutions often precludes the degree of detachment which is necessary for constructive theorizing. The behavioral scientist is not immune to moralistic attitudes. As a member of a society which makes laws, he is susceptible to a belief in the inherent moral correctness of the law. As a result, a great deal of theoretical inquiry into the causes of crime has been subtly dominated by the assumption that all crime is bad or evil.

The approach maintained throughout the first part of this book will be somewhat different from that taken by many psychiatrists. I shall examine legally designated criminal behavior without bias as to the rightness or wrongness of the illegal act and without judgment as to the responsibility or nonresponsibility of the offender. I shall examine crime as a natural phenomenon and shall attempt to understand it in terms of the advantages it offers to the criminal. Yet such an approach may not provide easy answers, such as society seeks, for the causes of crime lie in the sordid realities of our existence. There will never be a society that is free of criminal behavior, and whether we should even try to create such a world is debatable.

Society must defend itself against crime. It must punish those who violate its laws, and may not feel it can afford to redefine offenders as sick people. Yet should a society also become interested in reforming the criminal, it becomes involved in an ambiguous situation; it is then that psychiatric techniques of treatment begin to appeal to those who wish to help the criminal. Unfortunately, the marriage of medical models and punitive models has spawned a complicated and confusing variety of philosophies and treatments. The various roles which the psychiatrist has assumed in the correctional setting are especially complex.

These roles have led to profound social consequences. Any psychiatric role may be abused so as to deprive some individuals of their liberty unnecessarily. On the other hand, most psychiatric activities can benefit both the individual and his society. Therefore, one of the efforts of this book, especially in the second part, will be to consider both the dangers and the advantages of each psychiatric role. I shall also examine related correctional practices in terms of their relative advantages to the individual and his society.

Any procedure which a society or profession invokes to help or to hurt the criminal must ultimately reflect ethical and social beliefs. The efforts of individual psychiatrists to deal with the criminal are no less motivated by value judgment than those of anyone else. The reader is, therefore, entitled to a frank statement of the ethical and social biases which influence the viewpoints I shall offer:

First, a stable society may need to punish its criminals, but rehabilitation is a more important goal than punishment. If this value is accepted, our current correctional system must be seen as more concerned with punishment than is necessary, and its efforts to rehabilitate the criminal begin to appear shabby and insincere.

Second, the psychiatrist as a physician must be wary of participation in any procedure that is designed to hurt the criminal. Deliberate punitiveness is not consistent with the ethical codes of the medical profession.

Finally, the psychiatrist has a social responsibility to use his medical skills to prevent emotionally disturbed offenders from hurting others and a moral responsibility to try to prevent any persons from hurting themselves. At the same time, the physician is ethically bound to avoid imposing arbitrary or unnecessary social restrictions upon the offender. Putting this differently, our view is that an individual's right to liberty should be put ahead of all other values except when he endangers the lives of others or is acting in a manner which will ultimately bring great harm to himself. The reader may wonder how the psychiatrist can prevent the offender from harming himself or others without periodically imposing restrictions which the offender experiences as punitive. This is indeed a thorny problem and does not have an easy answer, but, as does the entire question of crime, punishment and treatment, it possesses in its very difficulty an importance to society and to every individual which makes the effort to find answers not only worthwhile but imperative.

SEYMOUR L. HALLECK

*University of Wisconsin*

# PART I

## CAUSES OF CRIME

*Chapter 1*

# PROBLEMS IN EXPLAINING CRIMINAL BEHAVIOR

EVERY society which hopes to preserve a reasonable degree of stability must find a way of dealing with those who violate its criminal code. Yet nowhere in the history of mankind has there been a culture which has found a satisfactory solution to its crime problem. We do not even understand why men commit crimes. Modern biology, psychology and sociology have taught us a great deal about man's behavior, but they have failed to provide a comprehensive or scientific explanation of crime. Development of research and theory in criminology lags behind most of the other behavioral sciences.

There are many reasons for this lack of progress. Certainly society's punitive and often irrational attitude toward the criminal has made it difficult to study crime in a scientific manner. But even if we were more humane and rational, certain methodological problems would still occur. First, crime encompasses an enormous variety of behaviors ranging from mass murder to evasion of income tax. Since almost any form of social behavior might in some circumstances be defined as criminal, the task of explaining all crime can assume overwhelming proportions. Furthermore the criminologist is usually uncertain as to which subjects should be studied as criminals. He finds that it is relatively easy to define crime but that it is much harder to decide who is a criminal. Crime can be defined as "any act or omission prohibited by public law for the protection of the public and made punishable by the state in a judicial proceeding in its own name."[1]* But this (or any other) definition does not provide the criminologist with a consistent means

* Superior numbers refer to Notes, beginning on page 351.

of identifying the law violator. To be labeled a criminal, an offender must not only be apprehended but he must also be convicted in a judicial proceeding. This means that many people who break laws are never designated as criminals. Two individuals may show almost identical behaviors, yet one may be called criminal and the other not. Thus when the behavioral scientist uses legalistic definitions of criminality he can study only the selected offenders whom society chooses to put before him and often he is unable to study similar classes of deviant behavior.

We must also note that it is often difficult to relate definitions of criminality to consistent social needs or purposes. There are many acts which our statutes define as criminal which neither the society as a whole nor any subculture would consider deviant or harmful. As sources of power in the community change, normal behaviors may be redefined as criminal (or vice versa) so quickly that the question of deviancy becomes entirely arbitrary. The criminologist may be asked to study behaviors that a generation later would not be called crimes.

In reflecting upon the difficulties of relating scientific data to legally defined concepts, the sociologist, Thorsten Sellin, urges the scientific student of criminology to abandon legal definitions of crime and instead to study more measurable behaviors such as deviations from cultural norms, whether such behaviors are called criminal or not.[2] In a similar vein, the psychoanalyst, Kurt Eissler, has advised that we utilize psychological concepts to study any person who lacks the emotional capacity to integrate the values of the community—again ignoring the question of arbitrary legal designations.[3] Sellin's and Eissler's suggestions would direct our attentions to a larger group of individuals than those who are ordinarily considered criminal. In substance they ask that we derive a consistent definition of antisociality and then study the antisocial person rather than the legally convicted criminal.

This interesting suggestion has appealed to many criminologists. There are, however, a number of cogent counterarguments which have discouraged its general usage. First of all, theories derived from examination of the antisocial person may tell us very little about criminals. No matter how we define antisociality, we will find many people who fit the definition but never commit a crime. We can mention three other serious objections to this approach.

Antisocial behavior may be easier to measure than criminality, but it must be remembered that antisociality is also an arbitrary, moralistic concept, the definition of which must be dependent upon the value judgments of the investigator. Generalizations about antisocial behavior are subject to many of the same criticisms directed to generalizations about the criminal.

There are important legal and ethical reasons for not mingling additional groups of antisocial individuals (who may not have committed illegal acts) in classifications that include the criminal. Such indiscriminate classification encourages society to direct punitive measures against allegedly antisocial individuals without providing them with the benefits of judicial process. Paul Tappan has noted that our judicial agencies have an increasing tendency to label juveniles as delinquents solely on the basis of the recommendations of welfare workers.[4] He justifiably fears that widespread use of similar nonlegalistic definitions of crime would lead to an eventual erosion of civil liberties.

Finally, it is difficult to consider a scientific basis of behavior and the cultural terms which define behavior as entirely separate dimensions. If we are to be precise, we cannot ignore the impact of social definitions of behavior upon a behavioral system itself. Much of the conduct of the deviant person is dependent upon what the society chooses to call him or upon what he expects the society to call him. If we focused exclusively upon an artificial category such as "antisociality," we might lose those insights which are derived when we follow the *"in vivo"* behavior, or the natural history of the criminal as he influences and is influenced by our society.

The criminological theorist is faced with an almost insurmountable task. If he adheres to legalistic definitions of crime, he must formulate theories which explain such variant behaviors as murder, embezzlement, treason, failure to pay income taxes, sodomy and adultery. On the other hand, if he eschews legalistic definitions and elects to look upon crime as a form of antisociality, he can approach his task more systematically but must face the possibility that the subjects whom he studies will not always be law violators. The theoretical criminologist has never found a satisfactory resolution of this dilemma.

Many criminologists have failed even to acknowledge the existence of the problem. They have viewed crime as a legally defined behavior but have nevertheless attempted to explain it with a single theory. Their explanations have usually been based upon knowledge borrowed exclusively from one other field such as biology, psychology or sociology. This approach not only fails to explain adequately the diverse phenomena of crime, but it has also resulted in a fragmentation of the field of criminology. Too often the study of crime causation has been limited by a situation in which we have either a biological criminology, a psychiatric criminology or a sociological criminology and in which each approach ignores the knowledge available in the disciplines of the others.

A more integrated and more useful approach has been developed by other criminologists, who view crime as a legally defined behavior but seek to understand it only through the study of a wide variety of causative factors. Their eclecticism has led to what is called the multiple-factor approach to crime causation. The pattern for this approach was set by the American psychiatrist William Healy[5] and was later adopted in England by Cyril Burt.[6] Healy rejected any preconceived theoretical framework and meticulously set about to document every possible factor associated with criminality, be it biological, psychological or sociological. This approach makes it possible to investigate the influence of a wide number of factors in a given crime, and since it is primarily concerned with causative factors in individual cases, it does not easily lend itself to the formulation of all-inclusive theories.

The multiple-factor approach has engendered a great deal of controversy. Some criminologists view it as the most scientific approach to crime causation while others believe that it has little if any theoretical usefulness. To understand both the value and limitations of Healy's method, we must first appreciate that multiple factors can be used for explanation in one of two ways. Each factor can be considered to have a weighted or additive degree of influence in eliciting a criminal act, or each factor can be seen as a relative force which exerts a criminologic influence within a dynamic process or system. (There is still a third usage of the multiple-factor approach, which is not explanatory but more statistical or "actuarial." Some statisticians are merely interested in determining the frequency with which various factors such as race, age and place of residence are associated with delinquency. These observers do not impute causal power to the factors which they study, and they should not be considered criminological theoreticians.) The two major uses of the multiple-factor approach are related to different models of scientific explanation. In order to clarify the manner in which criminogenic factors will be studied throughout the remainder of this book, we must digress for a moment and review these explanatory models.

One way of looking upon causality in human affairs is in terms of a consistent association between a given factor (or factors) and a given behavior. If factor A is always present when behavior B is observable, it is sometimes assumed that factor A is the cause of behavior B. This is a linear type of explanation, which can be phrased in terms of the question "why." If we ask "why" behavior B is present, the answer would be that factor A has caused it. In a more complicated form of "why"-type explanation, we might assert that behavior B could also be caused by the additive influence of factors A, C and D.

This type of explanation was predominant in the latter part of the nineteenth and the early part of the twentieth centuries and was given special impetus by new and useful discoveries in medicine. For instance, in 1882 Robert Koch, a German physician, was able to explain the occurrence of tuberculosis by demonstrating that the tubercle bacillus was always associated with the clinical picture of the illness, that the bacillus could be cultured from the sick person, that it would cause the same disease in laboratory animals and that it could later be cultured from the same animals. This logical and methodical demonstration of an association between the symptoms of a disease and an external causative agent encouraged some to believe that the disease itself was thus explained and that similar modes of causality could be demonstrated for other varieties of behavior. Many illnesses were explained on the basis of "why." "Why does this man lose weight, have a fever and cough up blood-tinged sputum? It is because he is infected with the tubercle bacillus. Why does this man feel weak and have sugar in his urine? It is because his pancreatic cells are defective and he cannot produce enough insulin." These, of course, are partially correct explanations. They provide only limited knowledge, however, insofar as they do not tell us how the tubercle bacillus causes tuberculosis or how insulin deficiency causes diabetes.

It is especially tempting to ask "why"-type questions in attempting to explain criminal behavior. In response to the question, "Why does this man violate laws?," criminologists have sometimes accepted answers such as "It is because he has an inborn intellectual deficiency." "Because he comes from a broken home," or "Because he is poor." Sometimes one of these factors is invoked as the complete cause of crime and sometimes it is asserted that a combination of factors is necessary for the criminal act to occur. Such explanations suffer from the same defects as similar explanations of physical illness except that they are based on even weaker evidence of a consistent association between the causative factor and the behavior. Furthermore, these explanations tell us little about *how* intellectual deficiency, a broken home or poverty causes crime.

In recent years physicians and other behavioral scientists have come to appreciate that behavior is better understood if we study the manner in which causative factors exert their influence. We then become concerned with processes, and the question "how" becomes more important than the question "why," however valuable the latter may be. Recognizing that not all people exposed to the tubercle bacillus develop an illness, the physician must now ask, "How do many complex, physical, psychological and social factors interact so that some individuals are incapacitated by an illness such as tuberculosis?" When the behavioral scientist examines the processes of criminality, he asks, "How does the individual interact with the society in a manner that eventually leads to his violating a criminal law?"

Modern psychiatry is particularly concerned with the processes by which an individual adapts himself to his surroundings. At any given moment the individual is exposed to a wide degree of influences, some emanating from within himself (the internal environment) and some from without (the external environment), which interfere with satisfaction of his basic needs or which threaten to disturb his biological or psychological equilibrium. These influences or stresses require the individual to alter either his internal environment or his external environment in a manner which is need-gratifying and which preserves his equilibrium. The direction of this alteration or adaptation is determined not only by stressful factors in the immediate environment but also by the individual's patterns of previously learned reactions, which in turn have been determined by his adaptations to past stressful experiences. Most human behavior can be described in terms of the processes by which the organism adapts to stress. Criminality can thus be viewed as a legally punishable action which an individual takes as a means of adapting to biologically, psychologically and sociologically stressful occurrences in his past life and present circumstances.

In models of crime based on processes of adaptation, stresses or factors exert only a relative influence, and all the factors (to be equated with stress*) we might choose to study have a certain interrelatedness. When any single factor changes, it is likely to exert some influence on every other factor. Process models obviously provide more complicated but also more sophisticated and more useful explanations of crime.

It should be apparent that Healy's approach could be an instrument for answering the question "why" as well as a frame of reference for approaching the question "how." Unfortunately, in the hands of many behavioral scientists it has become a static, multilinear approach in which factors are seen as distinct variables whose relative influence can be precisely weighed or measured. The totality of criminal behavior in an

* The reader will note that we are now equating the term "factor" with the term "stress." Most of the factors which Healy found to be related to criminality (for example, broken homes, poverty, exposure to delinquent values) can be looked upon as stresses.

individual is too often looked upon as a sum of the influence of various factors upon him. This direction of multiple-factors theorizing has been justifiably criticized by sociologists such as Albert Cohen[7] and George Vold.[8] Both Cohen and Vold correctly insist that a theoretical approach must describe the means by which various factors exert their influence. They point out that the multiple-factor approach has little theoretical usefulness if it is based upon a naïve linear or multilinear model of causation.

The study of multiple factors in conjunction with a process model of behavior is a far more useful approach to theoretical criminology. In itself, however, this approach still is not a sufficient methodology for theory formation and research. The factors which act upon one individual in a manner which eventually leads to the commission of a criminal act are unlikely to be identical with those which act upon any other individual. Process models which are concerned with many factors are most useful in describing the origins of criminality in a given case, but they are less useful in suggesting hypotheses which allow for generalization between groups of cases. If the theoretical criminologist is to formulate and test hypotheses, he must find some means of restricting the type of criminal behavior to be studied.* We have previously noted that no single factor or group of factors could be even partial explanations of the wide variety of human actions which are defined as criminal. By focusing upon specific types of crimes the criminologist increases the likelihood that his experimental subjects will show more homogeneous characteristics and that their illegal behavior will have similar causes.

A methodology which seeks to examine multiple causes of specific categories of criminal behavior is implicit in much of the current research in both sociology and psychiatry. Sociological theories of causation which consider several factors have been proposed for criminal behavior such as naïve check forgery[10] and embezzlement.[11] Similar psychiatric theories have been advanced to explain specific crimes such as homosexual molestation of children[12] or some types of murder.[13]

Although such restrictions allow for a more scientific study of categories of crimes, they nevertheless move us further and further away from an integrated approach to criminology. One important question in modern criminology is how to determine the number of categories into which we have to divide criminal behavior before it can be studied systematically. Some sociologists have advocated use of a criminal typology which would

* In formulating hypotheses he must also restrict the number of factors to be studied and must state the reasons for choosing these factors. The need for taking these steps has been carefully explained by Marvin Wolfgang and others.[9]

direct us to study crime as a highly differentiated series of behaviors. Don Gibbons, for example, has described nine specific categories of juvenile delinquency and fifteen categories of adult criminal behavior each of which is alleged to have a unique etiology.[14] Even though there is some merit to this approach, the author doubts that such an extensive compartmentalization is either useful or necessary. The number of theories required by this approach makes for a quite unwieldy discipline of criminology. Some types of criminal behavior are so unique as to require special explanation, but it is our conviction that a significant proportion of criminal actions are closely related behaviors which share a common causality.

Throughout the first part of this book we will use a process-oriented multiple-factor approach to examine the question, "How do certain broad categories of legally defined criminal behaviors arise?" No effort will be made to present a comprehensive psychiatric theory of crime. Such an effort would be fruitless, first, because it is unlikely that all crime could ever be explained by a single theory and, second, because it is unlikely that any single crime could be considered a wholly psychiatric problem. Our goal rather is to demonstrate that many criminal actions can be best understood by utilizing a conceptual framework which is based upon psychiatric models of adapation and which integrates knowledge derived from the study of a large number of stressful factors.

To place the potential contributions of modern psychiatry in proper perspective, it is first necessary to examine other efforts to explain crime. We will begin with a brief review of the major biological and sociological theories. A few of these are based on a process orientation, but most of them, particularly biological theories, are not. As biological and sociological theories are examined, we will frequently note that what has initially been invoked as a complete or major cause of crime is better considered only a single factor or stress which sometimes favors a criminal adaptation.

*Chapter 2*

# BIOLOGICAL THEORIES

IF CRIME is studied exclusively as a legally defined behavior, the criminologist can lose sight of the forces which determine society's definitions. As a member of a community which must define illegal behavior according to its own needs, the criminologist is not immune to a belief that his community's laws have an inherent moral correctness. Once he ceases to inquire as to the natural or historical reasons behind the need for specific laws, he is more inclined to see the law violator as a different kind of human being. If the criminal cannot adhere to inherently correct precepts, it is easy to believe that he has a defect which separates him from his fellow man.

The criminal is often looked upon as defective in moral character, will power, conscience or superego. In the sense that there might be "something wrong with him" he is similar to a sick person whose disease is commonly thought of as a defect. Physicians and other biological scientists have at times sought the roots of both illness and crime in biological defects. The importance of anatomical or physiological abnormality in some forms of physical illness is often apparent. It is then tempting to reason as follows: "We have learned that people who behave in a sick manner have something wrong with them, a biological defect. People who behave in a criminal manner also have something wrong with them. Perhaps their defect, too, is biological and perhaps that is why they are criminals." This approach implies a biological correctness to conforming behavior, assumes an inherent wrongness in criminality and ignores the adaptive value of deviant behavior. Nevertheless, it has great popular appeal and has led to the development of a number of interesting theories, each of which has time or another been invoked as a direct and complete explanation o Each has since been rigorously scrutinized and rejected. Few criminologists are impressed with the relevance of physical factors to but it will be of value, I believe, to point out the defects of these t and to place biological stresses or factors in a proper perspective.

## Constitutional Theories of Crime

Constitutional theories of crime arose out of what has been call positive school of criminological theory. Previously, the most enligh criminology belonged to the so-called classical and neo-classical sc which viewed man as a reasonable and responsible individual, who sessed a "free will" and who could be taught to abstain from crimina through a rational system of control and punishment. With the adve Darwin's theories of evolution, it no longer was possible to be assur the special qualities of man as opposed to other members of the a kingdom. Some began to ponder whether man's behavior was "determi by his biological endowments and cultural experiences. In this intelle climate, it was possible for a school of positivism based on determinism the application of scientific methodology to develop. One early direc of this movement was an effort to prove that the "biologically determ criminal could be distinguished from the "normal" man through a stud physical or constitutional variations. Implied in this search was the b that a biological defect was in some undetermined way capable of produ criminal behavior.

Phrenology (the study of the faculties of the mind as determined by shape of the skull) represented an initial effort to relate constitution determined structure to behavior. Throughout the earlier part of nineteenth century phrenology was especially popular. Many physic of this era attempted to prove that criminal behavior was directly rel to specific defects in the structure of the skull.[1] Until this hypothesis discredited, it held considerable influence in psychiatric criminology.

In 1876 the Italian psychiatrist, Cesare Lombroso, first presented doctrine of "criminal atavism," based on his contention that criminals not advanced as far along the evolutionary scale as normal men.[2] Lombo examined the skulls and brains of criminals and was convinced that resembled those of prehistoric and primitive men. He then concluded the criminal must possess primeval instincts which would preclude effective functioning in an advanced civilization. The law violator had choice but to lead a predatory life similar to his ancestors because he was a "born criminal" endowed with a "criminal brain." Lombrosian doctrine became the most important scientific theory of crime throughout the latter part of the nineteenth and early part of the twentieth centuries.* For several decades it engendered wide enthusiasm and bitter controversy in American and European criminology.

A crushing refutation of Lombroso's theory came in 1913 with the publication of Charles Goring's *The English Convict.*[3] Using Lombroso's own critical measures, Goring compared thousands of criminals with control groups which included college students and sailors. He was unable to find significant differences between the criminal and noncriminal groups and concluded that there was insufficient evidence to support the notion of a physical criminal type. This repudiation of Lombroso's evidence did not, however, fully discourage belief in similar theories. The conviction that inborn constitutional traits produce criminal behavior has continued to receive periodic reinforcement through new studies which propose to link these two variables.

In our own era major studies supporting constitutional theories of crime have been presented by Ernest Hooton and William Sheldon, whose publications were originally hailed as new proofs of the existence of the "born criminal." In 1939 Hooton, a physical anthropologist, revived interest in constitutional criminality when he published the results of studies of eleven thousand prisoners.[4] A provocative and earthy spokesman, Hooton insisted that criminal behavior was a direct result of inherited biological inferiority and that particular types of crime could be related to specific anatomical traits. He was so convinced of the validity of his data that he made sweeping recommendations for social change, some of which had frightening implications. Hooton argued, "It follows that the elimination of crime can be effected only by the extirpation of the physically, mentally and morally unfit or by their complete segregation in a socially asceptic environment." Hooton's work has been criticized on the grounds of his basic assumptions, his selection of subjects, his controls, his disregarding of contradictory data and even for his anthropological criteria.[5]

A psychiatrist, William Sheldon, is the most prominent contemporary advocate of a constitutional theory of crime.[6] Influenced by the work of the European constitutionalist, Eugene Kretschmer,[7] Sheldon devised a new series of measurements of body build or physique which he then attempted

* It has been Lombroso's unhappy lot to be remembered for his constitutional theories and for little else. In later years, his approach became more eclectic and he gradually began to focus on a broad group of factors in addition to "criminal atavism."

to relate to personality. The asthenic, pyknic and athletic types of K schmer's earlier constitutional psychiatry became the endomorph, me morph and ectomorph, terms derived from analogies to the three ba cell structures found in early stages of embryological developme Sheldon developed a rating system which described the relative exte of ectomorphism, mesomorphism and endomorphism in a given individu In applying these indices of body development to a group of delinque boys, he discovered high degrees of mesomorphism. In a later stud Sheldon and Eleanor Glueck partially replicated William Sheldon's fin ings insofar as they found delinquent boys to be more muscular mesomorphic than nondelinquents.[8] Unlike Hooton, Sheldon avoide sweeping recommendations for social intervention, but his research h been severely criticized because of similar inadequacies in basic assum tions and methods.

## Heredity

If defective constitution is to be accepted as a major cause of crim we must ask how the criminal comes to be born a susceptible individua It is possible that prenatal influences or birth trauma could determin the constitutional limitations with which an individual enters this worl For the most part, however, constitutional defect implies transmissio through heredity. If one is born a criminal, it is most likely because he i herits criminalistic tendencies from his parents. This is implied in th writings of constitutionalists such as Lombroso, Hooton or Sheldon.

Charles Goring, whose intricate measurements of the physical chara teristics of criminals so effectively refuted Lombroso's doctrine of crimin atavism, still held that criminality was inherited. His conclusions were base on detailed statistical studies in which he found that correlations of crimina ity among fathers and sons and brothers were identical with similar correl tions among ordinary physical traits or inherited defects. He then reasone that criminality was inherited in the same manner as a physical characteri tic. Obviously, in such a study many environmental factors had to b controlled. Goring attempted to control for some environmental facto but ignored many others. In the absence of such controls his evidence usually considered to be no more than suggestive of a linkage betw heredity and crime.

The most impressive evidence for a genetic factor in crime has be derived from studies of twins. This controversial method, which has al been applied to conventional psychiatric syndromes such as schizophren or manic depressive psychosis, requires the discovery of a twin who has committed a crime and an observation as to whether the other twin has also engaged in criminal acts. Twins are either produced by the fertilization of a single egg (monozygotic twins) or by the simultaneous fertilization of two eggs (dizygotic twins). Monozygotic twins tend to be closely alike in physical characteristics while dizygotic twins have no more of a common heredity than ordinary siblings. If crime is inherited, one could anticipate a high rate of concordance (association of crime in both twins) in monozygotic twins and a low rate (about at the level one would anticipate in ordinary siblings) in dizygotic twins. Ashley Montagu has summarized the results of such twin studies in the following chart.[9]

CRIMINAL BEHAVIOR OF TWINS*

| Author of Study | One-Egg Twins (Monozygotic) | | Two-Egg Twins (Dizygotic) | |
|---|---|---|---|---|
| | Concordant | Discordant | Concordant | Discordant |
| Lange (1929) | 10 | 3 | 2 | 15 |
| Legras (1932) | 4 | 0 | 0 | 5 |
| Kienz (1936) | 20 | 12 | 23 | 20 |
| Stumpfl (1936) | 11 | 7 | 7 | 12 |
| Rosanoff (1954) | 25 | 12 | 5 | 23 |
| Total | 70 | 34 | 37 | 75 |
| Percent | 67.3 | 32.7 | 33.0 | 67.0 |

* From Ashley Montagu's "The Biologist Looks at Crime," *Annals of the American Academy of Political and Social Science,* 217 (Sept., 1951), 53. Courtesy of the author.

Approximately two-thirds of the one-egg twins show concordance in criminal behavior. Only one-third of the two-egg twins show concordance. These data seem to indicate that twins with a similar heredity are also likely to be more similar with regard to criminal behavior.

Again, however, major critcisms have been directed against this research on the basis of inadequate sampling, insufficient criteria for distinguishing one-egg from two-egg twins and insufficient attention to environment factors.[10] This last criticism is especially relevant. Identical twins do tend to be treated in a special way by family and friends, and one aspect of this specialness is to emphasize their "sameness." They are more likely to be exposed to a similar environment (in a broad sociopsychological sense) than are fraternal twins. Thus there are alternative explanations for a high concordance in the criminal behavior of identical twins, explanations which need not invoke heredity.

The modern criminologist must concede that although constitutional factors based on heredity could be a factor in criminality, research favoring this viewpoint has failed to withstand criticism. Consistent differences in the body structures of criminals have not been found. No evidence of an hereditary factor that is present in criminals but absent in noncriminals is available. Even had such evidence been uncovered, the inherited-physical-defect approach would not resolve still other problems.

Although constitutional and hereditary theories assume in the organism a structural defect which allegedly influences behavior, they fail to deal with the problem of how this influence is exerted. None of the theories deals with the problem of causality in terms of mechanisms or dynamisms. They either attempt to prove the presence of certain physical differences or simply allege that because they are present such differences are causes of crime. There is something almost mystical or demonological in this approach.

Furthermore, all constitutional and hereditary theories seem to neglect the fact that criminality is an arbitrary status that is defined only by the legal statutes of the community. Behavior which is criminal in one country may be perfectly acceptable in another. To talk about single physical causes of crime, one would have to devise relatively consistent criteria of criminality and then restrict observations only to offenders who met these criteria. This approach has not been followed by any of the proponents of constitutional or hereditary theories.

Finally, in their extreme form, and when invoked as monistic cause of crime, constitutional or hereditary theories often encourage totalitarian methods of social control. If one has a simplified view of the causes, it is tempting to adopt simplified and nonhumanistic solutions for the elimination of crime, for if criminals are born "bad," then it might be prudent to "control" them by execution, exile, castration or sterilization. We recall, for instance, that Hooton emphasized the need to "extirpate" or "segregate" all criminals.

## Crime and Mental Deficiency

Another theory of causation based upon concepts of constitution and inherited abnormality is that crime is the result of inborn intellectual deficiencies. In 1910 the psychologist, Henry H. Goddard, began administering the Binet-Simon intelligence test to criminals. Prior to the development of this test the diagnosis of feeble-mindedness had been based on unstandardized interview techniques, observation and clinical judgment. When Goddard began formalized testing, he discovered that 25 percent of the criminal population performed at a feeble-minded level.[11] A few years later he had revised this figure upward to 50 percent. In the decade 1910-1920 a number of investigators tested large groups of prisoners and concluded that 28 to 89 percent should be considered feeble-minded.[12]

While no physician ever claimed that intellectual deficiency was the cause of all crime, many believed that it could account for most crime. In the decade 1910-1920 few would have disagreed with the psychiatrist Walter Fernald when he asserted that feeble-mindedness was the most important cause of crime, degeneracy and pauperism.[13] The doctrine of the feeble-minded criminal was strong enough to encourage coercive legislation which led to the sterilization of many criminals. It was not until psychological tests were standardized with army recruits in World War I and not until other inadequacies in test administration were discovered that the doctrine of the feeble-minded criminal began to decline, although even into the 1930's mental defect was considered by many to be the primary cause of crime.

Today most behavorial scientists find little evidence to support the hypothesis that crime is caused by defective intelligence. Some criminals, particularly institutionalized offenders, may demonstrate a slightly higher incidence of mental deficiency than a noncriminal population, but these findings do not prove that mental deficiency leads to crime. They are more easily explained as the result of the general social ineffectiveness of the intellectually limited person. The defective criminal is not only likely to be more easily apprehended, but he also experiences greater difficulty in defending himself in court and in avoiding conviction and incarceration.

## Endocrine Abnormality

In the past fifty years the influence of physical defects or disease upon behavior has been increasingly clarified by medical scientists. The role of the endocrine glands is particularly intriguing. We know, for example, that an individual with hyperthyroidism is nervous and excitable and that an individual with hypothyroidism may be dull and lethargic. The dysfunction of any endocrine gland has some impact upon the emotional state of the individual. It is tempting to go beyond such observations and theorize that endocrinological dysfunctions could be related to specific kinds of behavior. Predictably, some medical scientists have attempted to derive an endocrinological theory of crime. Although these theories ordinarily assume an hereditary or constitutional cause of endocrine dysfunction, they do not rule out the possibility that the physical disorder can be acquired as well as inherited.

In 1928 M. G. Schlapp and E. H. Smith published a text
criminology which advanced the thesis that all criminal behav
based on biochemical dysfunction.[14] Several years later, Lewis
asserted that all crime could be understood as an imbalance or a de
of the endocrine glands and that specific types of crime could be
ated with specific endocrine malfunctions.[15] More recently Edward P
has argued that many types of criminal behavior are caused by
insulinism and hypoglycemic crises.[16] For the most part such theori
not created the same degree of interest and enthusiasm as consti
theories. At the same time, however, they suffer from similar defic

More careful endocrinological studies indicate that criminals exp
adequate nutritional and hygienic conditions do not differ from the no
Even if consistent endocrinological differences were found, it would
enormous and unjustified inference to argue that a physical def
specifically determine such a narrowly defined behavior as crime
because we know that it has a general and undifferentiated
upon the psyche. Undoubtedly, endocrine dysfunction is sometime
ciated with behaviorial changes, which may or may not be condu
law violation. The problem, however, is too complex to talk about
causal relationships. It could just as easily be argued that psycho
dysfunction could lead to endocrine dysfunction, and indeed we do
more about the effect of psychological stress upon glandular secre
about the reverse effects of glandular disturbance upon the personal

## Neurological Disorder

While neurological abnormality has never been consistently ad
as the sole cause of criminality, there have been many who reason
the criminal must be neurologically different. There are many
logical conditions which influence behavior, and some (particularl
types of epilepsy) may be directly related to certain crimes of vi
No physician, however, has attempted to generalize from these con
to develop a neurological theory of crime. These neurological defe
acknowledged to be related to only a very small percentage of crim
will be more appropriately discussed in later chapters. Some th
have been tempted to relate the behavior of large categories of
to the preserve of an ill-defined but generalized neurological
The evidence for such theories is scanty. One approach has been t
abnormalities in brain function through the electroencephalogram.
Hill and D. A. Pond found that the electroencephalograms of 70

of murderers who did not appear to have good motives were abnormal.[18] In studying the electroencephalograms of a group of individuals called psychopaths (psychopaths are usually described as being especially prone to criminality) and comparing them with other groups of normal and disturbed people, Hill and D. Watterson reported the following:[19]

INCIDENCE OF EEG ABNORMALITY

| Category | Percent Abnormal |
|---|---|
| Highly selected flying personnel (successfully completed training) | 5 |
| Royal Army Medical Corps personnel | 10 |
| Mixed control | 15 |
| Mixed psychoneurotics | 26 |
| Inadequate psychopaths | 32 |
| Aggressive psychopaths | 65 |

Other researchers have found high incidences of abnormal EEG's in criminals defined as psychopathic and in other groups of criminals as well. Mortimer and Miriam Ostrow, in a study of prisoners at the Medical Center for Federal Prisoners, reported the following percentages of abnormalities according to diagnostic or legal category.[20]

| Category | Percent Abnormal |
|---|---|
| Psychopaths | 50 |
| Homosexuals | 56 |
| Epileptics | 98 |
| Schizophrenics | 80 |
| Conscientious Objectors | 65 |

This study illustrates some of the problems in utilizing electroencephalographic data in determining abnormality. One would wonder why conscientious objectors, who are minor rule breakers at best, would show a higher incidence of abnormality than the more antisocial psychopath. The electroencephalogram is simply not so highly standardized an instrument as we often assume it is. Interpretations of records are dependent upon judgments of the reporter and vary with his theoretical orientation. Thus there have been other studies which report far lower percentages of abnormal EEG's among criminals.[21]

The potential value of the EEG as an instrument for studying criminal behavior is far from clear. Electroencephalography is a relatively new field. With increased technical progress and more careful studies, differences between criminal population and normals may yet emerge. If we could establish such differences, we still would be faced with the problem of determining the manner in which electrical changes in the brain could be

directly related to legally defined behaviors. At this moment, we m
acknowledge that EEG studies are inconclusive and add little to our th
retical knowledge of criminology.

Another approach has been to compare the degrees of abnormal
found in the neurological examinations of criminal and noncriminal grou
George Thompson has noted a high proportion of "soft" or minor sig
of neurological deviation among offenders.[22] He found the following in
dence of neurological signs among 280 delinquents.*

| Findings | Number | Percenta |
|---|---|---|
| Abnormality of cranial nerves | 176 | 62.8 |
| Altered deep reflexes | 154 | 55.0 |
| Pathological reflexes | 118 | 42.1 |
| Associated glandular and other physical disorders | 51 | 18.2 |
| Clonus, ankle or wrist | 31 | 11.0 |
| History of head injuries and/or unconsciousness | 24 | 8.5 |
| No neurological abnormalities | 18 | 6.4 |
| Ataxia | 9 | 3.2 |
| Tremors and forced movements | 8 | 2.8 |
| Left-handedness | 6 | 2.1 |
| Altered associative movements | 5 | 1.7 |
| Stammering | 5 | 1.7 |
| Altered superficial reflexes | 3 | 1.0 |
| Cerebellar signs | 1 | 0.3 |
| Convulsions | 1 | 0.3 |

In comparing this group with noncriminal patients, whom he saw
private practice, Thompson noted that only 28.57 percent of his privat
practice patients had abnormal neurological signs while 71.43 percent
delinquents demonstrated such pathology. He concluded that many cri
inals (particularly those whom he called psychopaths) were subject
some type of neurological defect.

It is difficult to know how to interpret such data. Certainly the neur
logical examination is somewhat subjective. The discovery of certa
physical signs as well as their interpretation is to a large extent depende
upon the orientation and experience of the examiner. We also know th
an unselected group of criminals is more likely to have had head injuri
or a history of heavy use of alcohol than a noncriminal population. Su
experiences would favor a higher incidence of "soft" signs of neurologi
abnormality.

In recent years there has been some experimental evidence which
gests that the nervous system of delinquents may quantitatively differ f
that of more law-abiding citizens.[23,24] H. J. Eysenck has summarized

* From G. N. Thompson's *The Psychopathic Delinquent and Criminal,* 19
Courtesy of Charles C Thomas, Springfield, Illinois.

search findings which suggest that the criminal has an "innate predisposition to form weak and fleeting conditioned responses."[25] Eysenck assumes that criminality is a continuous trait of the same kind as intelligence, height or weight and that its ultimate hereditary basis lies in the low conditionability and extroverted nature of the criminal. A linkage is suggested between a continuum of introverted-extroverted behavior and the degree of activity of the reticular system of the brain and spinal cord. While insisting that hereditary defects of conditionability are powerful causes of criminal behavior, Eysenck acknowledges the complex social and psychological nature of crime and concedes that environmental learning experiences can modify disposition.

In looking upon criminality as a trait, Eysenck equates crime with a nonlegalistic concept of antisociality which he fails to define. In spite of this limitation his suggestion of a biological basis of rule-breaking behavior is carefully documented, ingeniously formulated and certainly worthy of further investigation. Although Eysenck's recommendations for treatment of criminals are reminiscent of the coercive inclinations found in other biological theorists (he implies that there is "something wrong" with the criminal which must be corrected), his theoretical speculations are consistent with modern knowledge of genetics and represent a new and exciting approach to a constitutional basis for criminality.

## Current Concepts of Biological Factors in Crime

In spite of the inadequacies of all-inclusive biological theories, we cannot completely discount the relationship of physical characteristics to criminal behavior. Certain inherited biological traits could exert a profound influence upon the direction of the adaptational process.

According to modern theories of genetics, behavioral potentialities are definitely inherited but the emergence of behavioral traits is dependent on environmental conditions. (Environment here is to be understood in the broad sense, beginning with the physical and biochemical environment of the womb and encompassing every aspect of the society.) This does not deny the existence of innate differences in people. We know that children differ in their motoric patterns from the time of their birth. Certain aspects of human development patterns do appear to be preordained. While the language a child learns to speak is entirely a function of his culture and upbringing, the time in his development when he is ready to begin to learn language is not susceptible to change by environmental tampering.

Viewed in this light, heredity appears to set upper limits or potentialities which can be brought out by a given environment. The environment is not capble of influencing change beyond those limits. Yet many inherited potentialities may never be realized if a propitious environment is unavailable. A child born with perfectly adequate or even exceptional abilities may never become capable of leading a socially acceptable life if he is deprived of adequate physical and emotional nurturance during his first few years.

The question, "To what extent might constitution based on heredity be involved in causation of criminality?," might better be replaced by a new question: "In what ways do environmental and hereditary influences collaborate or interact so as to lead to criminality in a given individual?" It is apparent that once the second question is asked, it is no longer meaningful to construct a general theory which supposes a linear relationship between heredity and crime. Instead, we are obliged to adopt a process approach in which the criminality of each individual has a distinctive dynamic basis in the constant interplay of constitutional and environmental factors.

If a child is born in the slums of a large city in the United States and if he is a Negro, the color of his skin may be a factor favoring criminality. A muscular boy from the same environment may find that his innate physical endowment provides him with better equipment for criminal activity than his pyknic counterpart. In different environments, however, neither dark skin or muscular habitus would necessarily encourage criminality. Similarly, the child born with a speech defect or an unattractive appearance might in some circumstances be so rejected as to develop personality traits conducive to later participation in antisocial behavior. But the same child could be reared in an environment which would help him to overcome these handicaps. He could conceivably even become an exceptional person by virtue of his efforts to overcompensate for his hereditary defect. Gerald McLearn has succinctly described the need to account for such individual differences by noting, "What is sauce for a goose may not only not be sauce for a gander, it may be poison to a different goose."[26]

Chapter 3

# SOCIOLOGICAL THEORIES

DURING the past two decades the influence of biological and psychiatric approaches in criminology has gradually waned. Especially in the United States, scientific criminology has been increasingly dominated by the sociological viewpoint. This is evident in the orientation of criminology textbooks and in the trend toward designating departments of sociology as the principal teachers of criminology. The sociologist seems to have replaced the physician as the major protagonist in the battle against irrational treatment of the criminal.

Sociological explanations of crime differ markedly from those held by physicians. As we shall see in later chapters, even the process models of modern psychiatry bear little resemblance to those of sociology. At times members of both professional groups have identified themselves as adversaries in a struggle to understand crime. Interdisciplinary communication between the two professions is often limited to polite acknowledgment or intemperate criticism of the other profession's approach. While this estrangement is unfortunate, it seems to have deep roots in the differing social roles and perspectives of each profession.

The psychiatrist comes to know the individual criminal through his role as a healer. Seeing the criminal as a patient, he often fails to perceive an enormous amount of data relevant to that individual's life as a nonpatient. The psychiatrist tends to turn away from the problem of crime as a whole and directs his interest to the individual criminal. His theoretical models of criminality are derived from his work with the mentally ill, from his efforts to explain individual variation or individual suffering. As such they bear the imprint of a highly individually oriented bias. Consider such theories as "the criminal from a sense of guilt," the neurotic character, psychopathy or latent delinquency. They are all derived from work with individual patients and are almost devoid of sociological perspectives. These models are also limited insofar as they are derived from experiences with middle-class patients and may reflect the class values of the psychiatrist. Furthermore, the psychiatrist is not driven to test his hypotheses with regard to crime. The healer is interested in the pragmatic. Concepts or theoretical frameworks which help him to work more efficiently with patients are sometimes maintained even when they do not comprehensively explain facts or are incapable of validation.

The sociologist approaches the problem differently. His major concern is with the crime process as a whole rather than with the individual criminal. He is often more interested in the deviant act itself than in the man who committed it. Treatment for the sociologist may be any technique that helps to diminish deviant behavior. This type of social control is impersonal. Its total impact on the happiness or future life span of the individual is often ignored.

The sociologist is deeply committed to a research orientation and to the elucidation of criminology as a science. He is extremely wary of any viewpoint or doctrine that "explains" the phenomenon of crime in a way which precludes scientific investigation. Thus any biological or psychiatric theory that is naïvely advanced as a unilateral explanation of crime has been carefully scrutinized, vigorously attacked and rejected.

Sociologists have sensed a serious inadequacy in those conceptualizations of criminal behavior that have been derived from psychiatric studies of motivation. They argue that even if the psychiatrist succeeds in a painstaking unraveling of the motivation of crime, he still cannot explain causation since similar motivations exist in people who do not commit crimes. Failure of psychiatrists to appreciate the fact that "motivation is not enough" has often led them to reject prematurely the importance of sociological data.

It must also be noted that the psychiatrist's familiarity with criminals is limited. Less than 50 percent of all offenders are actually apprehended and punished. The undetected or unconvicted offender does not seek medical attention unless by circumstance he finds himself in need of consultation for personal problems. The psychiatrist is ordinarily requested to examine only two groups of offenders, those whose sanity has been questioned and those who have been legally designated as criminals. Even his familiarity with the latter group is likely to be restricted to offenders who seem to be strange, peculiar or unreasonable. When viewing the crime problem as a whole, therefore, the psychiatrist deals with biases emanating from the study of an eccentric sample. This consideration is often neglected by both psychiatrists and sociologists. Many psychiatric postulates with regard to criminals may be true, but they are true for only a limited group of criminals. At the same time, the "normal criminal" described by sociologists may seem like an overly naïve concept to the psychiatrist simply because he rarely sees criminals who behave in a reasonable manner.

## The Sociological Viewpoint

Some sociological theories are based upon efforts to apply general knowledge of social deviancy to legalistic definitions of criminality. Others are broader and utilize more professionally derived concepts. An example of the broader sociological viewpoint is the concept of "white-collar crime" developed by Edwin Sutherland.[1] Sutherland maintained that extensive but unpunished lawbreaking regularly occurs among business and professional groups. He pointed to many instances of collusion, fraud, misrepresentation and profiteering which are not punished because they are difficult to detect and because society is unable to organize a substantial degree of resentment against such activity. The concept of "white-collar crime" has engendered much controversy. Since the "white-collar criminal" is not a person who has been actually apprehended and convicted, there is some question as to whether his illegal activities should even be referred to as crime. Most sociologists, however, have argued that any comprehensive theory of crime must somehow account for "white-collar" offenses.

Most sociological theories are based upon more precise definitions of criminality. Sociological criminology can be viewed as a study of the manner in which criminal behavior arises, is maintained and is controlled in a given community. It does not search for defects within the individual but either assumes that crime can arise out of processes common to any society or that a defect can be found within social units. Frank Hartung has described the two major sociological theories of crime:

The social psychological hypothesis asserts that "The criminal is a normal person in a normal society whose criminal behavior is learned in a process of symbolic communication with other human beings." The social disorganization hypothesis maintains that "The criminal is a normal human being but he is today living in a disorganized society which tends to disorganize its individual members."[2] In other words, society is sick.

These two major viewpoints provide a convenient starting point for our discussion.

## The Normal Criminal

The concept of the criminal as a normal person living in a normal society was developed by Émile Durkheim, who attempted to relate criminality to inevitable social forces present in every society.[3] Later sociological theorists have stressed a "process of criminalization," or the means by which social patterns and events ultimately lead to a criminal act. The criminal is viewed as a normal person who learns his criminality through a process of unfortunate but natural happenings.

Many sociologists see the future criminal as a person who has been exposed to an excess of learning experiences favorable to a violation of law over learning expriences unfavorable to a violation of law. This statement roughly describes Sutherland's theory of "differential association," which for the past two decades has been the most prominent sociological theory of criminality. The theory is summarized from Sutherland and Cressey's textbook of criminology.[4]

1. Criminal behavior is learned.

2. Criminal behavior is learned in interactions with other persons in a process of communication.

3. The principal part of the learning of criminal behavior occurs within intimate personal groups.

4. When criminal behavior is learned, the learning includes: (a) techniques of committing the crime, which are sometimes very complicated, sometimes very simple; and (b) the specific direction of motives, drives, rationalizations and attitudes.

5. The specific direction of motives and drives is learned from definitions of the legal code as favorable or unfavorable.

6. A person becomes delinquent because of an excess of definitions favorable to violation of law over definitions unfavorable to violation of law (this is essentially the principle of differential association).

7. Differential association may vary in frequency, duration, priority or intensity.

8. The process of learning criminal behavior by association with criminal or anticriminal patterns involves all the mechanisms that are involved in any other learning.

9. While criminal behavior is an expression of general needs and values, it is not explained by those general needs and values since noncriminal behavior is an expression of the same needs and values.

The differential-association theory has received incisive criticism from

Sheldon Glueck, who points out that it fails to account for the impact of innate biological differences, the influence of early character structure, or the fact that various forms of aggressiveness seem to be present even in little children.[5] Glueck and other critics[6] doubt that the differential-association hypothesis can explain criminality as long as it ignores the emotional origin of those responses which influence the learning situation. Furthermore, the differential-association theory cannot fully explain why some people who are exposed to an excess of criminal associations become criminals, while others do not.

As it now stands, the greatest appeal of differential association is as a "pure" theory of criminality which avoids the pitfall of seeing the criminal as a type or criminality as a defect. Unfortunately, this theory has been promulgated mainly by sociologists who are indifferent or unfriendly to the teachings of psychiatry. This is in spite of the fact that the genetic approach involved bears some marked similarities to the genetic approach which is characteristic of psychoanalysis. Psychiatric and especially psychoanalytic insights might have substantially added to the explanatory and predictive value of the differential-association theory, but unfortunately few integrative efforts have been made.

Faced with the problem of explaining differential responses to similar learning experiences, a few sociologists have begun to examine psychological variables. One interesting theory which integrates the differential-association hypothesis with psychiatric concepts has been presented by G. M. Sykes and D. Matza.[7] Under Sutherland's "definitions favorable to the violation of the law," they would include defensive personality patterns which are used to rationalize and justify a criminal act, even before it is committed. Other sociologists have suggested that susceptibility to learning criminal behavior is related to the individual's self concept (a poor self concept would favor criminality),[8] or that it is related to the extent to which the individual identifies himself with real or imaginary persons from whose perspective his criminal behavior seems acceptable (referred to as his differential identifications).[9] The concepts of rationalization, self concept and identification are important parts of psychiatric and psychoanalytic theory. When sociologists use these concepts, however, their approach is somewhat different insofar as they are less concerned with the unconscious aspect of personality defenses, self concept or identification.

## "THE SOCIETY IS SICK"

The hypothesis of social disorganization as a cause of crime is familiar to psychiatrists as well as sociologists. The phrase, "It is society that is sick," is heard with increasing frequency. In his book *Who Are the Guilty?* David Abrahamsen implies that the delinquent is less to be impugned than are certain large segments of our society.[10]

The inconsistencies, stresses and conflicts in Western society have been a major concern of many professional and nonprofessional groups. Psychiatrists as well as sociologists have been interested in the way in which a need to resolve contradictory value systems influences psychological adjustment. Anxieties engendered when an individual is forced to adjust to new value systems which may contradict previously learned standards of conduct are crucial to the etiology of that condition which psychiatrists refer to as the "identity crisis."[11] The sociological criminologist is concerned with the "sick society" insofar as he seeks to examine critically those conflicts and disorganizations within a given culture that tend to increase potential for criminal behavior.

Thorsten Sellin has examined the problem of conflict between the norms of divergent cultural codes.[12] He concludes that criminality can result when the individual is placed under social pressures which direct him to respond to norms or values that are at variance with those of the general culture. "Culture conflict" arises either when the norms and values of different cultures clash or through inconsistencies in the values of the divergent social groupings which are present in a complex heterogeneous society. Another social theorist, Robert Merton, focuses upon value conflicts specific to American society.[13] He argues that success goals in the United States are not coordinated with available means to obtain such goals. He states: "The cultural demands made upon persons in this situation are incompatible. On the one hand they are asked to orient their conduct towards the prospect of accumulating wealth and on the other hand they are largely denied effective opportunities to do so institutionally." Merton believes that these inconsistencies are conducive to a condition of anomie which produces social deviancy. Richard Cloward and Lloyd Ohlin have expanded upon Merton's theories and have pointed out that in the absence of legitimate means for obtaining success and wealth, the direction of criminality will also be dependent upon the kinds of "illegitimate means" to similar goals available in a given culture.[14]

In an interesting variation of the sick-society theme, Albert Cohen has demonstrated how a delinquent subculture can arise as a reaction to middle-class values.[15] He notes the nonutilitarian, malicious and negativistic actions of juvenile delinquents and argues that such behavior exists only because it is supported by a delinquent subculture. But the existence of that subculture, he reasons, is dependent upon an imposition of middle-class values upon people who have little opportunity to live up to them. The values of the delinquent subculture then become a perversion or mockery of middle-class values. The juvenile delinquent finds encouragement within his peer group for behavior that is nonutilitarian or almost the opposite of what is expected from a middle-class boy.

An extreme view of the sick society as related to delinquent behavior has been offered by Paul Goodman.[16] He argues that delinquency may be a "healthy" but pathetic attempt to do battle with a society that cynically advocates platitudinous standards of conduct while failing to provide worthwhile values or even the opportunity for "honest work."

Most psychiatrists would agree that psychological conflicts cannot be understood outside of a social framework. Even the psychoanalytic notion of conflict between id and superego cannot be defined without taking cognizance of conflicting ethical standards and cultural expectations. The process by which a person eventually achieves emotional maturity requires that he encounter, struggle with and resolve literally thousands of issues which Sellin would call "conflicts of cultural norms." There is no doubt that adaptation to a rapidly changing society such as exists in the United States is growing increasingly difficult. While the extent to which these complexities contribute to criminal behavior cannot be measured with any degree of exactness, the importance of cultural or ethical conflict in the genesis of crime cannot be discounted.

## Other Sociological Theories

Somewhat related to theories of crime as social pathology are those sociological theories which seek the roots of crime in the physical and social structure of selected neighborhoods or cultures. Ecological theories assume that the means by which humans compete for space and economic advantages in any given community will influence the direction of behavioral patterns. Starting with this analogy to Darwinian struggles for survival, a number of sociologists have examined city neighborhoods, areas which contain the most extensive concentration of human competitors, in an effort to relate human ecology to deviant behavior. Ernest Burgess postulated that if one demarcated specific zones in a city radiating outward from the center, each zone would demonstrate different stages of competitive adjustment and different rates of crime.[17] He focused upon the "interstitial zone," that area in the throes of change from residential dwellings to business activities, and suggested that to this zone would migrate those casualties of the survival process who would be most prone to delinquency. Investigation of the city of Chicago by his students, Clifford Shaw and Henry McKay, did demonstrate that crime rates were highest in the "interstitial zones" and that criminal behavior was less prevalent as one moved away from the center of the city.[18] Subsequent studies in other cities revealed similar findings. Although exceptions to this patterning were eventually found, ecological theories of crime dominated sociology up until the 1930's.

Eventually social scientists realized that the physical factors of a neighborhood environment were not sufficient to account for delinquency patterns. The concept of the neighborhood milieu had to be broadened in a way which recognized the importance of individuals and their relationships to one another. The need to focus upon interpersonal factors in the community milieu has encouraged those sociologists who adopt the ecological viewpoint to become more aware of the importance of psychiatric determinants. Their concern with the individual as he exists within a disturbed community and as he is affected by that community has in recent years led to a limited degree of interdisciplinary research and theory. The original ecological studies of "sick neighborhoods" ultimately laid the groundwork for current community mental health projects which represent the most sociopsychologically integrated approach to mental illness or antisocial behavior.

The relationship of family pathology to the genesis of juvenile and adult crime has for the most part been documented by psychiatrists.[19, 20, 21] Maternal deprivation, inconsistencies in rearing patterns and family stress have all been cited by psychiatric observers as crucial factors in delinquency. The sociologist is primarily interested in the way in which the family transmits socially acceptable values to the child and how the family prevents the child from being influenced by deviant values. This has led to an investigation of such factors as the presence of other criminals in the family, lack of parental control through ignorance or illness, home uncongeniality, racial and religious differences and economic pressures. Particular attention has been paid to the broken home, the home in which one or both parents are absent because of death, desertion or divorce. When the first juvenile courts were established at the turn of the century, statistics were compiled which indicated that a disproportionate number of delinquents (40 to 50 percent) were products of broken homes.[22] For a time sociologists were convinced that the broken home was the most important cause of delinquency. Later studies, which compared delinquents with nondelinquents of similar social class, showed a less significant incidence of broken homes among delinquents.[23] There is still much dissension in this area, but commitment to the factor of broken homes as a major cause of crime has gradually lessened.*

A unique contribution of the sociological method has been a clarification of the selective impact of the disrupted home on different social groups. Sociologists have demonstrated a significantly high relationship between broken homes and delinquency in preadolescents, girls and Negroes and also a lack of such a relationship in white male delinquents who have reached adolescence.[24] While the broken home does not explain all criminal behavior, it is nevertheless a stress which under some circumstances could contribute to a criminal adaptation.

The problem of any theory of crime which recognizes the importance of personality variables has been clearly stated by Richard Korn and Lloyd McCorkle:

> The obvious error in any attempt to relate an individual's personality directly to his overt activities is the failure to realize that certain other factors may intervene between his inner state of mind and his ultimate responses—factors which may change those responses radically. A factor intervening between a causal or *independent variable* and an end effect or *dependent variable* is technically known as an *intervening variable*. A theory which ignores these intervening factors is incapable of dealing with findings that different people behave similarly and similar people behave differently.[25]

Korn and McCorkle offer the concept of role as a clarifying intervening variable.† By applying this concept, one can construct a theory of crime in which personality factors contribute to the motivation of crime but where the actual question of whether or not a delinquent act is committed is determined by the particular social role the individual either chooses or is forced to play. Criminality then becomes the result of certain motivations which may be shared by many noncriminals but which find expression only through previously learned social patterns of action.

Some of the wide variety of social roles available in our complex culture would appear to be more conducive to criminality than others. The lower-

* It is also possible that children from broken homes are referred to juvenile courts more frequently because their parents are less concerned with their welfare. The apparent high correlation between broken homes and delinquency may reflect the fact that children from broken homes are more likely to be taken to court than children from intact homes.

† No attempt will be made in this brief discussion to adequately define the concept of role. A simplified definition of role is that it is a "pattern or sequence of learned actions and attitudes which a person takes in an interaction situation."

class adolescent who comes from a broken home and lives in a disorganized neighborhod may have little alternative but to adopt social roles which encourage antisocial conduct. In this frame of reference some roles are "chosen" by the individual while others may be forced upon him by his social situation.

Role theory helps to answer the question, "Why out of a great number of individuals with antisocial motivations do only certain of these individuals commit crimes?" The reply might be: "Many individuals experience difficulty with the control of impulses, but it is only the person who for various reasons is put into a role (such as that of the delinquent gang member) who is likely to commit an aggressive crime. Similarly, the person who is driven to steal as a symbolic equivalent for obtaining affection would be more likely actually to commit the crime if he perceived his social role as that of an abused and rebellious outcast." The concept of role as an intervening variable offers a means by which knowledge of emotional states can be integrated into broader theories of crime causation. It does not actually offer a theory of criminal behavior but does provide a frame of reference to which we will have occasion to refer in subsequent chapters.

## Limitations of Sociological Theory

Psychiatric criminology during the latter part of the nineteenth and early part of the twentieth centuries often resorted to global explanations which could not be validated, which discouraged research and which in practice encouraged questionable coercive procedures. Experiences with the suppressive potentials of earlier medical theories of crime seem to have made sociologists unusually skeptical of all psychiatric theory and practice.

In being alert to the dangers of naïve theorizing the sociologist has performed a valuable service. But too often he has made the familiar mistake of throwing out the proverbial baby with the bath water. Much of the sociological literature (particularly that which favors theories of criminality as a learning process) is directed toward a repetitive criticism of the psychiatric approach.[26, 27, 28] Whatever the motivations for such criticism, there is no question but that it is intense, passionate and often destructive. Arguments are often directed against earlier biological or Freudian theories which have since been modified and refined. The "straw man" of the all-pervasive medical psychiatric theory of crime is repeatedly invoked in spite of the fact that few if any modern psychiatrists either claim or believe that all crime can be explained in medical or psychiatric terms.

An unfortunate outcome of this rejection of psychiatric theory has been a failure of sociology to be fully aware of the total picture of criminal behavior. Insights derived from the study of individual criminals are too often ignored. In many instances less plausible sociological theories have been advanced to explain behavior that could be more comprehensively understood in psychological terms (e.g., the failure to utilize knowledge of family psychodynamics to explain the impact of the broken home upon the delinquent). In other instances sociological theories are rendered sterile by virtue of their neglect of unconscious motivation (e.g., in a situation of value conflict or identity crisis a great portion of the conflict may be influenced by drives or motivations which are out of the individual's awareness and which exert their influence through mechanisms that have been carefully elaborated by psychiatrists). Certain process theories of criminality such as differential association might have been practically broadened had they incorporated available knowledge of the influence of unconscious motivation in the learning process. The neglect of unconscious motivation can be especially misleading when applied to research. Much sociological data of criminology are derived from studies of directly expressed attitudes and from descriptions of observable conduct. Granted that the attention to the unconscious meaning of behavior enormously complicates any research enterprise, data which neglect this parameter are limited in their validity.

Just as psychiatry has failed to account for the selective criminality of individuals with similar personality traits, so has sociology been unable to account for the selective criminality of individuals exposed to similar social situations. It would seem obvous that some factor has to be invoked to account for the great differences in behavior encountered in individuals of similar social background. The differential-association hypothesis is too broad and general to account for these differences. Theories which focus on social disorganization, such as those which postulate a delinquent subculture, are interesting, but have been criticized even by sociologists as being insufficiently precise.[29] Sociological theory pays scant attention to the influence of innate biological or personality differences. Yet individuals do differ in physical capacity, in motivation and in personality. Any theory that is to account for the great varieties of crime and criminals must at some point recognize these differences. (It should be added that sociologists have more recently become interested in the study of behavioral systems which are associated with specific crimes.[30, 31, 32] In their new-found concern with typology, sociologists have become somewhat more alert to biological and psychological variables.)

Finally, psychiatry and medicine are not alone in their unfortunate propensity to attribute all crime to a unilateral cause. The sociologist has not been totally immune to this temptation. At one time or another many of the prevailing sociological theories have been advanced as complete explanations of all criminality. For the biologist, the devil to be exorcised has been the criminal brain, atavism and mental deficiency. For the sociologist, it has been poverty, bad neighborhoods, broken homes or criminal associations. Naïve single-factor explanations seem to crop up everywhere, even among disciplines which pride themselves upon precision and scientific methodology.

## *Chapter 4*

# MENTAL ILLNESS AND CRIME

SOCIETY often calls upon psychiatry for help in confronting the problems of crime, but society's need to deal with immediate ethical and legal questions has put demands upon the psychiatric profession that have interfered with detached or rational examination of the data. If the psychiatrist wishes to explain or treat criminal behavior, he should be able to demonstrate and describe a relationship between such behavior and mental illness. Unfortunately, the pursuit of a connection between illness behavior and criminal behavior has not been allowed to take place in an atmosphere of scientific objectivity.

The administration of criminal justice in Western society is deeply influenced by three basic assumptions: (1) Some offenders must be punished; others need not be punished. (2) Some offenders are responsible for their behavior; others are not. (3) Some offenders cannot be considered mentally ill; other offenders are mentally ill. Traditionally, punishment, responsibility and absence of mental illness have been linked together. If a man is believed to be psychologically intact, he is usually treated as responsible and punishable. Conversely, a mentally ill person is considered to be nonresponsible and frequently is not punished. These dichotomies have dominated psychiatric and legal thinking since the nineteenth century.

Whether society's assumptions are valid when examined separately or whether there is ethical or scientific justification for linking them together is debatable. What is important for our purpose here is to recognize the extent to which psychiatric criminology has been influenced by society's need to separate the "sick" criminal from the "normal" or "bad" criminal. Technically speaking, if an offender is mentally ill and nonresponsible, he is not a criminal. When we speak of mentally ill criminals, we are actually being somewhat imprecise. Psychiatry's determination of the emotional status of offenders is more accurately a part of the social process by which criminality is defined. Historically, the finding of illness in a man who has committed a criminal act has had profound social and legal repercussions. These conditions have made it extremely difficult to develop a dispassionate or scientific model of the relationship of psychiatry to criminology. In this chapter we will examine some of the possible linkages between mental illness and criminality. We will note that attempts to link these two behaviors through manipulation of arbitrary social definitions result only in agonizing inconsistency. On the other hand, we will argue that if these behaviors are examined in a more naturalistic manner they will be found to have many similarities and common origins.

## Social Definitions of Behavior

Neither mental illness nor criminality exists independent of social definitions. Any categorization of behavior must in large part reflect the needs of the society. In this sense mental illness is best considered a useful hypothetical construct justified by social and biological data and which has social value insofar as it insures humanistic treatment for disturbed persons. There can be no definition of mental illness outside of the value judgments of psychiatry and the society. As of this date the profession of psychiatry has not been able to come up with a consistent definition of mental illness which is acceptable to all its members. Criminality, on the other hand, is a form of social deviation which society defines as punishable in hope of protecting its institutions. There are other forms of social deviation, such as alcoholism, which might not be considered either mental illness or criminality. Increasingly, however, our society tends to define these behaviors either as illness or as crime.

Even if we examine the problem of physical disease, it is apparent that society plays a major role in defining when a man is ill. Diseases of organs are measurable in purely anatomical terms, but the authority to decide when a whole man is ill is ultimately relegated to society. To be labeled physically ill, a man must not only demonstrate objective signs of altered biological function but he must also communicate his suffering to others.

The designation of mental illness is even more dependent upon the wishes of society. Mental illness is diagnosed when the individual either behaves in a bizarre or unreasonable manner or communicates that he is experiencing emotional distress. Sickness, either mental or physical, also implies that the individual does not have sufficient capacity to control his behavior. Before calling a person mentally ill the society must be convinced that he "cannot help himself." The criminal who may behave in an extremely unreasonable manner will not be considered ill unless society is willing to believe that he is incapable of controlling his antisocial conduct.

It should be apparent that the designation of a particular act as unreasonable requires value judgments as to what behavior the society or the psychiatrist considers reasonable. The determination of whether a man can control his actions is an even more complicated philosophical question. It is not surprising, therefore, that the labeling of certain behaviors as normality,* illness or crime has always been somewhat arbitrary. During some phases of American and European history women who expressed certain bizarre ideas were burned at the stake as witches. Today they might be treated as mentally ill. Mystical experiences are considered normal and even desirable in some cultures; in others they are considered signs of illness. Behaviors which are crimes in one society may be praiseworthy or virtuous in another. Epileptic seizures have been considered signs of spiritual affliction in some cultures, but in others they have been thought of as evidence of special powers.

It is generally true that any gain in our knowledge of the determinants of behavior encourages society to modify its definitions. If a man molested a five-year-old girl, society would almost immediately seek to define him as a criminal. If he were examined by a psychiatrist, however, and found to have been motivated by delusional ideas, he might never be convicted of a crime and would be called mentally ill. If through further medical diagnosis it was discovered that he had a brain tumor, society would redefine him as physically ill.

While society increasingly utilizes biological and social knowledge in categorizing its troubled citizens, tradition and expediency continue to exert considerable influence. Definitions of physical illness have the greatest stability and scientific accuracy because structural or chemical change is relatively easy to measure. Even here, however, there is much ambiguity as to what should be called physical illness, particularly in borderline areas such as psychosomatic disorders. Definitions of mental illness vary with the cultural setting and with the orientation of the behavioral scientist. Although society allows the psychiatrist some freedom to devise his own criteria of mental illness, cultural biases are still imposed upon him, and

* For our purposes here, we will define normality as an absence of illness or other deviant behaviors.

the most objective criteria the psychiatric profession can devise are incapable of precise measurement. Definitions of criminality need not, of course, be based upon knowledge of human behavior. They are mainly influenced by the needs of society or by tradition.

When the physician or social scientist views physical illness, mental illness or criminality as distinct entities, he is in danger of making the automatic assumption that society's definitions are based mainly on scientific fact and therefore have an inherent "correctness." Actually, placing any individual into a behavioral category is largely a matter of value judgment. Nevertheless, the designation of physical illness, mental illness or criminality has enormous social meaning, and a person is subject to quite variant attitudes and treatment depending on what he is called. The relative solicitousness and unconditional tolerance afforded to the physically ill contrast with the relative unconcern and uncertain tolerance which are afforded the mentally ill. The attitudes and treatment which society maintains toward any sick person are even more strikingly different than those directed toward the criminal.

At one point in history no distinction was made between the mentally ill and the criminal. Any variety of deviant behavior which seriously interfered with the smooth functioning of society was treated in a similar manner. Both the criminal and many who would now be considered mentally ill were punished or sent into some type of exile. Concern for the welfare or rehabilitation of either group was nonexistent. In the past hundred years the situation has changed. In modern society some socially deviant individuals are defined as mentally ill and are approached with attitudes and treatments which are increasingly more similar to those previously reserved for the physically ill. Others, particularly those who have violated laws, are defined as criminal and are still likely to be punished.

This newer model for the treatment of social deviancy functions smoothly only so long as we are not too ambivalent about what should be done with those who have clearly violated our laws. In Western culture there are strong forces toward humanizing the plight of all the socially deviated, including the convicted offender. Influenced by a humanistic tradition which argues for the dignity and worth of each individual and finding increasing enlightenment as to the changeability of man's nature, modern society does have some wish to provide better treatment for all its deviant citizens. Friendly attitudes toward law violators, however, do not come easily. The criminal has wronged us, and our concern for his rehabilitation is also accompanied by our urge to punish him. This ambivalent attitude has led to a number of compromises in our treatment of offenders. Among them is an increased willingness to call upon psychiatrists to find arbitrary linkages between mental illness and criminality. Society is willing to define some law violators as "sick" rather than "bad." It is also willing to acknowledge that some may be both "sick" and "bad." As long as a designation of sickness leads to more humanistic treatment definitions there is a tendency to increase the percentage of offenders who are placed in the illness category.* Society will not, however, accept the proposition that all criminals are sick and insists that the majority of offenders continue to receive punishment.

Psychiatric criminology has been deeply influenced by society's need to have a professional person provide a rationale for categorizing some law violators as ill, thereby to allow the community to take a selectively non-punitive approach. Almost from the time that psychiatry became an organized profession its practitioners have been directed to a preoccupation with the question, "Which criminals are mentally ill?"

## "Which Criminals Are Mentally Ill?"

It has not been easy for psychiatrists to derive criteria for determining which criminals are mentally ill. Part of the problem lies in our changing concepts of mental illness. Initially, the medical profession viewed mental illness as a state or condition, a discernible entity which could be defined with precision through medical criteria. According to this viewpoint an individual is either schizophrenic or not schizophrenic. If he is schizophrenic, he is believed to have a disease which exists independently of his social environment. Although this kind of thinking is not compatible with current psychiatric knowledge, it continues to exert considerable influence upon psychiatric practice. Insofar as it emphasizes the existence of a variety of illnesses which are likely to have distinct etiologies it is quite similar to older medical conceptualizations of disease. It suggests a qualitative difference between those who are judged to be ill and all the rest of society's members, who are considered normal.

This model of mental illness is based upon static and linear explanations of behavior. It is primarily concerned with the question "Why?" "Why does this man behave in such a peculiar manner? It is because he has a disease or condition which we call schizophrenia." As applied to the criminal it also leads to rigid dichotomies between the "sick criminal" and the "normal" criminal. An offender either has a mental disease or he

* It must be acknowledged that this is certainly not the only way in which society has attempted to humanize its treatment of criminals. There are many ways of helping criminals without calling them sick. Society has at times attempted to provide humanistic treatment for offenders while continuing to call them criminals.

doesn't have. Usually his criminality is explained as being caused by his disease or defect. Again, this explanation is based on a "Why?"-type question. "Why did this man commit a crime? It is because he has a mental illness, schizophrenia."

Most modern psychiatrists look upon mental illness as a process. Mental health and mental illness are both viewed on the same continuum. The behavior of some individuals may at times become so ineffective, so self-punitive or so irrational that the psychiatrist deems it advisable to define them as ill. Mental illness in this sense is a temporary state of disorganization; it is part of a process and always subject to change or reversibility. This model is compatible with newer theories of medicine insofar as it relates disease to internal or external stress. Karl Menninger has been the most articulate spokesman for such a unitary viewpoint. He states:

> We insist that there are conditions best described as mental illness. But instead of putting so much emphasis on different kinds and clinical pictures of illness we propose to think of all forms of mental illness as being essentially the same in quality and differing quantitatively. That is what we mean when we say that all people have mental illness of different degrees at different times and that sometimes some are much worse or better.

Menninger goes on to say:

> Gone forever is the notion that a mentally ill person is an exception. It is now accepted that most people have some form of mental illness at some time and many of them have a degree of mental illness most of the time. This really should not surprise anyone, for do not most of us have some physical illness some of the time and some of us much of the time?[2]

Menninger and other psychiatrists who adhere to process models of behavior would visualize both mental illness and crime as efforts of the organism to find a sustaining adaptation.[3, 4] An individual might respond to certain stresses by adopting behaviors which are defined as mental illness. If these stresses are slightly modified, however, or if they are perceived in a different manner, they could lead to behaviors which are called criminal. The same individual may show symptoms of schizophrenia on one day and of obsessive preoccupation on the next. On the third day he might commit a crime, and on the fourth he might be entirely docile and comfortable.

While field or process models of behavior help the psychiatrist to discover important relationships between illness and crime, they do not help society to decide who is to be given medical treatment and who is to be punished. Categorization is an essential need of the society. Under pressure from the community it is extraordinarily easy for the psychiatrist to abandon his newer scientific models and to rely on static models which give more definitive answers. It is often difficult to determine whether psychiatrists' criminological observations are based upon static or process models. Thus some writers state that only a small portion of criminals are mentally ill (implying a static model in which mental illness is a definite entity),[5,6] and others discuss the abnormalities of all criminals (implying a process model in which mental illness is defined in a quantitative manner).[7,8]

As long as the psychiatrist adheres to a static model of illness his decisions as to which criminals are mentally ill are relatively straightforward. He needs only to define what degree of unreasonable and maladaptative behavior will be called illness and then note if the offender has demonstrated such behavior and therefore should be considered mentally ill. The more the psychiatrist becomes involved with process models, however, the more difficult is his problem. If he finally comes to a unitary viewpoint and agrees with Menninger that "All people have mental illness of different degrees at different times," then the question of which criminals are mentally ill becomes almost meaningless. We can illustrate some of the complexities and confusions surrounding the question by examining four different classes of answers.

Answer A. Illness and criminality can be viewed as distinct behaviors which have no relationship to one another. This is a strictly legalistic way of looking at the problem. If a man commits an illegal act and is found to be mentally ill and nonresponsible, he cannot be called a criminal.

Answer B. Illness and criminality can be viewed as patterns of behavior that might be characteristic of the same person. In this sense some people could be both sick and criminal. Although these behaviors could theoretically have no influence upon one another, this answer lends itself to linear models in which criminality is seen as determined by the illness.

Answer C. In addition to answer B, it has been more recently argued that many criminal behaviors are determined by processes which are identical with or similar to those involved in mental illness. Since the processes are the same, some psychiatrists would argue that such offenders should also be considered mentally ill. An increasing use of this answer has led to a great deal of debate and controversy.[9,10]

Answer D. If a unitary model is accepted, all criminal behavior and all illness behavior represents a form of adaptation. This would make it possible to argue either that all criminals are sick or that no criminals are sick. Admittedly, this answer is socially impractical.

We can illustrate these four viewpoints by the following diagrams:

ANSWER A

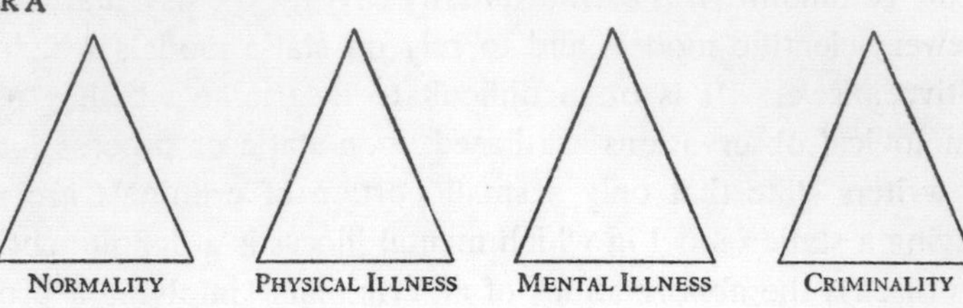


Each of these four triangles stands for behaviors that are defined by the culture as normality, physical illness, mental illness or criminality. Each behavior is considered a separate entity. To be precise, this response is not really an answer to the question, "Which criminals are mentally ill?," but is rather a model of social and legal definitions to which the psychiatrist has contributed.

ANSWER B

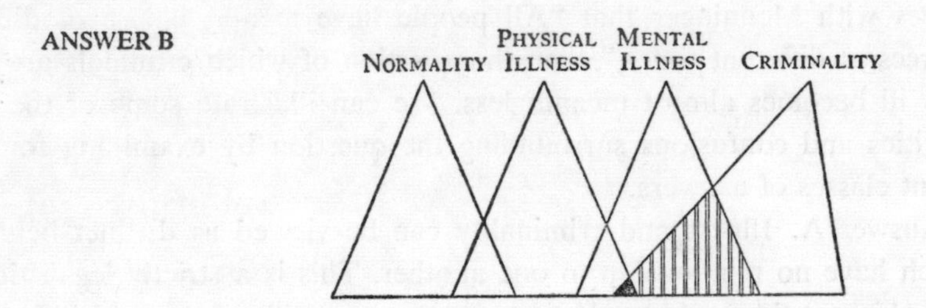


In this answer the triangles begin to merge. The psychiatrist who supports this position would argue that some of the behaviors that are ordinarily thought of as criminal must be redefined as illness once we become aware of the individual's true mental or physical state. The black area would represent those criminal behaviors "caused" by physical disturbance and the hatched areas those criminal behaviors "caused" by mental illness. This is a theoretical position often taken when psychiatrists view mental illness as a distinct entity. If one holds to such a view, it is possible to describe a

ANSWER C

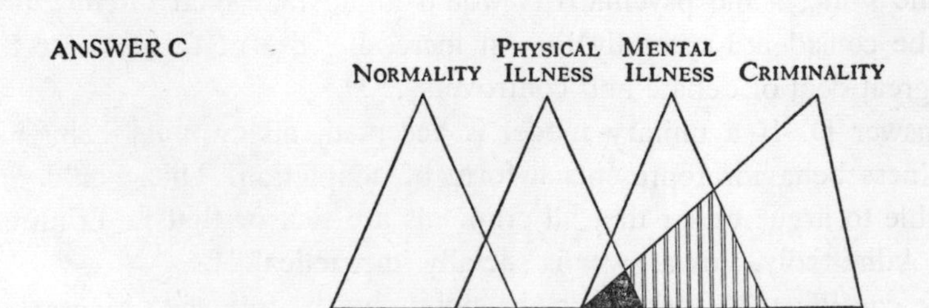

given percentage, for example, 20 percent, of criminals as mentally ill and the rest as normal.

In this diagram the area of the criminality triangle which falls within the illness triangle is much greater. The blackened and hatched areas represent criminal behaviors which are alleged to be determined by illness or by processes which are similar or identical to those which determine illness.* There is enormous disagreement as to the extent to which the criminality triangle should be merged with the illness triangles. As society attempts to humanize its treatment of the offender, there is much pressure to bring them closer and closer together.

If we look upon all behaviors as communications or as methods of adaptation, we come closer to the conviction that physical illness, mental illness, criminality and normality cannot be understood as independent entities, but must be considered together. Answer D would be best illustrated through a three-dimensional model.

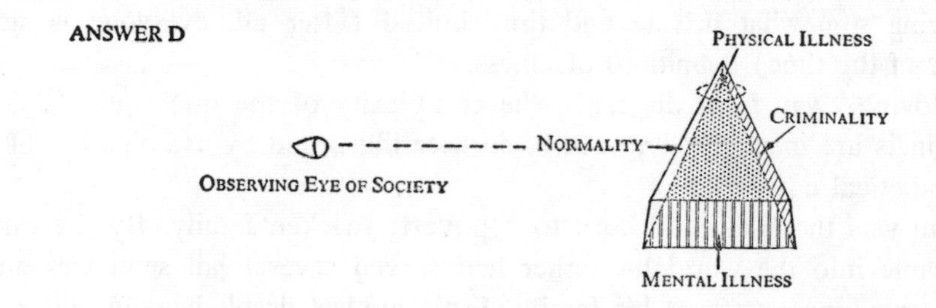


Physical illness, mental illness, criminal behavior and normal behavior are represented as triangles which have become the four sides of the same pyramid. This pyramid represents the total behavior of a given individual. If we now picture the pyramid as rotating very slowly and assume that the "observing eye" of society is at a level at which it can observe only one side or a portion of two sides of the pyramid at any given moment, we have a crude analogy to the way in which society imposes social definitions upon an exceedingly complex situation. Cultural definitions deal only with behavior that is observable at any given moment and are easiest to describe in terms of one category or in terms of parts of two categories. (We talk about two categories at the same time when we consider psychosomatic medicine, the insane criminal or the normal criminal.) The psychiatrist who holds to a unitary viewpoint believes that behavior does not remain con-

* Most sociologists and some psychiatists would also be interested in the extent to which the criminality triangle fused with the normality triangle. For the sake of convenience and clarity, we will ignore this issue in this chapter.

stant and is always subject to rapid change. This means that in our diagram the pyramid would be rotating so fast that the four sides would be blurred and would actually appear as a single cone. This cone would represent the totality of all factors involved in the genesis of all behavior. This is a diagrammatic way of saying that if society took into consideration the question of history (experience and the passage of time) and the complexities of the adaptational process, all behavior, including crime and illness, would have a high degree of interrelatedness.

The problem with this answer is that it does not really allow society to deal with questions which involve categories. A unitary model of behavior would allow us to find some illness and some normality in any criminal or some criminality and some mental illness in any person called normal. These findings might have a certain scientific validity, but they would have very little social usefulness. Unfortunately, when some psychiatrists have argued that all criminals are sick, they have actually been basing their statements on a unitary model and have allowed themselves to take great liberties in deriving somewhat private and time-limited (after all, everyone is sick some of the time) definitions of illness.

Moving away from diagrams, the complexity of the question, "Which criminals are mentally ill?," can be further illustrated by examination of a hypothetical case.

Jim was the fifth child born to a poverty-stricken family. By the time he came into the world his father had served several jail sentences and could no longer support his family. Jim's mother drank heavily and was promiscuous. During the first three years of his life, Jim was neglected and received only the barest amount of maternal care necessary for survival.

At the age of three Jim's mother remarried and he was sent to the home of his grandparents. Shortly after this he developed a high fever, became quite ill and was diagnosed as having a form of encephalitis. His grandparents noticed that following his recovery he appeared to be restless and hyperactive. When Jim was six his grandmother died, and since his grandfather could not care for him he was sent to an orphanage. During the first two years in the orphanage he was described as a withdrawn and nervous child. Periodically, he had symptoms of asthma, bed-wetting, nail-biting and temper tantrums. By the time he reached the age of ten, however, these symptoms had diminished, and since Jim was an attractive, retiring and quite peaceful boy, it was possible to place him in a foster home.

With the onset of puberty at the age of thirteen the brief period of quiescence in Jim's life ended. Faced with the problems of sex, approaching manhood, school and work, he found himself inadequate to the task. He could not sleep, he worried about pains in his stomach, he had difficulty breathing, he often felt an urge to cry, he was not comfortable with people and often when in the presence of adults had to restrain an overpowering urge to lash out and strike somebody. Jim frequently felt that he was "falling apart." He lived with an unremitting and unbearably high level of anxiety.

At the age of fifteen Jim discovered a gang of boys who had had experiences similar to his. They seemed to understand him. When he was with them, he did not feel rejected but was rather "one of the boys." He no longer felt inadequate but was able to think of himself as a responsible man. Over a period of time Jim found that as long as he was involved in antisocial ventures with his gang he was relatively free of anxiety. He and his friends continued to engage in acts of petty theft and aimless destruction until the age of sixteen, when after several arrests he was sent to a training school for boys. As soon as he arrived at the school, Jim became moody, sensitive and withdrawn. His symptoms of severe anxiety returned. One night he had a severe asthmatic attack which almost resulted in his death.

Jim's case is similar to that of many boys who are ordinarily considered juvenile delinquents. We must note, however, that much of the time his behaviors are of a type that could just as easily be defined as mental illness. At other times he could be considered physically ill. At still other times he appears to be functioning at a normal level.

Would Jim have been delinquent if he had not had asthma? Would Jim have been delinquent if he had not been so anxious? These are relevant questions, but they can also be asked in a quite different way. What effect did Jim's delinquency have upon his asthma? Would Jim have suffered greater anxiety if he had not been delinquent? The totality of the person that is Jim is much more than the behaviors that we can observe at a given moment. He cannot be understood unless we observe him as an individual with certain innate endowments who is constantly responding to his past experiences and his present environment. Society might elect to treat Jim harshly or kindly. It cannot, however, find a scientific rationale for either a humane or punitive action in a psychiatric determination of mental illness.

## Linkages Between Mental Illness and Criminality

The pursuit of linkages between mental illness and criminality will remain hopelessly muddled as long as such linkages are sought against a background of preoccupation with questions of punishability, responsibility and man's capacity to control himself. The only way in which we can describe consistent relationships between crime and illness is to divorce ourselves from a consideration of society's needs and examine only the behaviors themselves. We can then argue that mental illness and crime are related in two major ways:

Mental illness and crime are both adaptations to stress. The stresses that lead to mental illness are often the same stresses that lead to crime. We will note in subsequent chapters that many of the psychiatric concepts which explain mental illness can also be modified to explain crime.

While both mental illness behaviors and criminal behaviors provide a certain degree of mastery over stress, the adaptations themselves often lead to some difficulty with the environment. Mental illness always has a maladaptive quality and criminality usually has a maladaptive quality. In a later chapter we will attempt to define the maladaptive aspect of crime.

It is also of interest to note that if society were more consistent about its judgments and was not concerned with a need to punish, it would be relatively easy to find other descriptive similarities between mental illness and crime. A designation of illness or crime must be partly determined by value judgments. There are, however, some consistencies in our judgment of deviant behavior in general which do not carry over once we begin separating deviancy into crime and illness categories. Consider the following examples. A man in apparent good health who suddenly picks up a sledge hammer and deliberately smashes his foot will likely (if the facts are known) be called mentally ill. At the same time a man who is not in dire financial straits who impulsively robs a grocery store of ten dollars and then turns himself in to the police is called a criminal. There are many similarities in the behavior of these two men. Both have hurt themselves. Both have indulged in behavior that few would define as rational. Yet because the burglar's behavior has violated the law the issues of punishment and responsibility are immediately raised, and he is likely to be met with quite different attitudes than the man who has more directly injured himself.

If we carefully note the factors involved in the definition of mental illness, we will find that some of these same factors are consistently present in many of the behaviors we call crime. We have previously noted that mental illness is characterized by communication of personal suffering, by communication of an inability to control one's behavior and by society's judgment of unreasonableness of behavior. If we examine the first criterion, communication of personal suffering, it must be admitted that most criminals do not show evidences of psychological pain. It is always difficult to determine whether the anxieties and depressions seen in the apprehended offender are related to his immediate situation or whether they were present before the crime took place. If we believe what offenders tell us, however, it would appear that they suffer less, or are less aware of or less willing to communicate the extent of their suffering, than those we think of as mentally ill.

The issue of being able to control one's behavior is an extremely complicated one which touches on questions of free will and determinism. At this point we need only note that when a person commits an objectionable act and states, "I couldn't help myself," we are sometimes inclined to accept his explanation and sometimes eager to reject it. If we accept his explanation, we classify his behavior as a form of illness; if we reject it, we look upon it as "nastiness" or sometimes criminality. In everyday life our judgment as to whether or not an individual can "help himself" is based upon two factors: (1) the degree to which the offender has wronged us or the extent to which we wish to punish him and (2) a judgment as to how unreasonable or nonutilitarian his behavior appears to have been.

Ultimately, most of our decisions to call people mentally ill are based upon judgments of unreasonableness. Even when a person communicates suffering we do not diagnose illness unless psychological pain seems inappropriate. The person who panics in battle or the person who is depressed after losing a loved one is ordinarily looked upon as behaving in a normal manner. It is only when he appears to be anxious or depressed in the absence of any reasonable stimuli that we are willing to call him sick.

Although judgments of unreasonableness are always somewhat arbitrary, they do have a certain consistency which carries over between different societies. One consistent criterion of unreasonableness is the existence of goals or motivations which are grossly deviant from the norms of the society. In almost any society, for example, a man who wished to molest his own infant child or a man who wished to destroy his own property would be looked upon as unreasonable. Another way in which we define unreasonableness is in terms of the manner in which a person goes about achieving his goals. If we can accurately determine his motivations, it is possible to assess whether he acts upon them in a logical, consistent and effective manner. A person who wishes to gain affection from another and seeks it by aggressive or insulting actions is behaving unreasonably. So is the person who in a quest to gain wealth indiscriminately gives away all his holdings.

There are certain types of crime in which the offender's behavior suggests goals or motivations which seem so unacceptable and so incomprehensible that they are readily looked upon as unreasonable. This is especially true of sex offenses. A man who molests a child, steals undergarments or exhibits his genitals is usually considered to be a special class of offender. Society is often willing to categorize him as mentally ill. Even when society seeks to punish the sex offender, however, our uneasiness as to his potential irrationality seems to lead to programs marked by a peculiar admixture of punitive and treatment goals.

Sometimes the society is completely puzzled as to the goals which lie behind a crime. A woman who kills her children and can provide no explanation of why she did it, or an adolescent who wantonly destroys property and states, "I just felt like doing it," is usually judged to be behaving in an unreasonable manner. Again, society is quite ambivalent as to what to call such behaviors but is sometimes willing to acknowledge the possibility of including them in an illness category.

In most instances of criminal behavior, however, particularly where crimes against property are involved, society is much less willing to designate unreasonableness. It is assumed that the criminal is seeking goals which everyone can understand and accept, goals such as financial profit or status. It cannot be denied that a great deal of criminal behavior does seem to meet these goals very well. Crime undoubtedly pays well for some, and it would be ridiculous to argue that the man who steals one hundred thousand dollars from a bank is not satisfying a reasonable goal. Some criminal behavior is encouraged and condoned by the criminal's own subculture and endows him with a considerable degree of status. It is difficult to think of an offender whose criminal activities serve acceptable goals as a disturbed person. He may hurt the society, but he does not seem to hurt himself.

Many other offenders to whom society ascribes similar reasonable goals, however, simply fail to act in a manner which would be conducive to gaining such goals. Let us for a moment consider how a reasonable criminal might behave if he were seeking the reasonable goals of profit or status. He would first make every possible effort to avoid apprehension and legal punishment except in those rare instances where great status could be gained by going to prison, and, second, he would take a legal risk in order to obtain material gain only if there was a possibility that he could "earn" a sufficient amount of money or property to compensate for his risk.

A great number of criminals simply do not follow this rational code of behavior. Some make virtually no effort to avoid apprehension or are at best pitifully inaedquate in their efforts. Two types of crime in particular, check forgery and auto theft, are often carried out in an absurd manner. The offender is frequently intoxicated, and his behavior during and shortly following the criminal act often draws attention and arouses the suspicion of the law. A reasonable man would not undertake a difficult criminal task while intoxicated. If he must depend upon crime to earn his living, he is behaving no more reasonably than a surgeon who would try to operate while inebriated.

Even if we examine individuals who commit burglary or robbery, we often find that they have failed to exercise rational caution or restraint in their efforts to avoid apprehension. The fact that legal officers are more likely to apprehend and convict lower-class people does not negate this observation. One would suspect that a reasonable offender who knew he was under greater observation would exercise more caution.

The assumption that the criminal is out to make a profit does not always find support in observations of the manner in which he handles his illegal activities. Many criminals spend years in prison for crimes which even if successful would have netted only a paltry sum. The number of imprisoned criminals who have earned more than a few thousand dollars in many years of illegal activities is probably a fraction of one percent. Even if we talk of possible earnings, many crimes against property seem to be totally ineffective. Few criminals undertake illegal ventures which would earn more than two to three thousand dollars per year, although most of them risk many years of imprisonment. It could be argued that a small amount of money would not impress an upper- or middle-class person but might be quite meaningful to a lower-class person. Even if we knew the offender's needs, however, and attempted to measure his total possible earnings in a criminal venture against his risks, we would still wonder if that offender could not have earned more money through legitimate means. We might also note that it is almost as easy to "steal big" as to "steal small," and the possibilities of apprehension and the penalties are not too dissimilar.

When the criminal fails to pursue acceptable goals in a logical, consistent or effective manner, we must assume either that he is inept at solving ordinary problems, that he has met with environmental circumstances which he cannot master, or that he is driven by motivations which are not apparent and which deviate from those which society would consider reasonable. These are all qualities that could just as easily describe the mentally ill. We therefore must return to our earlier assertion that if the judgments by which we designate unreasonable behavior were consistently applied to the law violator, we would have to agree that many criminals behave in a manner that is not too dissimilar to that of the mentally ill.

It is not possible to estimate what percentage of criminal behavior should logically be described as unreasonable. Unreasonableness is almost as value-laden a concept as mental illness, and the writer does not wish to suggest that we replace the question, "Which criminals are mentally ill?," with the question, "Which criminals are unreasonable?" There is no question that the psychiatrist is likely to encounter many more criminals who look no different to him from those he has come to know as mentally ill. This perception is determined by much more than his skills or his biases. It has a great deal to do with the fact that the psychiatrist it familiar with only a selected group of offenders. To be seen by a psychiatrist, an offender must first be apprehended, must be charged with a crime and must be given a court trial or incarcerated. There is no precise way of knowing whether or not apprehended or convicted criminals differ sociologically or psychologically from their more fortunate brethren. If reasonable and self-serving criminal behaviors do occur, however, they are not likely to be seen in that criminal population which eventually comes to prison. The incarcerated offender is by definition an inefficient offender, and just like a person who is inefficient at anything else he is more likely to be disturbed.

Finally, we must note that the community bases its judgments of reasonableness only upon behavior it can observe plus certain inferences and prejudices as to what is going on in the mind of the deviant person. The judgments of society are not based on a complete knowledge of the many complex motivations which act upon a given individual. Nor does society consider those aspects of the offender's personality and situation which might have made his behavior appear as something totally different to him from what it did to the community. If we look at the way an individual perceives his own actions or if we try and enter into his phenomenological field, much of his behavior which initially appeared to be unreasonable becomes more understandable and hence more reasonable.

When the society asks a psychiatrist to explain unreasonable behavior, it is really asking him to discover the rationality (those factors which consciously or unconsciously influence the individual) which lies behind a behavior the community cannot accept or understand. Stated differently, a major task of the psychiatrist is to uncover what the patient is looking for and describe how his perception of the world leads him to adopt certain means of finding it. This kind of inquiry is as relevant to unreasonable criminals as it is to the mentally ill.

# Chapter 5

# CONCEPTS OF ADAPTATION

SO THAT we may better understand the concept of crime as adaptation, we should consider other, pertinent ideas, such as those of steady-state mechanisms, interpersonal relations and phenomenology. It may also be helpful to examine briefly more general psychoanalytic theory.

## Steady-State Mechanisms

Much of the psychiatric view of adaptation is derived from the physiological principle of homeostasis, or the tendency of living organisms to maintain a relatively constant internal environment. In 1865 Claude Bernard supplied a foundation for the steady-state or organismic theory when he asserted that "it is the fixity of the internal environment which is the condition of free and independent life."[1] Bernard looked upon all the body's mechanisms as having only one purpose: "preserving constant the conditions of life in the internal environment." In 1926 Walter Cannon elaborated these concepts and gave the name "homeostasis" to the constancy which was maintained by continually active regulatory processes, and the name "stress" to those external and internal conditions which tended to disturb the constant state of the fluid matrix.[2] Cannon saw adaptations to stress as automatic and always directed toward bringing an unbalanced situation back to a prior state of equilibrium. The principle of homeostasis makes it possible to look upon physiological reactions as adaptive. Under stress the organism makes a number of internal readjustments which unify the body for maximum physical effort. These reactions may themselves disturb the internal environment, but they disturb it in a manner that leaves the organism better prepared to retain ultimate total stability. What the physician defines as symptomatic physiological disturbance can also be looked upon as the organism's effort to protect its state of equilibrium and ultimately its own existence.

The principle of homeostasis, which has proved so useful in integrating biochemical and physiological knowledge, has also been extended to explain more complex psychological and social adaptations. It has been pointed out that man ultimately seeks to maintain a constant external environment (for example, by collecting money and food or building shelter) in an effort to guard against potential external threats to internal consistency. G. L. Freeman states: "Although it may sound farfetched at first, we should properly regard complicated total behavior and maintenance operation of such organs as the liver as both directed to the same ultimate end—internal quiescence, relaxation and the preservation of essential constancies."[3]

Edward Dempsey has noted: "Just as the appearance of salt conserving mechanisms allowed marine animals to invade fresh water so has the ability to manufacture clothing and to build houses permitted man to live in climates otherwise inimical to his existence. The intellectual processes by which this problem was solved must therefore be regarded as a homeostatic mechanism."[4]

The principle of homeostasis can be extended to describe the total biological, psychological and social behavior of the organism as it seeks to maintain a state of equilibrium.

Extension of the principle of homeostasis to "higher" forms of psychological and social behavior brings us to a consideration of psychological stress. There has been some disagreement as to whether psychological stress can be considered as the same type of phenomenon as physiological stress.* Psychiatrists, however, have generally held to a unitary viewpoint and have viewed the principle of homeostasis as applicable to both physiological and psychological behaviors. Menninger has presented perhaps the most comprehensive conceptual framework, which views all behavior as seeking

* As we begin to examine psychological stress in man, the problem is complicated by the fact that similar stress situations have different impacts upon different people. If we speak of stress as a stimulus, we assume a potential effect but must recognize that we cannot predict the effect of a given stress upon a given person. If we view stress as a response, we must limit the variety of stresses to be studied and will have difficulty in defining the kind of response to measure. This is an extremely difficult problem and has led to a variety of approaches. Some writers define stress as stimulus, others as response, and perhaps most use the term to refer to a broad class of events involving interaction between environmental stimulus and the adaptive capabilities of the organism. Our use of the term "stress" will be somewhat imprecise, and we will adhere to broader definitions which consider stress in terms of stimulus, response and intervening phenomenological states.

certain conditions of equilibrium or a "vital balance."[5] His model of adaptation goes beyond earlier physiological concepts of homeostasis insofar as it also considers the principle of heterostasis, a concept which must be used to explain such phenomena as organismic growth and change. Menninger defines heterostasis as "the progressive moving away from the status quo, the search for new and unsettled states, in contrast to the automatic return to the comfortable and relatively tension-free previous state of balance." This modification of the organismic viewpoint seems to be essential to explain the tendency of the organism periodically to move away and then return to stable conditions.

Menninger views adaptation in terms of the mechanisms the organism utilizes to control disturbances of equilibrium. Adaptations to severe stress are somewhat expensive insofar as they lead to a certain amount of dyscontrol and dysorganization. The adaptation itself leads to a new kind of internal and external balance, which may or may not be effective. If it is not effective, the organism must invoke more drastic mechanisms which lead to a greater degree of dyscontrol. Menninger states: "Increasing dysfunction, increasing dyscontrol, increasing dysorganization can be identified empirically in a series of hierarchical levels, each one reflecting a stage of greater impairment of control and organization." Deviant behaviors or psychiatric symptoms are then looked upon as devices employed by the organism to deal with emergencies, disturbed equilibrium and threatened dyscontrol.

This viewpoint can be applied to the problem of criminal behavior. At some moments an individual may experience stresses which for him are most efficiently adapted to (in a manner which preserves organismic integrity) by a behavior which may violate the criminal code. The performance of the criminal act holds out the promise of gratification and relief of tension, which will restore a state of balance. If the individual did not indulge in the prohibited behavior, he would have to find an alternative adaptation which might be more incapacitating or more expensive. The "choice" of the criminal adaptation is dependent upon many factors, including the nature of the stresses impinging upon the individual, his state of anxiety or tension and those previously learned attitudes and reaction patterns which lead him to perceive the situation in a given manner.

## Interpersonal Relationships

The most important stresses contributing to crime as adaptation arise in disturbed interpersonal relationships. Man is psychologically dependent upon his fellow man for gratification and survival. He begins his life in a completely dependent state, and although he may grow to a greater independence, his need for contact with others is never substantially diminished. Children who do not receive adequate interpersonal gratification during the first year of life may become ill and may even die.[6] Increased evidence from human experience and animal experimentation tells us that isolation from others leads to severe and sometimes irreparable damage.[7] Man must derive his satisfactions in life through a constant process of interaction during which he both satisfies and is satisfied by others. Frequently, however, his needs are frustrated. Failure to find gratification of interpersonal needs engenders powerful and often maladaptive emotions.

While painful interpersonal experiences are a constant threat throughout life, psychiatrists have discovered that the most critical experiences are likely to occur within the first few years. Unsatisfactory interpersonal relationships, particularly with the mother and father, are believed to engender ineffective patterns of behavior which become firmly entrenched within the structure of the personality. Individuals so damaged tend to live out their lives continually repeating behaviors which do not have optimum adaptive value. They are unable to obtain gratification from others in a direct and socially acceptable manner.

Interpersonal relationships are easiest to study if only two people are involved. Many of the concepts of psychiatry are derived from examination of dyadic relationships such as mother-child, father-child, sibling-sibling or husband-wife. The concept of the dyadic interpersonal relationship can also be extended to include the individual's relationship toward a group (society) or toward himself. Attitudes and behavior toward society are ultimately derived from the experiences one has had with others. The image which any single person has of society as a whole is, in a sense, a personification which represents the intertwining of a myriad of images of important people in his past life.

Similarly, the individual's attitudes and behaviors toward himself are determined by interpersonal experience. A large part of our personality reflects the identifications we make with others. Each of us takes into our own personality a part of another person's personality, to which we continue to react in our daily behavior. A different way of looking at this is that we are continually "on stage."[8] Even when we are alone, most of what we do or think is in some way related to recollections as to how others have reacted to us or expectations as to how others will react to us.

One important aspect of interpersonal behavior is that any given interaction is determined not only by the immediate situation but also by past interpersonal experience. Let us consider the example of a delinquent boy who when approached in a kindly manner by a well-meaning counselor reacts in an angry manner. There are many possible explanations for this response, but one way of looking at the boy's behavior is that he does not respond to the realistic intentions of his counselor because the interpersonal situation brings out attitudes related to past experience. If the boy has previously been treated badly by other authority figures, his communications to the counselor may not be specifically directed to him but may also be aimed toward all those who have treated him poorly in the past. To the extent that such interpersonal behavior is not a response to present realities, it is likely to have an apparently unreasonable quality.

Much of our behavior can be looked upon as out-of-awareness efforts to relate to and to communicate with introjected objects, individuals who still reside within us even though they are not physically present.[9] The concept of communication with introjects is extremely useful in explaining inappropriate behaviors. A person who becomes depressed when there is no observable reason for sadness may be responding to realistic interpersonal stress which is not apparent, but it is also possible that he is locked in an unresolved communication process with an introjected figure. This mechanism is especially apparent and useful in understanding the behavior of severely disturbed people such as schizophrenics. The verbalizations and actions of the schizophrenic may seem to have little relevance to anything that is going on in the immediate environment. The schizophrenic's behavior is often more adequately explained as an effort to communicate with internalized objects.

Crime is a distinctively interpersonal phenomenon. The criminal act usually involves an infringement upon another person's physical being, his beliefs or his property. Particularly when criminal behavior is maladaptive and unreasonable, the psychiatrist seeks its psychological causes in the stresses which arise between people. Some of these stresses are based upon the realities of the immediate interpersonal situation. Others are based upon past interpersonal experience.

Man cannot live in society without experiencing needs and desires toward his fellow man which are incompatible in the sense that one cannot be gratified without sacrificing another. Some of the conflicts engendered by social forces have been described earlier. The psychiatrist sees conflict as arising when the organism is faced with the need for reconciling discordant desires, needs and values. Such conflicts take many forms. Physical needs may conflict with the needs of society. The desire to have a person behave in a certain way may conflict with the desire to have him behave in a different way. The individual's impulses may conflict with his internalized values and standards. Or the individual may be faced with conflicting messages from others, each urging him to behave in a manner which is incompatible with the demands of the others.

The existence of conflict is itself a stress. When the organism is confronted with a conflict, it tends to develop anxiety, an unpleasurable emotion characterized by physiological changes (such as increased heart rate, heart activity, muscular tension or weakness) and by psychological experiences (perception of unpleasant feelings and sensations, a feeling of apprehension and impending harm or disaster). Anxiety as a by-product of conflict thus also becomes a powerful stress upon the organism. Unreasonable criminal behavior can frequently be viewed as an effort to ward off or alleviate the unpleasant effect of anxiety.

## Phenomenology

We have noted that different subjects respond to similar stresses differently. A given psychological response is always dependent upon the manner in which a stress is perceived. It is not easy to study objectively the manner in which an individual perceives stress. We can observe a subject or we can develop rating scales, psychological tests and sociometric measures of his behavior, but we may still not know what he actually is experiencing. To understand a person truly, we must enter into his subjective world. This requires a departure from traditional methods of inquiry and has led psychiatrists to borrow philosophical insights which help them understand the phenomenological world or subjective experiences of their patients.

Psychiatric phenomenology is based upon Edmund Husserl's methodological principle of unbiased observation. It is described by Henri Ellenberger as follows:

> In the presence of a phenomenon (whether it be an external object or a state of mind) the phenomenologist uses an absolutely unbiased approach; he observes phenomena as they manifest themselves and only as they manifest themselves. This observation is accomplished by means of an operation of the mind which Husserl called the *epoche* or "psychological phenomenological reduction." The observer "puts the world between brackets," i.e., he excludes from his mind not only any judgment of value about the phenomena but also any information whatever concerning the cause and background.[10]

Psychiatrists began their studies of phenomenology by examining in detail their patients' descriptions of their own illnesses. Descriptive phenomenology now also attempts to learn about the patient's inner world by intensive and unbiased interviewing. Listening to the patient talk about his perceptions of the world and attempting to avoid all value judgment enable the phenomenologically oriented psychiatrist to approach an understanding of what his patient is experiencing. It is thus possible to obtain an understanding of adaptation which would be unobtainable if behavior were studied simply in terms of stimulus and responses. If the psychiatrist is able to obtain a picture of his subject's intervening emotional state, he is in a better position to understand how a given stress directs the subject toward a given adaptation.

## Some Psychoanalytic Concepts

The conceptual framework which psychiatrists find most useful for clarifying the meaning and impact of psychological stress upon the personality is based upon the insights of psychoanalysis.

Psychoanalytic theory is based on two fundamental hypotheses. The first, that of psychic determinism, asserts that nothing within the mind happens by chance and that each psychic event is determined by the one which precedes it. The second hypothesis, that of the unconscious, suggests that the linkages of causality or determinism in our psychic lives are not apparent because the most important psychic processes take place at a level below our awareness. Both hypotheses are extremely useful in clarifying the genesis of unreasonable behavior.

According to psychoanalytic theory, the forces which provide energy for the direction of psychic processes reside in motivational tendencies or drives. Some students of psychoanalytic theory see drives as hypothetical constructs or intervening variables between stimulus and response.[11] If viewed in this way, motivations are learned action tendencies which need not be visualized as inborn biological needs. Classical psychoanalytic theory holds that a drive is a genetically determined constituent, an instinct, and that instinctual forces produce states of excitement or tension which in turn impel the individual to find gratification. In his later writings Freud distinguished two basic drives, the sexual and the aggressive, and looked upon these as inherited instinctual tendencies.[12] More recent psychoanalytic concepts of motivation suggest the existence of innate forces or energy sources, but offer alternative explanations of aggressive behavior which rejects Freud's notion of the aggressive instinct.[13, 14]

Most psychiatrists posit the existence of some biological source for drive energy. The development and expression of the sexual and aggressive drives are believed to be partially determined by the anatomical and physiological changes which occur as the child grows. Such evolvement of drive direction, however, must be examined against the background of the child's interpersonal relationships, particularly with his mother, who in the earlier years is the primary source of gratification.

The psychic representation of the mainly unconscious drive tendencies is conceptualized as the *id*. If the child were allowed to do so, he would constantly seek immediate gratification of his id impulses whether they were socially acceptable or not. He would seek pleasure and avoid displeasure (the pleasure principle). However, the child is a helpless organism completely dependent upon others. He cannot dictate the terms of drive gratification. As he is repeatedly frustrated by others, he learns that there is a real world outside of himself, a world which can inflict pain and deprive him of pleasure. He learns to take account of this world and develops an *ego,* which is the part of the psyche concerned with gratification or discharge of the id and adaptation to the external environment.

The ego must accurately perceive and accomodate itself to the realities of the external environment (the reality principle). It is a central control system of the personality, which directs the expression of biological drives in a world in which others will not tolerate certain direct manifestations of these drives. The ego seeks mastery of the environment by accurate perception, logical thinking, motoric activity and by constantly testing the accuracy of the stimuli it receives (reality testing). The ego can also be looked upon as the mediator of the adaptive process. Its major functions include maintenance of the steady state and preservation of organismic integrity.

A third conceptualized part of the psyche is the *superego*. The superego is a part of the ego which contains the representations of parental and societal values and standards. The concept of the superego, however, also includes an unconscious component of conscience. The superego is believed to undergo its most important development during the third to fifth years of life as a consequence of the need to control specific aggressive and sexual drives which are directed toward the parents (the Oedipus complex). As the child is forced to repudiate his wishes toward his parents, he internalizes their own values and morals. He identifies himself with them, and parental or societal prohibitions become permanently installed within his personality. With the formation of the superego the child sacrifices some freedom to act in a pleasure-seeking manner, but at the same time he gains a certain degree of social independence.

The ego is assisted by the development of the superego, but as a consequence it is also confronted with new problems. It now must not only coordinate the expression of id impulses with the dictates of society but also deal with an internalized representation of society which is constantly present. The ego now must be seen as serving three masters: reality, the id and the superego.

Within this structural conceptualization of personality the role of conflict is crucial. The ego itself can to a large extent be conceived of as having developed as a consequence of conflict between the needs of the individual (the id) and the needs of society. Once developed, the ego may find itself in conflict with both the id and the superego. It may have to restrain the expression of drives in order to preserve the individual's place in society or it may find itself in conflict with a superego which prevents the emergence of behavior that might be adaptive.

If the ego is ineffective, the organism experiences anxiety. In his later writings Freud defined anxiety as an effect produced by the ego whenever it was confronted with danger or the anticipation of danger.[15] Danger exists when the psyche can be overwhelmed by an influx of stimuli too great to be mastered or discharged. The individual is sensitized to danger through a series of inevitable experiences during childhood. These experiences create a fear of losing a loved object (the parents), a fear of losing love, a fear of bodily harm (castration anxiety) or a fear of disapproval or punishment from the superego. Many stressful situations can revive these fears. In the course of development the ego begins to utilize anxiety as a signal, or a warning of the possible emergence of conflict and the experiencing of danger.

If man is to survive in a civilized society, it is essential that his ego keep an adequate check or control upon his id. He must control the expression or even the perception of some unacceptable impulses lest they create conflict and unbearable anxiety. The mechanisms by which the ego controls the id, deals with the superego and thereby averts anxiety are referred to as defense mechanisms. They are actually adaptive processes which resolve conflict and allow the organism to maintain equilibrium in the face of stress.

Defense mechanisms achieve compromises between the motivations of the individual and the dictates of society. As compromises they have varying adaptive value. Some defense mechanisms strengthen the individual's ability to function within society. Others lead to behaviors which are not adaptive and which in themselves lead to further conflict and anxiety.

According to psychoanalytic theory, defense mechanisms are constantly in operation and are instrumental in determining the course of personality development. Character traits, personal attitudes and belief systems to a large extent develop out of conflict. It must be pointed out, however, that psychoanalysis does not teach that all adaptation must be understood in terms of unconscious defense mechanisms. Conscious efforts to master the environment through conflict-free adaptive mechanisms of the ego are also felt to be major determinants of behavior.

The psychoanalyst looks upon mental illness as behavior which arises largely out of conflict. Mental illness can be described in terms of the mental mechanisms which the ego employs to reduce tension and find a state of equilibrium. When the psychoanalyst examines adult subjects, he is primarily interested in the question of vulnerability to illness. Some individuals arrive at adolescence or adulthood already predisposed to various types of maladaptive behavior. Such people have immature or maladaptive personalities. Since they have not mastered the stresses and problems of early childhood, they remain peculiarly vulnerable or predisposed to mental illness. A basic psychoanalytic postulate states that mental illness does not develop unless predisposition is present. This concept helps us to understand the selective impact of stress upon different individuals, or why a stress that will not trouble one person will seriously trouble another.

Psychoanalytic theory attempts to explain all behavior, adaptive as well as maladaptive. The psychiatrist, on the other hand, is primarily interested in those forms of maladaptation that the society defines as mental illness. Although psychiatrists are painfully aware of the theoretical limitations of psychoanalysis, they do accept the basic principles of unconscious motivation and psychic determinism and find it useful to think of the ego as the mediator of the adaptive process. There is much disagreement, however, among all psychiatrists, including psychoanalysts, as to the nature, direction and classification of adaptive mechanisms.

## Psychoanalysis, Psychiatry and Crime

We are now in a position to examine how psychoanalytic and psychiatric concepts have been applied to the problem of criminal behavior. First, psychiatrists recognize the universal nature of unconscious sexual and aggressive drives, and they believe that any person is a potential criminal. The evidence for this belief is derived from the study of the fantasy and dream life of the so-called normal individual. The psychiatrist asks, "Who among us has not had a sexual or aggressive fantasy which if carried out would have resulted in a violation of the law?" or "Who among us has not committed crimes of violence or violated sexual laws during his dreams?" Every man has within him the capacity to commit the most objectionable antisocial acts, no matter how civilized or sophisticated his social training has made him.

Moving beyond notions of crime as a random expression of pleasure-seeking emotions, psychiatrists have turned to a study of the influence of organized motivation. While motivations are ultimately derived from some type of drive energy, they become structured by experience as the individual matures. Some motivations represent compromise wishes and some become distorted in ways that are socially maladaptive. Motivations also vary in the degree to which they are consciously recognized by the individual. Psychiatrists have learned that it is extremely difficult to unravel the motivations underlying criminal behavior. The criminal may hide the real motivations for his behavior from others; quite often he also hides them from himself. When the psychiatrist learns the motivations underlying a criminal act, he is able to offer only a partial explanation of that behavior. We must repeat again, however, that the criminal's motivation to violate a law can never be a total explanation of a crime.

The psychiatrist is also interested in the means by which the individual controls his antisocial impulses, and he is especially concerned with any defects in the internalized control system. Much psychiatric theorizing about crime focuses upon stresses which weaken the ego and superego. Any weakness of the control system is believed to be conducive to criminality. Unfortunately, many nonsophisticated students of criminology mistakenly see this concept as representing the entirety of psychoanalytic or psychiatric thinking. They believe that the psychiatrist is arguing that all crimes should be explained as a simple breakdown in control mechanisms. Actually, such beliefs are founded upon a gross oversimplification of psychiatric theory. Control in this sense refers to direct restraint of unacceptable impulses. It does not have the same meaning as control which is directed toward minimizing disturbances of equilibrium. Partial breakdown in the mechanisms which maintain equilibrium can eventually lead to behaviors such as crime. This is a complicated process, however, which is concerned with something quite different from control as simple restraint.

While some aggressive and some sexual activity is often correlated with a weakening of control mechanisms, similar statements applied to a legally defined criminal act can be misleading. The act of law violation is often a deliberate, planned and complicated operation which may require a great deal of ego strength. If the psychiatrist assumes that crime is related to abdication of controls, he must also assume that such abdication is always bad. If he accepts the belief that crime occurs only when controls are lacking, he is in danger of making the same error as earlier biologically oriented psychiatrists, namely, searching for a defect and moralistically accepting the inherent correctness of our laws. This argument can be clarified by considering the following hypothetical situation.

If the United States suddenly became a totalitarian state and the writer could no longer practice the kind of psychiatry he believed in, he would have to seek other means of sustenance. If he could not find such means legally, he might be reduced to seeking illegal means. He might even attack the existing social structure in an effort to bring back a world in which he could survive more efficiently. In either case there would be a good possibility that the society would label him a criminal. Yet nowhere have we assumed any defect in his control system. Only the situation has changed. Actually, the writer would need even greater ego strength to survive in what he perceived to be a predatory society. We might also note that there are some noncriminal activities which require a considerable abdication of control. Sexual intercourse, dancing and some athletic activities cannot be fully enjoyed unless the individual "lets himself go." One of the frequently voiced criticisms of our society is that our people are too controlled and nonexpressive.

Even if we consider those crimes which seem to be a clear expression of antisocial impulses, it is not possible to describe a linear relationship between such expressions and ego and superego defect. We must examine an alleged personality defect within the total situation. Let us consider the case of a brain-damaged child. Such a child will be looked upon as having a damaged ego. If he behaves in an antisocial manner, the psychiatrist is tempted to relate his behavior directly to a defect in his control mechanisms. More accurately, however, we are dealing with a general shift in equilibrium between the child and his environment. If he has a damaged ego, the child will be exposed to many new social stresses and will experience some lack of capacity to find useful adaptations. Antisocial behavior may now occur with greater frequency because in his new state of ego impairment the child finds himself in a world in which antisocial behavior is the best adaptation available. This is quite a different kind of causality from that implied in simplified notions of crime as a breakdown in control mechanisms.

The psychiatrist cannot derive an integrated conceptual framework for understanding crime simply through studies of motivational tendencies or control mechanisms. He must direct his attention to the processes by which the organism seeks to sustain itself. This means that he must concern himself with the ego as the mediator of the adaptive process. He must repeatedly ask himself why the criminal's ego "chooses" law violation as the most economical adaptational alternative.

*Chapter 6*

# THE ADAPTIVE VALUE OF CRIME

CRIME is an adaptation to life stress. It is best understood in terms of the manner in which the individual experiences the biological, psychological and socially determined situations of his existence. Since crime so often seems to be harmful to the criminal and since it represents only one of several possible adaptations, the criminologist must grapple with the question of why the criminal solution is "chosen." Our purpose in this chapter will be to suggest a conceptual framework which will clarify the psychological advantages of crime and which will help us to understand why an individual who experiences the world in a certain way finds crime to be the most desirable adaptation.

## Autoplastic vs. Alloplastic Adaptations

The criminal act involves either a motoric action or in rare instances a clearly defined refusal to perform a motoric action (crimes of negligence). A criminal act usually changes the external environment, while other types of adaptation are less likely to alter it. It is possible to adapt to stress, for example, by a change in physiology or personal belief systems. These latter mechanisms can be looked upon as efforts to alter the internal rather than the external environment. Freud, Sandor Ferenczi[1] and, later Franz J. Alexander[2] differentiated two major types of adaptation. When confronted with stress, the organism may change itself (the internal environment), or it may attempt to change the situation (the external environment). The first type of behavior is called autoplastic and the second alloplastic. The criminal act is almost always an alloplastic adaptation.

The concept of autoplasticity and alloplasticity admittedly represents an inherently inconsistent and oversimplified categorization of adaptive responses. It assumes a distinctiveness between the internal and external environments and ignores their continual interaction with one another. Once we recognize that any change in either the external or internal environment leads to a change in the other, classification of a particular adaptation in a single category has limited meaning.

The concept of autoplasticity and alloplasticity has also been misused in discussions of neurosis vs. crime. Most psychoanalytic writers correctly assign the criminal act to alloplastic defenses. They assume, however, that neurosis is a purely autoplastic adaptation. This latter assumption is not valid. Some mental illnesses (e.g., catatonic excitement) are a direct attack upon the environment, and in fact most mental illnesses are subtle efforts to alter the environment through a communication of helplessness and suffering.

Being aware of the limitations and potential misuses of the terms "autoplastic" and "alloplastic," we will still find them useful in attempting to describe adaptations. (The reader will note that the terms "autoplastic" and "alloplastic" bear some resemblance to the categories of stress response defined as coping vs. defense or attitude vs. behavior in sociological literature.) Once the reader is forewarned as to the artificial nature of these terms, they can be utilized to describe certain complex issues without endless qualification.

What kinds of adaptations are available to man? Although alloplastic behaviors are easy to observe, they are extremely difficult to classify. They serve one of two major purposes: to gratify drives or to ward off attack. They therefore must include not only muscular activities of the body but also verbal behavior which is designed to change a situation. Both verbal and nonverbal efforts to alter the environment can be direct or indirect, gross or subtle, socially acceptable or nonacceptable.

There are other forms of alloplastic adaptation which can be considered either as primary tendencies of man or, in psychoanalytic terms, as derivatives of drive energy. One is creativity. Creating buildings, books, music or art is a highly prized form of adaptation. Another is play. While play can perhaps be seen as a form of creativity, it can also be looked upon as a seeking of motoric action for action's sake alone. Play serves as a reminder that man must have motoric activity to exist. If the world does not offer him sufficient outlets, he constantly strives to create his own. New games are created when the possibilities of changing the environment are diminished. Such games provide an artificial or substitute environment which requires constant mastery.

Autoplastic adaptations are somewhat easier to describe. They include efforts to adapt by changing beliefs or attitudes, by gratifying needs in fantasy or by altering the biological state. Changing personal belief systems allows one to live with many situations which would otherwise be intolerable. Gratification of needs through fantasy allows a person to tolerate many different kinds of deprivation. Man can sustain himself under adverse circumstances for long periods of time if his imagination is sufficiently productive. Physiological and biochemical responses of the organism to stress can also be looked upon as adaptations which primarily alter the internal environment. Originally designed to enable the individual to cope with changes in the external environment, they may through learning or conditioning be elicited in situations in which they are not needed. Extensive physiological modifications often change the individual without appreciably influencing his surrounding world.

Autoplastic adaptations imply a certain amount of motoric passivity and a great deal of compromise. They are more commonly associated with the experiencing and tolerating of painful affects. Autoplastic adaptations tend to take on greater significance as civilization becomes more complicated. It is likely that primitive man met his needs primarily through efforts to alter the external environment. With the advent of a complex civilization, stresses tend to be man-made rather than natural. This becomes increasingly evident in today's world. We have made enormous progress in mastering the elements, but ultimate destruction is threatened if man cannot change himself and learn to live in peace with his neighbors.

Up to this point adaptations have been considered only in terms of their capacity for reducing tension or gratifying needs. The most efficient way in which an individual can gratify a drive or modify the external stresses of his world is through a motor action. If such actions are not available to him, he must do something to change himself. In terms of purely biological needs alloplastic adaptations are clearly more advantageous to the individual. Autoplastic adaptations imply a lack of motoric action, and there are limits to man's ability to tolerate passivity.

Criteria for evaluating the favorable or unfavorable quality of a given adaptation are insufficient if they are framed only in terms of an adaptation's capacity to satisfy biological needs. A useful judgment of the favorability of any adaptation must be based on broader criteria. We can search for these criteria either in needs of the society or in the needs of the individual. In keeping with our approach throughout this book, we will describe additional measures of the value of an adaptation in terms of individual needs.

The advantages of a given adaptation can be measured by the extent to which the adaptation itself does *not* constitute a new stress. According to this criterion, some autoplastic adaptations are clearly more favorable than others. If a man is rejected by a lover, he is in a better position if he accepts his loss and prepares himself to accept another woman than if he develops a paranoid attitude toward all women or develops a psychosomatic illness. It is also possible to judge the favorable or unfavorable aspects of an alloplastic mechanism by the new stresses it creates. In this frame of reference, the stressfulness of an alloplastic adaptation is dependent upon the way in which it is interpreted by the society. If a man's behavior elicits angry and retaliatory actions in others, it has limited adaptive value. When considered together, the criteria of tension reduction, need gratification and tendency to produce new stress provide a frame of reference by which we can determine the maladaptiveness of criminal behavior for a given individual. If crime does not reduce tension or gratify, and if it brings the criminal new troubles, it is not a useful adaptational device.

There is another measure by which we can judge the favorable quality of either an autoplastic or an alloplastic adaptation. An adaptation can be evaluated by the extent to which it requires a sacrifice of a potentiality that is inherent in the individual and that is not denied to other, more fortunate members of the same society. We assume here that man is driven to fulfill his own potentialities. If he is not permitted to develop his inherent capacities, his existence becomes less meaningful. Alloplastic adaptations which attack a stressful situation indirectly and do not allow for fullest gratification or creativity are less advantageous than those that do. Autoplastic adaptations which require a permanent surrender of the possibility of mastery and gratification have similar disadvantages. These statements are based on a philosophical rather than a scientific point of view, for it is this writer's belief that any adaptation which results in an adjustment at a lower level of existence and which is far below an individual's capabilities is an unnatural and unhealthy state of being.

It is not possible to talk about man realizing his potentials without also commenting on man's desire for freedom. A wish to be free of oppressive control by others is a dominating force in the lives of many individuals. It is surprising, therefore, that with the exception of Erich Fromm[3] and Thomas Szasz[4] psychiatric and psychoanalytic theoreticians have given little consideration to this topic. Psychoanalysis tends to focus upon the individual's need for others and upon the restraints to individual freedom which are necessary for the maintenance of civilization. Obviously, man must sacrifice certain freedoms if he is to live within a civilized community. However, to the extent that he is denied freedoms that are available to others in the same community, he experiences himself as less fulfilled. A lack of freedom, then, can be looked upon as a limitation of available alloplastic adaptations. Autoplastic adaptations are primarily conciliatory and compromising insofar as they do no more than help the individual to adjust to an absence of freedom. They are advantageous only when they prepare the individual for some future reward or when they increase his potential for gaining more freedom at a later date.

## Oppression and Limitation of Adaptational Alternatives

To a certain extent the stresses of life are out of man's control and are determined by natural events. As our technological skills have increased, however, the number of natural stresses which threaten man has gradually diminished. The major problems of our era are man-made. Modern man experiences the most severe stresses when others attempt arbitrarily to control, deprive or abuse him.* We can speak of such stresses under the heading of interpersonal oppression. In this context oppression implies neglect, selfishness or malevolence on the part of others.

The meaning of an oppressive stress to an individual is influenced by a number of factors. Some interpersonal and social oppression is real, immediate and direct and is perceived as such by the individual. Other oppressive stresses may be indirect, subtle and insidious (but nevertheless real and observable) and will have an effect upon him even if he is totally or partially unaware of them. A child, for example, might be subtly rejected by parents who constantly verbalize attitudes of love and affection. Such a child would not be in a position to accurately experience and acknowledge the negative aspect of his parents' behavior and could not respond to it directly. The oppressive stress would influence his attitudes or behavior, but it would not be consciously experienced in its true form.

In other situations an individual may experience more oppression than actually exists. Many actions are experienced as oppressive even when the motivations of others are basically benevolent. Limitations of the individual's ability to obtain information from others and personality defects often

* The author does not wish to underestimate the importance of biological stress. Obviously some biological factors will contribute to interpersonal oppression. We are temporarily leaving consideration of such factors aside, however, in order to present a more simplified discussion.

lead to interferences in communication; thus benevolence may be misinterpreted as malevolence. A child, for example, may feel oppressed by his parents' setting limits on permissible behavior even when such limits are in the service of the child's own interest. A person who is plagued by his own conscience will experience oppression where none exists. So will one who projects his inadequacies and fears onto the external world and learns constantly to anticipate attacks from others. We must, therefore, distinguish between unrealistic and realistic oppression and between that realistic oppression which is perceived directly and that which is not.

For purposes of clarity oppression can be classified as follows:

1. Objectively measurable oppression
   a. Social and interpersonal stresses which are real, direct and recognized
   b. Social and interpersonal stresses which are real, but indirect and totally or partly unrecognized
2. Oppression which is perceived but which does not have an apparent source in the observable environment
   a. Misunderstood oppression
   b. Internal oppression (superego pressures)
   c. Projected oppression

Everyone feels oppressed at one time or another. Yet most of the time we find ways of adapting to minor stresses which do not substantially diminish our potentialities. We learn to fight for our gratifications, to find enjoyable substitutes or to delay our hopes of future rewards. Yet there are some situations in which oppression can become so severe that no alloplastic or autoplastic response seems capable of providing a favorable solution. There are millions of people in our country who encounter such situations with monotonous regularity. Oppression for such people becomes a condition of life. For many, social forces constitute the chief sources of oppression. These are the poverty-stricken and those subjected to discrimination on the basis of race or ethnic origin. For others, oppression takes place in a family or two-person situation. For still others, oppression operates as a continuous pressure from punitive internalized images and standards (introjects).

How can we describe the emotional state of an individual who feels so oppressed that his survival seems to require that he either abandon direct gratification and surrender potentiality or experience greater stress? The terms which come closest to describing this *subjective* experience are "helplessness" or "powerlessness." Freud used the term "helplessness" to describe a situation in which mastery of impulses was not possible and from this concept derived his later theory of anxiety.[5] The psychoanalytic model is only minimally concerned with that kind of helplessness which follows a surrender of potentiality, namely, that helplessness which might exist without an accompanying experience of anxiety. Yet a person can feel helpless or powerless and experience other kinds of painful affects such as resignation, apathy or despair.

Social theorists such as Karl Marx,[6] Max Weber[7] and C. Wright Mills[8] have employed the term "powerless" to describe a situation in which the individual feels that he is incapable of influencing his environment. Their concept would include as "powerless" or "helpless" many who do not manifest overt anxiety. For our purposes we will use the term "helplessness" and define it as the feeling of being oppressed and not being able to do anything about it. This definition includes those who experience both helplessness and anxiety and those who experience helplessness without anxiety. Helplessness is dependent upon the extent to which the individual perceives himself as being oppressed, the physical and mental strengths which he can mobilize to deal with his oppressors and the modifiability of the oppressive stress. Although helplessness thus varies in degree, as an emotional state it possesses certain consistent qualities. It implies not only fear of possible annihilation but also want without hope of gratification, a limitation of autonomy and a limitation of freedom.

The subjective feeling of helplessness plays an important role in the genesis of criminal action. Unreasonable criminal behavior in particular can be viewed as a direct effort to combat the painful affect of helplessness or as an indirect effort to defend against the emergence of this painful emotional state.

The relatedness of oppression, helplessness and the criminal adaptation can be clarified by examination of a hypothetical situation in which helplessness is almost complete. The phenomenological world of the potential criminal can be compared to that of an American prisoner of war confined in a Chinese Communist prison camp. He finds himself living in a situation in which he has some belief that he will stay alive but where the possibility of ultimate rescue is remote. In his day-to-day life he is regularly degraded, is completely dependent upon his captors for the barest necessities for survival and is deprived of opportunities for motoric action or gratification. How would such an individual attempt to adapt to this grievous situation?

Beginning with autoplastic adaptations, there is the possibility that the prisoner could modify his views of his captors in such a way as to make his punishment more acceptable. He might decide that he has been fighting for the wrong side and that he deserves to be punished. While this adaptation could lead to subsequent alloplastic behaviors (cooperating with the Communists) that might eventually improve his situation, it would require a painful acquiescence to the norms of a culture that has been treating him badly. The prisoner would have to reject his own values, risk losing the friendship of his fellow inmates and acknowledge that he is even less of a free man. The reader will recognize that this adjustment bears some similarities to that made by certain oppressed individuals in our society, the most notable example being the "Uncle Tom" or the "good Negro." The suspicious person would be least likely to accept this adaptation. It is interesting to note that those American prisoners who most successfully resisted efforts at brainwashing were later found to have the highest degree of paranoia.

Perhaps the most favorable kind of autoplastic response would be a strengthening of those belief systems which offer hope. A belief in eventual rescue or a strong religious conviction would have sustaining value. The prisoner's effort to strengthen this kind of belief system would be vigorously opposed by his captors. It would also be increasingly more difficult to maintain hope with the passage of time.

The use of fantasy for gratification would be one valuable means of sustenance in this situation. Fantasy could be used to preserve self-esteem and satisfy both aggressive and sexual needs. In view of the great amount of frustration the prisoner would experience, anger toward his captors would be particularly great. This could not be expressed directly, but in fantasy vengeance could be experienced many times over. The problem with this adaptational tool is that fantasy is not easily shared, and its continued use could drive the prisoner continuously further away from other people. Extreme reliance on fantasy for gratification might eventually lead to an impairment in ability to test reality.

Those mixed autoplastic and alloplastic adaptations which would result in physiological change or the communication of painful emotions would be particularly ineffective and damaging in this situation. Ordinarily, whatever gratifications an individual can gain by suffering are available only if others are concerned. Since the Chinese guards could not be expected to be solicitous toward the suffering prisoner, communication of any emotional or physical distress would be totally ineffective.

The prisoner's opportunities to alter the external environment through motoric activity would be meager. Opportunities for sexual gratification, expression of aggression, creativity and even play would be denied. If he were fortunate enough to be confined with other American prisoners rather than being kept alone, he could find certain substitute activities. In effect, he could become part of an inmate subculture which would allow him a number of outlets for motoric expression. Such a subculture could develop its own games. It could redefine a world in which there were still possibilities for gratification open to the prisoner, albeit substitute gratifications.

The prisoner of war in such a totally oppressive situation would find that most efforts at alloplastic adaptation would be defined as criminal. If he attacked his captors (the culture) verbally, through direct physical assault or through an attempt to escape, efforts would be made to restrain and punish him. Even though the likelihood of injuring or successfully escaping his captors would be extremely remote, there would still be powerful forces driving the prisoner into making this effort. The effort alone, irrespective of its outcome, would have certain favorable effects upon the organism.

Let us for the moment focus upon only one "crime," the attempt to escape, and list its immediate beneficial effects. (1) At the moment the individual is attempting to escape he is active. As long as he can keep moving he does not feel helpless. (2) The criminal act carries with it hope. There is always the possibility that it will be successful and that the environment will be changed. (3) The escapee, once he begins to act upon his plan, is a "free" man. At that moment he is not oppressed by others. (4) The planning and carrying out of an escape provides an opportunity for both creativity and play.

The value of such "criminal actions" are clearly recognized by military forces. Soldiers are frequently instructed that they are obliged to attempt to escape no matter how desperate the circumstances. Such behavior allows the prisoner to maintain his dignity, his self-esteem and his identity as a warrior.

Even within the limited situation we are attempting to describe here, there are apparent degrees of reasonableness to "criminal behavior." An escape attempt could be carefully designed either as a group or individual project. On the other hand, it could be a futile and unplanned lashing out against the environment. The reasonableness of the criminal act would be dependent upon such factors as the degree of helplessness or desperation experienced by the prisoner, which in turn would be related to the possible substitutive behaviors available to him and the level of his ego strength, that is, his intelligence, his ability to wait and so on.

The plight of our prisoner of war bears many resemblances to that which faces the potential criminal. It is, of course, unlikely that any American citizen ever experiences the degree of oppression we have described here. There are times in the lives of all of us, however, when we feel that we have no more alternatives open to us than our hypothetical prisoner. And many Americans have been exposed to this feeling on repeated occasions throughout their lives. If favorable opportunities for altering the internal or external environment are not available, criminal action looms as a seductive antidote to an unbearable feeling of helplessness.

We can extrapolate from this harsh example of total helplessness and make three general statements as to the genesis of criminality. (1) Criminality is one of several possible adaptations to a feeling of helplessness. (2) The "selection" of criminal behavior becomes more likely when gratifications are not available in other adaptations or when alternative adaptations are actively restricted by other people. (3) In situations of partial or total oppression criminal behavior has many inherent advantages of its own. It may be sought even when other adaptations are available.

## Normality, Mental Illness and Crime

Before examining the advantages of criminality it is necessary to take a brief look at some of the alternative adaptations to helplessness available in American society. These adaptations will be categorized in terms of the cultural definitions of behavior. In earlier chapters, normality, illness and criminality were discussed as potential adaptations, each of which over a period of time could be characteristic of the same person. Let us now examine the conditions under which each of these behaviors could serve as effective adaptations to oppressive stress. While we will refer mainly to sociological stress (such as poverty or persecution), everything we will say is equally applicable to a two-person situation in which one of the parties oppresses the other.

Society tends to define normality as an absence of deviant behavior. If a person is not behaving in a sick or criminal manner, he is usually considered normal. Normality encompasses such behavior as passive acceptance of a life of poverty. In a democratic society normal behavior also includes socially acceptable efforts to break out of an oppressive situation. In the United States, for example, an oppressed person can educate himself or drive himself tirelessly and win a battle against poverty or discrimination without violating any laws or group mores. It is also possible to make legitimate efforts (usually through group action) to change the society in a direction which provides the oppressed person with greater opportunities. The labor movement and the civil rights movement are examples of such efforts.

Society's definition of normality includes two major directions of adaptation to oppressive stress. One requires a passive acceptance of oppressive situations and an effort to live within the rules of the society (conformity);

the other represents an attempt to change an oppressive situation either by acting within the rules or by attempting to change the rules through legally approved individual or group action (activism).

The "choices" of illness or crime can also be looked upon as adaptations designed to deal with an oppressive situation. Illness begins as an alteration of the internal environment. Once the state of illness or suffering is perceived and communicated, however, the sick person has some capacity to alter the external environment through following specialized rules of conduct which society designates as the sick role. Crime, on the other hand, (and, to a lesser extent, such behaviors as hoboism or Bohemianism) can be looked upon as an adaptational alternative which attempts to ignore the rules of the larger society.

If we observe the oppressed person longitudinally, we find that at any given moment in his life he employs one or more of the adaptational alternatives we have listed. He either passively accepts his plight or actively tries to change it through socially acceptable channels, through illness or through criminal activities.

These adaptations are neither static nor exclusive of one another. Often, two or three adaptations will characterize the same person within a brief span of time. The "choice" of adaptation will be primarily influenced by two factors, the advantages provided by an adaptation plus its availability

Although it has been argued that man tends to seek freedom, there is also ample evidence that he is willing to abandon it with depressing regularity. The adaptational alternative of submitting to oppression is almost always available. Passivity is especially tempting when compliance is rewarded with security and abdication of responsibility. A woman, for example, can be dominated by an overbearing husband, but if he feeds her, clothes her, makes her decisions for her and occasionally shows his love for her, she may be persuaded to accept her role with little complaint. Her life may be characterized by ineffectiveness, lethargy and occasional despair, but society will consider her normal.

Passivity and compliance need not necessarily be maladaptive traits. Obviously, many freedoms have to be abandoned if society is to survive. Even a minimum degree of social stability requires that conformity must frequently take precedence over individual needs. Sometimes passive acceptance of an oppressive situation is absolutely essential for survival. At other times it may prepare the individual for future advantages.

There are certain factors in American life conducive to acceptance of oppression. Basically passive autoplastic adjustments are furthered by the increase in fantasy material provided by an enormous growth in mass communications media. Religion still plays a prominent part in enabling people to accept a difficult existence with some grace. There are constant diversions such as television and alcohol. Those who are willing to settle for an existence which precludes realization of potentiality and implies domination by others find this alternative readily available.

Active efforts to change the environment are most advantageous when they attack an oppressive situation directly, and are socially acceptable. When these conditions are met, such efforts would be regarded as the most desirable and perhaps "healthiest" adaptation, given the prevailing value systems in American life. The problem with this adaptation is its sparse availability. One must have the physical and mental tools to battle his way out of an oppressive state, and his opponent (the society or other individuals) must be willing to compromise. Unfortunately, opportunities for altering the environment in a socially acceptable manner appear to be steadily diminishing. This is particularly true of the poor, who are experiencing increasing difficulty finding a better level of existence.

Suffering, unhappiness and anxiety are not only characteristic of the mentally ill. The helplessness which is accepted when one conforms to an oppressed state undoubtedly carries with it similar miseries. Suffering and anxiety existed in the world long before mental illness was "discovered," and there is some truth in Thoreau's statement, "The mass of men lead lives of quiet desperation." *For a person to be defined as ill, however, he must take some action which communicates his suffering.* Mental illness is more than a passive withdrawal from the environment. The person who communicates his suffering through a conversion, a phobia, an obsession or a panic attack is making an effort to elicit a certain response from others. Once having made this effort, it is possible for him to exert some degree of control over what others can do to him. In our society, for example, a person who shows that he is depressed is usually treated with kindness. His symptoms bring him not only substitute gratifications but also some defense from the arbitrary attacks of others.

Of course, such a role is not always available. Society may not recognize the existence of mental illness for certain classes of people, or it may treat its mentally ill with cruelty and derision. The advantages of being mentally ill in our country are far greater for the rich than for the poor. If a wealthy person communicates his suffering, he will most likely be given excellent care and may be offered the prospect of a psychotherapeutic relationship. The poor person is most likely to be deprived of his freedom and sent to an understaffed hospital which does not provide the highly coveted experience of psychotherapy.

To the extent that the mentally ill are treated kindly, illness becomes a favorable alternative to crime. Many psychiatrists have argued that if the delinquent is to be successfully treated he must first become neurotic. Prison workers soon learn that when antisocial activities are denied to the criminal, suffering and illness often follow. It is also true that when a psychiatrist begins to work in a prison the number of mentally ill prisoners rapidly increases. This is partly because he brings new definitions of behavior, partly because many prisoners who have been silent will now communicate their suffering and partly because many prisoners will, on an unconscious basis, begin to behave neurotically if a sick role is available. Paradoxically, an increase in mental health facilities in a correctional setting will initially increase rather than decrease the incidence of mental illness.

Mental illness (particularly that behavior which is ordinarily considered neurotic) is an indirect and in a sense "dishonest" means of fighting off oppression. One condition which is always necessary for a person to be defined as mentally ill is that others believe that he cannot control his behavior, that he is not responsible for his unreasonable actions. In order to control others or defend against attack from others, the mentally ill person must adopt a lesser role in our society, one in which he can no longer be seen as a fully responsible or free citizen. Paradoxically, mental illness requires that the individual be looked upon as helpless in order to be less helpless in his relationship with others.[9]

The author does not mean that the mentally ill patient is consciously dishonest, nor does he wish to belittle the suffering of the sick person. There is no question that people whom we call mentally ill are subjected to the severest kind of pain and misery. We cannot forget, however, that their behavior always has a purpose, and insofar as there are interpersonal determinants of mental illness, the purpose is to influence others. The sick person may suffer greatly, but his suffering brings him a certain amount of power.

There are some behaviors which society defines as mental illness and which are not accompanied by the message of "I can't help myself." These are certain psychotic states, such as mania or catatonia, in which the individual may attack the environment more directly. He may firmly believe in the inherent correctness of his actions. In these cases the label of mental illness is attached to an individual who is reluctant to accept it. The society, impressed with the unreasonableness of psychotic behavior, assumes the existence of irrational motivations, and argues that anyone who would act in such a manner could not possibly be able to help himself. The psychotic, however, may feel that he is rational and perfectly capable of helping himself. Much like the criminal, he sees his behavior as a direct effort to alleviate an oppressive situation, and does not voluntarily accept society's efforts to designate him as a sick person.

### The Advantages of Crime

Earlier in this chapter we attempted to describe the phenomenological world of the potential criminal and compared it to that of a prisoner of war. Let us now discuss in greater detail the subjective advantages of criminal behavior and also attempt to clarify some of the more observable benefits which crime can provide in the American culture. If we assume that socially acceptable efforts to change the environment are most desirable, the adaptational advantages of crime must be ranked only against the merits of illness or conformity. As such comparisons are made it will become apparent that every criminal act, even an act which provides only indirect gratification or an act that would appear to be unreasonable, has certain inherent advantages.

When man is engaged in motoric behavior, he feels less helpless. The criminal act is most often an active effort to change some aspect of the environment. When it is performed, the criminal acknowledges his intentions and responsibility. Criminal action has a more direct impact on the environment than neurotic behavior. Because the criminal is more "the master of his own fate," he is less likely to feel himself directed by strange and uncontrollable forces. When the environment cannot be altered by legal means, illegal actions may offer the most direct vehicle for combating helplessness.

There is one obvious exception to the above statements. Presumably a person could be forced into committing a criminal act. In this case crime would not alleviate helplessness but would be a manifestation of it. It is doubtful, however, if many crimes occur in this manner. Occasionally a criminal will argue that he should not be blamed for his actions since society has forced him to adopt a criminal role. Although this statement may have some validity for a "hard" determinist, it is doubtful if the criminal himself actually believes it. He certainly does not believe it at the moment of the criminal action, and such statements are best considered as retrospective attempts to rationalize. Even if the criminal should feel that he has been forced into a criminal role, his experience is different from that of the neurotic insofar as he is often in a better position to identify the source of his oppression and does not have to convince himself that he is moved by invisible or mysterious forces.

However petty a criminal act may be, it carries with it a promise of change in a favorable direction. This is true while the crime is being planned and even more so when it is carried out. The adoption of a sick role cannot offer as much hope since the neurotic individual cannot admit to himself that his illness might lead to changes which would be advantageous. Adjustment to oppression also limits hopefulness to those people who have great faith in the future or in a superior being. The hopefulness of crime is related to the experience of redefining the rules of the world in a manner which holds out the possibility of a new and better existence. Sometimes the hopefulness of the criminal is exaggerated to grandiose proportions and becomes self-defeating. We occasionally see criminals who become so carried away with the certainty of new success that they neglect to take reasonable precautions for avoiding detection.

During the planning and execution of a criminal act the offender is a free man. He is immune from the oppressive dictates of others since he has temporarily broken out of their control. The value of this brief taste of freedom cannot be overestimated. Many of the criminal's apparently unreasonable actions are efforts to find a moment of autonomy, a moment of reassurance that he is "his own man." This advantage is difficult to find in neurotic adaptations, and is obviously unavailable to the person who conforms to an oppressive life.

More than other adaptations, crime offers the possibility of excitement. It involves high stakes, and its risks are real and stimulating. The dangers involved in the criminal act call for the highest use of faculties and talents which might otherwise lie dormant. Efforts to outwit or deceive others are traditionally among man's most coveted games. The future criminal is usually a person who has had little opportunity to use his creative abilities, and planning an illegal act provides an outlet for this potentiality. Crime is particuarly exciting when it is part of a group action. Those who have had the experience of engaging in a minor gang delinquency during adolescence will need no ponderous theories to convince them that crime can be fun.

Some criminals are driven by feelings of oppression that come from within. They constantly experience stress in situations which would not be defined as stressful by others. Oppression arising from a punitive superego is extremely difficult to master, since there is no palpable enemy to be engaged. Such persons may experience painful emotions without any awareness of the reasons for their suffering. Other criminals are subject to oppression which originates directly from other individuals but which may be so disguised that the oppressed person does not realize where it is coming from. Such people will also suffer without knowing why. If these people should begin to break the laws of society, however, the enemy is clearly defined. The culture as a whole, its symbols of conformity, and particularly its law enforcement agents, become the obvious source of oppression.

When realistic external stresses are increased, the organism tends to concentrate upon the most immediate threats to its equilibrium and temporarily "abandons" its more chronic intrapsychic problems. Displacement of oppression to an external source is often accompanied by a great increase in subjective comfort and effectiveness. In pretranquilizer days the author had the opportunity to observe that "backward" patients, who were characterized as hebephrenic or catatonic, responded in a perfectly normal fashion when threatened with realistic stresses such as physical illness or an approaching tornado. Malignant symptoms such as mutism, silliness or posturing disappeared in a startling, if temporary, manner when realistic external stresses appeared. There are many examples of this phenomenon in psychiatric medicine. Deeply disturbed neurotics may lose their mental illness when a crippling physical illness develops (and conversely some physically ill individuals may become mentally ill when they are "cured").[10] There are, of course, many complex factors involved in such a phenomenon, but it seems to be generally true that people are more comfortable and effective when they know (or think they know) where their trouble is coming from. Once a man becomes a criminal, he brings external stresses into his life which may actually make him feel better. This adds one more advantage to the criminal adaptation.

Once a person has convinced himself that the major pressures in his life come from without, there is less tendency to blame himself for his failures. The person who thinks he recognizes the source of his oppression is less likely to be self-punitive than the person who does not. It is also true that if a person can find a cause for his failures he will feel better. Many people go through life convinced that if only they had not been "afflicted" with a certain defect everything would have gone better. "If only I had been handsome; if only I did not have this birth defect; if only I didn't drink; if only I didn't have such bad nerves" are statements which imply that there is only one defect in the individual which accounts for all his failures. Such beliefs are often sustaining, and if they are discredited, the person tends to feel much worse.

Adopting the criminal role provides an excellent rationalization for inadequacy. The criminal is able to say (and often does say), "I could have been successful if I had not turned to crime. All my troubles have come to me because I have been bad." Once a person turns to crime as an adaptational alternative, he has a convenient resource for denying, forgetting or ignoring his other inadequacies. In many segments of our culture it is still more socially acceptable to be "bad" than inadequate. One can put many years of misery and failure behind him by convincing himself that criminal behavior has "caused" his trouble. More often, the painful truth is that life had been even more meaningless before the criminal role was adopted. The criminal who uses this defense is much like the alcoholic who says that everything in his life would be perfect if he stopped drinking. Actually, the reformed alcoholic often discovers that the despair in his life is greater than it had been when he was drinking heavily.

There are offenders judged to be grossly psychotic by competent psychiatrists who yet vigorously refuse to participate in legal proceedings which would label them not guilty by reason of insanity. The author has had the opportunity to examine a number of such cases.[11] These were individuals who were unwilling to define themselves as helpless or nonresponsible. Because their behavior was grossly unreasonable, there was almost unanimous agreement by others that they were mentally ill. In attempting to comprehend this stubborn refusal to accept hospitalization in place of prison, the author was struck with the social advantages of the "bad" role over the "sick" role. These men did not behave in a totally unreasonable manner. They seemed to recognize that crime has a more esteemed social status than is generally appreciated. If an offender is put into a situation where he can be "sick" or "bad," he may find greater satisfaction in being "bad."

A brief survey of crime reporting by the mass communications media would suggest that this nation struggles with a somewhat ambivalent attitude toward the criminal. Although crime is regularly condemned, it is also glamorized. Most of us find it relatively easy to identify ourselves with a criminal and his activities. Many of us ocasionally find ourselves cheering for the "wrong" side in the traditional police-against-crime movie. When a really masterful crime such as the Boston Brinks robbery takes place, almost everybody expresses a not too grudging admiration for the criminal. The honest and law-abiding American citizen sees himself as an enemy of crime and advocates its elimination, yet he is fascinated by the criminal and perversely tends to endow him with high status.

Deviant behavior sometimes helps the criminal to form close and relatively nonoppressive relations with other criminals. Particularly among adolescents, delinquent behavior seems to be a background against which moments of deep intimacy with compatriots can develop. The criminal finds that there are others who are on his side in a common battle against the "squares," the "straights" or the "fuzz."[12] The intimacy which results is somewhat akin to that which develops between soldiers who have fought in the same battle. No such *esprit* is available to the neurotic or to the person who passively accepts life in an unfriendly world.

Once the law violator is able to find alternative adaptations to criminality, it is relatively easy to stop being a criminal. His past may follow him, but not to the same extent as it would if he had been mentally ill. A reformed criminal is often able to achieve a considerable degree of status. One can picture such a person confessing his past crimes to a group of adolescent delinquents in an effort to dissuade them from further criminal actions. The author has had the opportunity to observe such interactions, and it is usually obvious that the ex-criminal thoroughly enjoys this role. Although he may speak of criminal activities with apparent shame, the obvious nostalgia, pleasure and humor in his reminiscences belie his avowed feeling. It is more difficult to picture an ex-mental patient talking in the same way to a group of neurotics. In this situation shame tends to overcome pride. The person about to commit a crime knows that even if he is caught and punished the social impediments to a better adaptation will be clearly defined and hence more capable of mastery.

Discussion of another advantage of crime has been deliberately left for last. Pleasure-seeking, or the effort to gratify needs, is often a sufficient explanation of criminality to the layman. Unfortunately, it is sometimes the only explanation offered by sociologists and psychiatrists. We have tried to demonstrate that crime has many advantages even when considered independently of the criminal's conscious or unconscious needs for gratification. The adaptational approach allows us to understand crime as an action which helps one to survive with dignity. We cannot understand the criminal unless we appreciate that his actions are much more than an effort to find a specific gratification.

Still, it must be admitted that each criminal act has its own distinctive motivations and pleasures. If one can avoid detection, crime can pay very well indeed. Certain types of crime offer substantial sexual gratification. Other crimes provide outlets for aggressive behavior directed against a clearly defined source of oppression. It is possible to look upon every criminal act as satisfying some pleasure-seeking tendency, whether it be greed, lust or vengeance. This is true even when criminal activities are thought of as symbolic or indirect efforts to obtain gratification. The fact that these benefits exist does not mean that they are necessary or sufficient causes of crime. When seen against the background of the adaptational needs of the organism, they are better looked upon as important fringe benefits which tend to encourage antisocial conduct.

It is possible to illustrate adaptational alternatives to oppressive stress in diagrammatic form as follows:

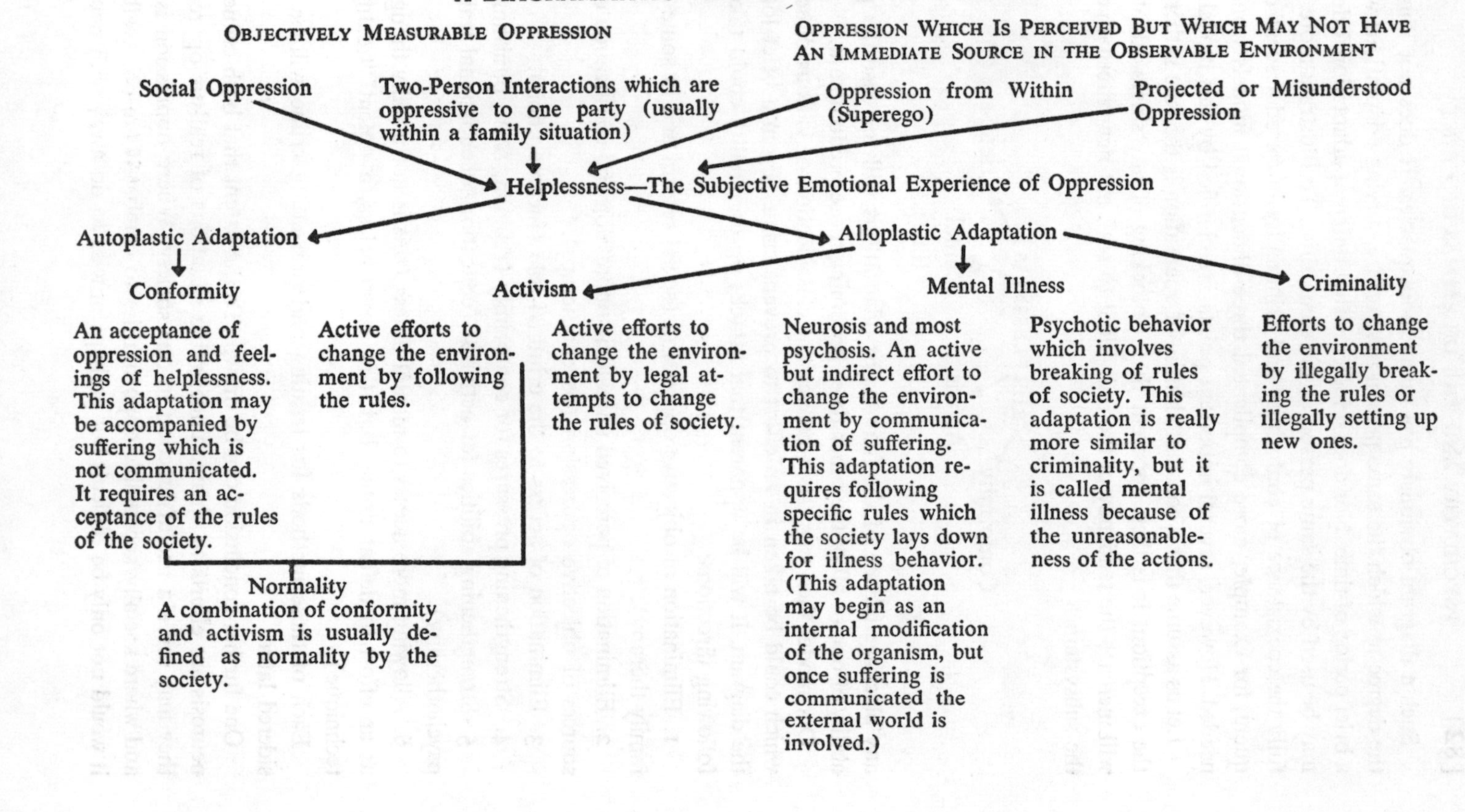

A DIAGRAMMATIC VIEW OF CRIME AS ADAPTATION
OBJECTIVELY MEASURABLE OPPRESSION
OPPRESSION WHICH IS PERCEIVED BUT WHICH MAY NOT HAVE AN IMMEDIATE SOURCE IN THE OBSERVABLE ENVIRONMENT
Social Oppression
Two-Person Interactions which are oppressive to one party (usually within a family situation)
Oppression from Within (Superego)
Projected or Misunderstood Oppression
Helplessness—The Subjective Emotional Experience of Oppression
Autoplastic Adaptation
Alloplastic Adaptation
Conformity
Activism
Mental Illness
Criminality
An acceptance of oppression and feelings of helplessness. This adaptation may be accompanied by suffering which is not communicated. It requires an acceptance of the rules of the society.
Active efforts to change the environment by following the rules.
Active efforts to change the environment by legal attempts to change the rules of society.
Neurosis and most psychosis. An active but indirect effort to change the environment by communication of suffering. This adaptation requires following specific rules which the society lays down for illness behavior. (This adaptation may begin as an internal modification of the organism, but once suffering is communicated the external world is involved.)
Psychotic behavior which involves breaking of rules of society. This adaptation is really more similar to criminality, but it is called mental illness because of the unreasonableness of the actions.
Efforts to change the environment by illegally breaking the rules or illegally setting up new ones.
Normality
A combination of conformity and activism is usually defined as normality by the society.

Such a diagram obviously has many inadequacies. It does not illustrate the degree to which the same person may utilize varying adaptations within a brief period of time. Nor does it indicate that different adaptational devices may be used by the same person at the same time. To illustrate more carefully the coexistence of conformity and criminality in an adolescent delinquent, for example, more complicated three-dimensional models would be needed. However, several important points are clarified by this model.

Let us assume that a constant shifting of adaptation is the rule rather than the exception. It is then apparent that a blocking of any single adaptation will increase the tendency of the individual to seek out new alternatives. In the subsystem

HELPLESSNESS
Conformity ← → Crime
Activism   Mental Illness

any blockage of one of the four major adaptations will increase the probability of one or all of the other three becoming more predominant.

Our model then suggests a convenient classification of various directions which could be taken in an effort to prevent crime. From a brief look at the diagram, it will be apparent that attacks on criminality could take the following directions:

1. Elimination of objective oppression (social reform and in some cases family therapy).

2. Elimination of perceived unrealistic oppression and clarification of the sources of objective oppression (psychotherapy).

3. Elimination of access to the criminal role (incarceration).

4. Strengthening pressures for conformity (religion, A.A., punishment).

5. Strengthening abilities for activism (education, occupational training, psychotherapy).

6. Allowing more access to mental illness (this is not usually thought of as an effort to defeat crime, but it is, nevertheless, a potent "treatment" technique).

Each of these methods for treating and preventing crime will be considered later.

One further conclusion can be drawn. To the extent that both crime and neurosis are efforts to change undesirable situations of realistic oppression they may serve a useful function in our society. Where oppression is real and where socially acceptable opportunities to combat it are not available, it would not only be difficult but perhaps unwise to do away with neurosis and crime. These behaviors represent forces for social and interpersonal change in cultures which do not provide more direct outlets for resolving inequities. As long as there is oppression in the world and as long as society provides for a mental-illness role, mental illness will remain with us. As long as there is oppression in the world people will also attempt to fight it through illegal means. The existence of social deviancy is a testimony to our own inadequacies. Crime (like mental illness) is a product of the selfishness, the cruelty and the neglect which lie within all of us.

*Chapter 7*

# EARLY STRESSES AND PREDISPOSITION TO CRIME

IN THE next six chapters we will examine those stresses which seem to favor a criminal adaptation. Sometimes these stresses are realistic and direct, sometimes they are realistic and indirect and sometimes they do not have an objectively measurable source. Some criminal acts seem to be determined mainly by realistic and direct stress (such as poverty or persecution). Others can be looked upon as responses to realistic stress which are not directly perceived (for instance, rejecting attitudes on the part of parents which are disguised) or to unrealistic perception of nonobjective stress (as in superego restrictiveness or paranoid fear of others). To the extent that any criminal act is *not* an effort to adapt to real and direct stress it is likely to have an unreasonable and maladaptive quality. We will be mainly concerned with those stresses that have a subtle and indirect influence and with those that are more subjective and are determined by perceptual distortions. Criminal adaptations to realistic and direct stress can be thought of as "rational crime"; this type of criminal behavior has been well studied by sociologists.

As we talk about stresses in early life, we are obviously concerned with predisposition to crime. If we accept the arguments of the previous chapter, predisposition to crime must be viewed as determined by the degree to which a person is prepared to experience oppression and by the kinds of adaptational alternatives he has learned and is flexible enough to use in his own interests. Some adults may not actually be oppressed at the time they commit a crime, but oppressive childhood experiences may have sensitized them to approach the world in a fearful or belligerent manner. Limiting experiences during the future criminal's childhood will also impair his capacity as an adult to evaluate and choose that adaptation which best serves his interests.

Predisposition to criminality is frequently looked upon by psychiatrists as a failure to develop adequate control mechanisms. Throughout this chapter we will find it useful to talk about control mechanisms, but we are not using this expression to describe a linear relationship between crime and an absence of restraining mechanisms. Our belief is that most crime is chosen because it is the best a person can do. Given a situation which a person perceives in a certain way and which he cannot master, these factors may lead to his committing a crime. We can speak of that act as occurring because of a defective system of controls, but we must be aware that nothing has actually broken down and that the criminal is still behaving in an adaptive manner.

Another aspect of predisposition to crime that must be constantly kept in mind is that predisposition is relative. Even the most predisposed criminal will be able to act in a law-abiding manner if his environment is favorable, and even the most predisposed conformist will react in a criminal manner if his environment is sufficiently unfavorable.

### Problems in Studying Predisposition

Confronted with an adolescent or adult delinquent, there are only a limited number of methods by which the criminologist can seek to determine which criminogenic stresses may have been present during that person's early life. The major methods for studying this problem are:

1. Reviewing histories of known delinquents to determine if certain stressful situations appeared in their early life with more frequency than in normal subjects.
2. Follow-up studies of individuals exposed to certain stresses as children for the purpose of observing if delinquent behavior during adolescent or adult years is greater in the "exposed" group than in control groups.
3. Examining the parents of delinquents to evaluate their personality defects and to obtain more accurate historical data as to their child-rearing practices.
4. Investigating the child through psychoanalytic treatment. In addition to being a method of therapy, psychoanalysis is also a research tool which provides an integrated picture of the interaction of various stresses upon an individual.

Each of these methods has serious limitations. Studies of the past histories of criminals usually take a correlative statistical approach, and such data tell us little about the manner in which a stress exerts its influence. It is possible, for example, to note that a significantly higher proportion of adjudicated delinquents come from broken homes, but a correlative approach tells us nothing more. It does not tell us how a broken home could engender delinquency, and it does not help us to understand those delinquents who do not come from broken homes. Although statistical correlations are of limited usefulness in explaining delinquency, they are of some value in predicting delinquency. The predictive tables of the Gluecks help to isolate factors which are highly correlated with delinquency and are of some value as adjunctive tools for parole boards and judges.[1] Follow-up studies of adults who as children were exposed to a stress such as maternal separation seem to provide a method of discovering a more meaningful linkage between that stress and delinquency. Once such a stress is carefully defined, however, it is difficult to find subjects or controls, and we are still left with little knowledge of the manner in which the stress exerts its influence. Studies of the personality of parents of delinquents are meaningful only if we extrapolate from these data and assume that they behaved in a specific manner toward the delinquent when he was a child. Obtaining information from parents of delinquents with regard to child-rearing provides more objective historical data about experienced stress, but still tells us nothing about why a particular stress can favor a criminal adaptation. Psychoanalytic studies provide information which may adequately explain an individual case, but such knowledge cannot readily be generalized to the problems of all delinquents.

At this point our methodology is not sufficiently refined to correlate meaningfully specific variables with criminality, and neither the more careful statistical studies nor the more insightful psychoanalytic explanations are definitive. Our techniques simply do not get at the complexities of the problem. A relatively straightforward event such as separation from the mother is influenced by many other variables, such as the child's age, where he is sent, the presence of other siblings or the father, how he is treated, intervening illness, previous separation experience and even his constitution. The developing child learns through participation in a complex system of interaction in which he is only one constantly changing element. Even if we restrict ourselves to studying the family, parental interaction with the child is at a minimum a three-person system, the complexities of which challenge our techniques for measurement. This means that it is almost impossible to anticipate consistent results when we attempt to relate one imprecisely defined independent variable such as maternal deprivation to criminality. Every factor which has been considered a cause of crime can also be found in the backgrounds of the mentally ill, and even in normal subjects. Throughout this chapter we will therefore avoid dogmatic statements about criminal predisposition. Rather, we will list the factors that have been suggested as important determinants of delinquency and will speculate as to how they might exert their influence.

It is difficult to examine stresses of childhood in terms of interpersonal oppression. First of all, we know very little about how the child actually perceives the world. When we talk of an infant experiencing oppression, we speak figuratively. We might speculate, however, that even benevolent actions on the part of adults could be experienced as deprivation and punishment by the child. If the child is to learn to survive in the world, he must be taught to abandon certain gratifications, to wait and to find substitute gratifications. This means that at times he will be restricted and punished. While such restrictions may be perceived by the child as oppressive, they certainly do not represent objectively defined acts of oppression on the part of the parents. They may have less to do with predisposition to maladaptive behavior than other factors which are not experienced as immediately stressful.

Some parental behavior may not be experienced as stressful but may still have a long-term maladaptive quality. Repeated instances of overprotection or inconsistency may not result in immediate discomfort, but they can teach the child to behave in a manner which is maladapted to adult life. The parent who invokes rules or punishments which are abusive or idiosyncratic imposes an unnecessary stress upon his child. In this sense, we can consider the failure to teach the necessity to tolerate some deprivation or to abide by standard rules as having a long-term stressful quality.

Although oppressive stress assumes some inadequacy on the part of those who deal with the child, many of the stresses of childhood are outside of anybody's control. Accidental events may lead to separation from the parents. The reactions of parents to a particular child may be determined by uncontrollable events such as a congenital defect or physical injury. Children differ at birth in their motoric patterns and their potential for conditioning. These variations will influence the manner in which the parents relate to the child. Other variables such as the child's sex and the time at which he comes into the life of his parents will be equally important. To obtain a reasonably accurate picture of the influence of predisposing stress upon a child, we must therefore examine a wide variety of factors which may not appear to be objectively stressful but which may have a crucial influence in shaping his ultimate behavior.

## INTRAFAMILIAL STRESS

Predisposition to criminality has to be understood largely in terms of stresses emanating from the parents. Although interpersonal relationships with grandparents, siblings, playmates, teachers and other adults are important, the major stresses of childhood related to criminal predisposition can be classified as parental deprivation, parental abuse, parental inconsistency and parental overcontrol.

It is extremely difficult to define a depriving parent. It is a little easier to study the effects of deprivation in a situation in which a parent is separated from the child and is clearly unable to provide love or affection. Early studies by René Spitz and other psychoanalysts suggested that maternal separation occurring during the first year of life would be followed by serious emotional disturbance.[2] Later, John Bowlby, an English psychoanalyst, concluded that deprivation of maternal contact before the age of three could result in crippling and unmodifiable personality traits.[3] More recent reviews of the earlier findings of psychoanalysts have emphasized the extreme complexity of the subject, so that the apparently simple problem of defining maternal deprivation has begun to assume monumental proportions. Leon Yarrow has noted that it is possible to distinguish a dozen major varieties of separation when separation is defined in terms of permanence, repetition, duration and coexisting degree of external stress.[4] Each could represent a psychologically different experience for the developing child. At this point students of the problem agree that maternal separation has an unfavorable impact upon the adaptive capacity of the organism, but they are uncertain as to the type of separation that is important or the relative influence of factors such as separation occurring at different ages and for different durations.

Attempts have also been made by Bowlby and other psychoanalysts to relate maternal separation to later development of specific character traits.[5] Lack of ability to make friends, inaccessibility, lack of emotional response, pointless lying and deceit are said to describe the "affectionless character," a person who is prone to criminal behavior. Bowlby argued that the "affectionless character" structure was directly related to maternal deprivation. His conclusions, however, were based on studies which were not sufficiently controlled. Later researchers have concluded that separation from the mother cannot be related to a specific constellation of personality traits.[6] Even if Bowlby's findings had been confirmed, they would have had limited relevance to the study of criminal behavior since not all "affectionless characters" are criminals and many criminals do not have this particular character structure.

Separation from the mother does not inevitably lead to personality disturbance. Much depends upon the circumstance in which the separated child finds himself. If the quality of maternal care is adequate, the shock of separation is modified. Some of the earlier studies of separated children may have reported a high incidence of morbidity because the children were exposed to an unfavorable institutional environment. Such factors as stimulus deprivation and lack of a personalized relationship with a single maternal figure may have been more crucial etiologic factors than separation from the mother.

There is no easy way to gauge the more general effect of parental deprivation when it is viewed in terms of a broad deprivation of the love, fondling and stimulation of some maternal figure. Most behavioral scientists, however, are in general agreement that prolonged neglect and an absence of a significant mothering person in the child's early life will have a profoundly unfavorable effect. Studies of children exposed not only to maternal separation but also to an absence of consistent substitute mothering suggest that an initial response of protest and anxiety is followed by a period of progressive withdrawal from the environment and from relationships with people.[7] Interestingly, children who previously have had a good relationship with the mother seem to become more withdrawn than those who did not. It is almost as if the child learns that his craving for love will put him in a situation in which he will be helpless if he is again deserted. Emotional closeness seems to become equated with a fear of helplessness.

The increased criminal potentiality of individuals who equate closeness with helplessness has been noted by a number of investigators. Irving Kauffman has suggested that most delinquents suffer from a chronic depression which, because of earlier inadequate mothering, tends to increase when close interpersonal relationships begin to develop.[8] He sees many criminal acts as efforts to adapt to the unpleasant affect of depression. Albert Bandura in his studies of adolescent aggression noted that some delinquents demonstrated more anxiety when they became aware of their need for others.[9] Any situation which threatened to remind them of their dependency or to make them more dependent could elicit "dependency anxiety," which was often followed by aggressive behavior.

Abuse and neglect have many common properties. Neglect is clearly a form of abuse when it is intentional, while direct verbal hostility, lack of warmth, depreciating attitudes, mockery and deliberate deprivation or rejection have considerable impact upon the developing child. Much of the psychological research on parental discipline suggests that aggressive and delinquent behavior is more likely to result when the parents express hostility toward the child and are at the same time lax in their modes of discipline.[10] It is difficult to imagine a more stark picture of helplessness than that of a child who must depend upon parents who openly show their disdain or hatred for him. The possibility of such a child expressing antisocial impulses would seem to be greater if he at the same time was deprived of the opportunity to learn techniques of conformity and restraint.

Sometimes parental abuse is even more serious and takes the form of physical attacks upon the child. Most of us recognize the possibility that parents can be unloving, overly strict or mentally cruel but tend to minimize the possibility of physical brutality. Recently the medical profession has presented us with the gruesome statistics of the "battered child syndrome."[11] We now know that brutality to children—even to infants—is not rare. Those psychiatrists who have worked with delinquents are familiar with histories of brutality which are shocking and sometimes difficult to believe. The author's impression is that similar histories are found less frequently in nondelinquents of similar social class. It would appear that a child exposed to physical cruelty would have difficulty in seeking closeness without being reminded of his earlier oppression. He would also have had the experience of seeing violence used as a resolution for problems. An inference that an experience with violence would encourage that child to be violent himself would be in accord with this writer's clinical observation that some of the most dangerous offenders have histories of having been abused or "battered" children.

In discussing the influence of parental inconsistency on predisposition to delinquency, most writers have focused upon inconsistency in discipline. Both psychiatric and psychoanalytic researchers are in remarkable agreement as to the criminogenic effects of this type of inconsistency. It does seem logical to anticipate that the learning of obedience and conformity would be impaired if the child was confronted with erratic disciplinary experiences. Many statistical studies of delinquents have supported this hypothesis.[12, 13, 14, 15]

The issue of consistency, however, encompasses many more factors than discipline. Inconsistent messages are involved in any communication process, including many which are less directly related to the learning of acceptable conduct. To define inconsistency with scientific rigor would be even more difficult than defining what is meant by maternal deprivation. There can be inconsistency between attitudes, between behaviors and between attitudes and behaviors. One of the most interesting forms of inconsistency which may be even more harmful than inconsistent discipline is inconsistent communication of goal expectations.

Jay Haley has demonstrated how a simple verbal directive can have two different messages which are not only inconsistent but contradictory or paradoxical.[16] The communication, "I would like you to grow up to be an independent young man," can be understood as having two contradictory messages. One is: "Do what I want you to do," and the other is: "Be independent." A different kind of inconsistent communication would be exemplified by a mother saying to her young son, "Don't come in the bedroom; I am undressing," a message which could have a seductive as well as a restraining quality. Recently a group of behavioral scientists have demonstrated the pathological impact of contradictory messages upon a person who is dependent upon the communicator and not in the position to comment upon the messages or to correct his discrimination of which message he can respond to.[17] Such situations, referred to as "double binds," increase the helplessness of the child and seem to have a close relationship to later disturbed behavior.

Inconsistency can, of course, occur between the communications of different people. When mother and father express different attitudes, the child is in a difficult position. His plight is even worse in those instances where he can sense disagreement but where agreement is pretended to preserve the illusion of consistency. Since there is no way of responding which will satisfy both parents, pathological reactions such as withdrawal, aggression or dishonesty may be the best that the child can produce. Although studies of inconsistent communication have thus far focused upon their importance in the etiology of mental illness, it must be noted that insofar as they increase the subjective experiences of helplessness they can also favor a criminal adaptation.

Sometimes a child is forced to adopt maladaptive patterns of behavior in order to satisfy unrealistic needs of his parents. Overprotected children, particularly those who are both protected and restrained, can be considered subjects of parental overcontrol. While some delinquents seem to have been exposed to exceptionally strict discipline on the part of the father, most psychological research suggests that restrictive or controlling parents are unlikely to produce delinquents.[18] In fact, parental overcontrol is usually thought of as a factor which predisposes to passive or neurotic personality traits. Presumably the child is made to feel helpless but is not allowed to combat this feeling directly and is encouraged to seek conforming or "sick role" adaptations. There are also, however, some subtle forms of parental overcontrol which do not have to do with discipline but which may have important criminogenic influence on some children.

The psychiatrist sometimes sees children who are "controlled" into fulfilling the needs of their parents through adopting deviant patterns of behavior. Adelaide Johnson and Stanley Szurek have described delinquents who can be thought of as having specific defects in the structure of their superegos.[19] Although conforming in most ways, they seem to be driven toward one specific type of antisocial conduct. Examination of the conflicts of their parents reveals that they have subtly encouraged their children to specific forms of misconduct which vicariously gratify their own needs. A sexually frustrated mother may, for example, indirectly encourage her daughter to be promiscuous or a timid father may raise a son who is a bully. The inadequacies of conscience formation, or "superego lacunae," which such children develop are not fortuitous characteristics but can be understood as predetermined or even planned.

There is a still more complicated form of overcontrol which seems to be directed toward satisfying the needs of the entire family unit. For lack of a better word this phenomenon can be called "scapegoating." When the dynamics of family interaction are carefully studied, patterns of behavior are sometimes found which seem to be directed toward forcing one of the members of the family to behave in a way which satisfies the needs of all the others.[20] When only one child in the family seems to behave in an antisocial manner, enormously complicated and largely hidden intrafamilial conflicts may be pushing him in this direction. The rebellious conduct of such a child may actually help his family to sustain a degree of equilibrium.

## Biological and Social Stresses Which Influence Predisposition

Parental deprivation, abuse, inconsistency and overcontrol must be examined against the background of the child's biological and social situation. It may be that some children are, on a constitutional basis, more susceptible to stresses such as neglect or inconsistency. Most of our thoughts in this direction remain highly speculative. The influence of social factors such as poverty or persecution, however, seems to be clearer.

Any kind of interpersonal stress has a greater impact upon those who are at the same time exposed to more general forms of social oppression.

Biological and social stresses can be thought of as influencing the child in at least two ways. They may directly impair his capacity to find favorable adaptations or they may encourage reactions of increased oppressive behavior on the part of the parents and the community. Either effect will increase the child's experience of helplessness. Some of the more important stresses are constitutional physical or mental defects, physical illness, poverty and persecution on the basis of race or ethnic origin.

A child born with a physical defect may be met with a variety of parental reactions. He may receive extra attention or he may be neglected. He may become highly prized, but he may also be unloved and rejected. There is no evidence that children born with physical defects are more likely to become criminals, but there are some offenders whose criminality seems related to oppressive experiences centered around an infirmity. Rejection by parents, teasing by playmates and denial of outlets for learning experiences available to others are only some of the possible stresses which can be imposed on such a person.

The child who enters the world with a constitutional impairment of his ability to learn is subjected to even greater difficulty. We have previously noted that during the first four decades of this century many scientists were convinced that the genesis of crime could be found in hereditary defects of the intellect. Today we know that mental deficiency is closely related to environmental experience and cannot be understood as a fixed inherited trait. We have also learned that when criminals are compared with carefully matched control groups they do not differ from noncriminals in intelligence. There may, however, be a significant relationship between mental deficiency and criminality in those offenders who are in prison. This has usually been explained in terms of the diminished capacity of intellectually limited criminals to avoid detection, but it may represent a tendency of defective criminals to commit more desperate and ill-conceived crimes as a means of combating helplessness. A child limited in his capacity to learn will be subjected to many oppressive situations and will be limited in his quest for socially acceptable adaptations.

Physical illness occurring during the early years of life could result in handicaps which would have the same influence as constitutional impairment. The chronically sick child would be likely to experience himself as a person limited in ability to master his environment. Chronic illness also incapacitates some children for long periods of time and could lead to parental attitudes and reactions which might be unfavorable.

Efforts have also been made to relate criminal behavior to specific physical illnesses which influence the nervous system. Brain-damaged children are likely to show disturbances in their motoric behavior and in their capacity for learning. Either type of abnormality could favor a criminal adaptation. An unusual relationship of neurological illness to crime was noted following the sleeping-sickness epidemics of the 1920's.[21] Children who had been disabled by a specific type of viral encephalitis seemed to be more prone to delinquent behavior. This illness had the apparent effect of increasing the need for motoric activity and led to an excessive restlessness. Some psychiatrists attempted to generalize from these cases and speculated that a defect in brain metabolism could account for the behavior of selected criminals. Actually, there has never been substantial evidence for such a belief. Nobody is certain that criminals differ significantly in motoric behavior from noncriminals, and even if we could discover defects in brain metabolism which increased the need for motor activity, we would still wonder if the delinquency of such damaged children was not ultimately dependent upon the secondary impact of parental reactions toward a hyperactive child. In recent years cases of antisocial behavior following viral encephalitis have been reported with far less frequency, and interest in this hypothesis has waned.

The overwhelming majority of imprisoned offenders are members of the lower socioeconomic class. The disproportionate rate of crime and illness among the poor is so great that some have wondered if it is the only factor in social deviancy. Poverty would at first glance appear to be a realistic and direct stress whose effects could be accurately perceived by the oppressed individual. Actually, however, poverty also leads to many indirect stresses which are not immediately apparent. Recent studies of poverty emphasize its impact upon the total development of the child.[22, 23] To be exposed to a life of deprivation is particularly serious in a culture where affluence is practically available to many and theoretically available to all. Poverty not only leads to deprivations of physical needs but also undermines the psychological stability of parents. Poverty-stricken parents tend to subject their children to greater deprivation and abuse because their own despair infiltrates into every aspect of the child's intrapsychic and interpersonal life. The impoverished child learns to see himself not only as an unfortunate being but also as a lesser being, someone who never is entitled to the same high assessment of his worth that is given to others. His repeated experience of helplessness makes him a more likely candidate for crime.

The obvious oppressive effect of racial or religious persecution need not be detailed here. We are more interested in the psychological damage which is done when a child grows up in a society which aggressively treats him as a lesser being, as "humanoid" rather than human. The Negro child who experiences discrimination can hardly be expected to avoid a deep sense of inferiority and distrust. As is the case with poverty, any existing family difficulty is aggravated by the oppression which every member of the family experiences.[24] Even if the Negro child is in later life exposed to a more tolerant and benevolent set of conditions, he is ill-prepared to accept them. He has not been given sufficient training nor has he developed skills which allow him to master his environment. We know that crime rates are proportionately higher among Negroes, Indians and other groups subject to intense discrimination, which should not be surprising. These people are badly oppressed by other elements in society and are denied outlets for favorable adaptations. Children of minority groups are more likely to learn the advantages of crime as an antidote to helplessness.[25]

## Psychoanalytic Concepts of Predisposition—Latent Delinquency

Psychoanalytic models of mental illness are largely dependent upon the concept of predisposition. Freud believed that a neurotic symptom would not accur in an adult unless some basic trauma had sensitized or predisposed the personality earlier in life. It is not surprising, therefore, that many efforts to understand psychological predisposition to crime have come from the psychoanalytic study of the child. The Viennese educator, August Aichorn, was among the first to apply psychoanalytic principles to the problems of delinquency.[26] Aichorn examined and treated individual delinquents and concluded that the impact of stress in the immediate social environment would be unlikely to result in criminality unless a psychological state of preparedness already existed. He described this state as "latent delinquency." The traits of Aichorn's latent delinquent include a tendency to seek immediate gratification (impulsivity), a tendency to consider satisfaction of instinct more important than gratification from objects (poor relationships with other people), and a subordination of regard for right and wrong to instinctual gratification (lack of guilt).

Psychoanalysts who have subsequently made important contributions to the understanding of predisposition to crime include such prominent figures as Kate Friedlander,[27] Kurt Eissler,[28] Edward Glover,[29] Adelaide Johnson[30] and Franz Alexander.[31] The writings of Kate Friedlander are most representative of psychoanalytic concepts of latent delinquency.[32, 33]

She ascribes such qualities as impulsivity, poor object realtionships and lack of guilt to defects in the development of the ego and the superego. In the first three years of life the child must learn to tolerate delay of gratification and must learn to accept substitute gratification when needs cannot be satisfied directly. (In psychoanalytic terminology, the child must learn to abandon the pleasure principle and accept the reality principle.) Any factor which interferes with the establishment of a firm and loving relationship with the mother will impair this learning process. Parental inconsistency, deprivation or other stresses such as overcontrol or abuse are seen as making the child less willing to abandon the pleasure principle. His inability to delay or resist gratification of instinctual wishes is then thought of as a defect in the ego.

Friedlander believes that the latent delinquent's apparent lack of interest in object relationships is related to insufficient exposure to maternal love. The child who does not feel loved will withdraw interest from his mother and will stay fixated at a developmental level which is primarily concerned with gratification of needs. As he grows older, his object relations tend to be dominated by primitive sadistic and masochistic drives. The future delinquent will see others as objects to be used for his own purposes, and more reality-oriented or mature interactions based on mutuality will be lacking. This, too, can be considered as a defect in ego structure.

If a child enters the Oedipal period with a weak ego, his superego formation will also be impaired. The formation of the superego requires a certain amount of ability to renounce instinctual gratification plus a sufficient interest in others to be able to internalize their values. The child traumatized in the first few years of his life may be unable to accomplish the task of finding his own internalized control system. He will then lack what Aichorn has referred to as an independent superego, that is, one which is not dependent upon external control and reinforcement. Where there is no internal system which automatically evaluates an act as right or wrong, control of impulses is governed by the chances of being discovered and punished.

Friedlander and other psychoanalysts argue that the incipient delinquent differs from the neurotic child. The neurotic is believed to pay more attention to the reality principle and is better able to develop an internalized superego. Psychoanalysts thus classify delinquents on the basis of the degree of mixing of neurotic and antisocial character traits.

One psychoanalyst, Jean Lampl-DeGroot, sees the basic defect in the character structure of the delinquent as residing in only one portion of the superego.[34] The superego is usually considered to have two parts, an inhibiting or punishing portion which metaphorically says to the child, "I must or must not do this or that," and another more benevolent portion which internalizes standards and says, "I want to be like my parents and have their ideals." The second part of the superego is called the ego ideal. Lampl-DeGroot sees the potential delinquent as having a reasonably normal development of the punitive part of the superego but as lacking in a healthy development of the ego ideal.

Psychoanalysis offers a comprehensive explanation of predisposition and describes mechanisms by which behavioral patterns conducive to criminality can become a part of the character structure. Much psychoanalytic theorizing as to latent delinquency, however, seems to be subtly dominated by moralistic notions and does not adequately distinguish between adaptive and maladaptive criminal behavior. If it is assumed that deviancy from social standards is generally bad, then there is a tendency to consider all deviant behavior as defect, and, indeed, psychoanalytic theory too often seems to be searching for a defect in the superego, a defect that allows for direct expression of antisocial impulses. An emphasis upon a linear concept of control mechanisms rather than upon adaptive processes weakens many of the psychoanalytic models and also narrows their applicability to the problem of crime.

## Aggressive Personality Traits

Implied but not always explicitly stated in psychoanalytic concepts of criminality is the belief that the future criminal is an aggressive person. The delinquent does behave more aggressively when exposed to stressful test situations, but we cannot be sure whether aggressivity is a cause of delinquency or whether it is an effect dependent upon the social consequences of being labeled delinquent. Recently efforts have been made to understand predisposition to criminal behavior as a learned pattern of aggressive responses to frustration. Using a learning theory approach, Albert Bandura[35] and, more recently, Leonard Berkowitz[36] have attempted to relate laboratory studies of aggression to the question of predisposition to crime. Berkowitz suggests that the potential criminal may, because of repeated frustration, develop a group of habits which can be viewed as latent response tendencies. The predisposed criminal perceives more frustrations than are actually present, reacts intensively to such frustrations and fails to develop adequate controls. Given these habits, suitable situational cues tend to elicit aggressively antisocial responses.

While psychologists have accumulated a great deal of knowledge with regard to aggressive behavior, there are many problems for the scientist who wishes to relate aggression to crime. If we look upon aggression as Berkowitz has defined it, that is, as "behavior whose goal is the injury of some object," it becomes very difficult to envision most criminal acts as aggressive. The key word in this definition is "goal." Once crime is understood in terms of the adaptive needs of the organism, aggression must be viewed as only one of the motivations for criminal behavior. This is true even when the criminal act itself appears to be aggressive. Furthermore, any argument which insists that the check forger, the burglar, the nonsupporter or the sex deviate wishes to hurt some object requires highly speculative and unjustifiable interpretations of motives.

We must also recognize the social usefulness of aggression. A person with an aggressive personality could theoretically be very successful in our society without ever resorting to crime. It seems that a more precise relationship of aggressive personality traits to crime should emphasize the inability of the potential criminal to find socially acceptable outlets for aggressive energies. Aggressiveness could be either a useful or poor way of dealing with oppression and helplessness. If the criminal is unable to find a socially acceptable outlet for aggressive tendencies, we are not justified in considering him to be any more aggressive than the noncriminal.

*Chapter 8*

# PSYCHOPATHY AND RELATED TRAITS

AUGUST AICHORN and other psychoanalysts have, as we have seen, described the latent delinquent in terms of such traits as impulsivity, aggressivity, inability to make adequate object relations and absence of guilt. When all these traits apply to a child, he is presumed to be predisposed to antisocial behavior and can be described as having an antisocial personality. Quite often this same cluster of traits or tendencies is found in adolescents or adults. Psychiatrists then describe such people as psychopathic or sociopathic personalities, and their behavioral patterns are often referred to as psychopathy or sociopathy.

During the past two centuries psychopathic behavior has intrigued psychiatrists of all theoretical persuasions. The subject of psychopathy always seems to create confusion and dissension. Few laymen are willing to acknowledge that the psychopath is a sick person. Even within psychiatry there is widespread disagreement as to whether psychopathy is a form of mental illness, a form of evil or a form of fiction. Most of the major disagreements within psychiatric criminology have originated in efforts to understand and treat the psychopathic personality.

The great humanitarian psychiatrist, Philippe Pinel, was the first to suggest than an individual who repeatedly involved himself in aimless antisocial behavior might be mentally ill. Shortly afterward, the English psychiatrist, J. C. Prichard, described a syndrome in which the "moral and active principles of the mind are strongly perverted or depraved."[1] His description of this condition, which he labeled "moral insanity," is quite similar to current descriptions of the sociopathic or psychopathic personality. However, the inclination of some psychiatrists to include selected forms of antisocial behavior in the category of mental illness was vigorously resisted. Philosophers, clergymen, attorneys, social scientists and other psychiatrists repeatedly warned of the dangers inherent in defining individuals who regularly transgress our laws as mentally ill and nonresponsible. Nevertheless, by the latter part of the nineteenth century psychiatrists were becoming more active in redefining some forms of antisocial behavior as illness. The "morally insane" were now being described as "constitutional psychopathic inferiors," a term more in keeping with a medical, as opposed to a moralistic, orientation.[2]

In 1930 Franz Alexander used psychoanalytic concepts of character formation and alloplasticity to describe certain antisocial individuals as "neurotic characters."[3] According to Alexander, the neurotic character was a disturbed individual who was in conflict but who, instead of developing psychic symptoms, resolved his conflict through alloplastic activity. While the provocative quality of such an individual's behavior was recognized, his behavior was also seen as self-injuring. He was pictured as a guilt-ridden person who ultimately suffered "just like the neurotic." Alexander's neurotic character can be looked upon as a grown-up and milder version of Aichorn's latent delinquent.

Alexander also postulated the existence of a condition in which both the expression of conflict through behavior and lack of guilt or self-punishment might be characteristic of the same individual. He referred to this state as "pure criminality," and thought of it as a hypothetical condition. Alexander doubted that the "pure criminal" actually existed and insisted that on closer examination most offenders could be included in his category of neurotic characters. The idea of "pure criminality" is interesting, however, insofar as it is a description of a personality type which roughly coincides with descriptions others have made of the psychopath.

In 1956 William and Joan McCord, on the basis of an exceptionally thorough study of the literature, described psychopathy as an emotional disorder or syndrome, and listed the characteristics of the psychopath as follows: "He is an antisocial, aggressive, highly impulsive person who feels little or no guilt and who is unable to form lasting bonds of affection with other human beings."[4] They distinguished the psychopath from the neurotic character and contended that while psychopathy could predispose the individual to crime, the psychopath himself would not necessarily be a criminal. For the McCords, psychopathy is a specific syndrome which rates an important place in psychiatric classification and nomenclature. Many psychiatrists are in substantial agreement with this view. The official nomenclature manual of the American Psychiatric Association, for example, includes the term "sociopathic" or "psychopathic personality" as an acceptable diagnosis.[5]

In current literature the term "psychopathy" is defined vaguely and because of arbitrary usage tends to assume multiple meanings. At its worst the term is used in its invective sense to describe people who are personally disliked or whose values differ from our own. Another unscientific use of the term equates all criminality with psychopathy. Generally, however, two major usages predominate. There are those persons who would agree with the McCords that psychopathy is a personality disorder, a discernible clinical entity which can be isolated from other disorders and which is clearly diagnosable. There are others who see the psychopath as similar to Alexander's "pure criminal" and visualize psychopathy as a hypothetical rather than an absolute condition. They would view psychopathy as a response to the same kinds of conflicts that produce neurosis but would recognize that some individuals have a tendency to develop hypertrophied alloplastic behavioral patterns. Psychiatrists who support this position argue that one does not see real psychopaths, only individuals who are more or less psychopathic. Unfortunately, these two meanings of the term, one referring to a distinct emotional disorder and the other to an abstract or hypothetical state, are often used interchangeably.

Whichever concept of psychopathy we may choose to explore, perplexing inconsistencies are encountered when we think of psychopathic behavior as mental illness. Certainly the psychiatrist frequently encounters individuals who fit the McCords' or the APA description of sociopathy. All the traits listed in these definitions, however, are derived from the values or morals of our culture. The diagnosis of psychopathy is not based on the presence of pain or communication of personal suffering. The psychopath does not communicate personal anguish unless we restrain him, and he rarely adopts the pose of being unable to control his behavior. When psychiatrists encounter him in the state hospital they are never sure that he really belongs there. Even when we agree that he is a legitimate object of psychiatric scrutiny, we have considerable difficulty in deciding what to call him. Repeated efforts to replace the phrase "psychopathic personality" with friendlier terms such as "sociopathic personality," "neurotic character" or "simple adult maladjustment" have met with limited success. The term "psychopath" seems to be retained because it has communicative value.

The case for defining psychopaths as sick people must be made on the basis of their unreasonable behavior. Yet it is not always easy to discern the unreasonableness of the psychopath. There are times when his goals and his efforts to obtain his goals appear to be entirely reasonable. When psychiatrists insist that psychopathy is a form of mental illness, it is with a quality of overdetermination, almost as if they have to reassure themselves and others that people who commit objectionable acts and do not seem to be guilty about it must be suffering from an affliction.

The concept of psychopathy as a disease is put on tenuous grounds when we consider the surprising versatility and flexibility the psychopath is able to demonstrate in certain circumstances. Sir David Henderson described a type of psychopathic state which was associated with genius and unusual creativity.[6] In Henderson's classification, a brilliant but erratic person, as, for example, T. E. Lawrence, was considered a "creative psychopath." Even if creative individuals are excluded as not meeting the usual definitions of psychopathy, there remain many less colorful psychopaths who are still able to demonstrate peculiar and unusual strengths.

Much of the behavior of the psychopaths depends on the social situation. People described as psychopaths are often able to function better under wartime conditions than many who would be considered normal. On the athletic field the relatively nonself-conscious psychopath may perform better than his neurotic teammate. The psychopath's capacity for success with women has been frequently noted, sometimes with a restrained note of envy. In frontier societies or under conditions of relative lawlessness, he has a higher survival potential than many other individuals. Even in the prison or mental hospital many psychopaths have the capacity to create a comfortable niche for themselves and survive with grace under circumstances that would overtax the resources of a "healthier" person. Admittedly, the gains accrued through utilization of these strengths may later be dissipated through impulsive or inappropriate behavior. A high capacity for adjustment and survival under adverse circumstances for a limited time remains, however, an aspect of psychopathy that is difficult to explain.

The individual diagnosed as a psychopath is often a charming and exciting person. While it is tempting to dismiss this charm as superficial or manipulative, it is still intriguing to almost everyone. Moments of involvement with the psychopath are often remembered as moments of pleasure, excitement and even exhilaration. The literature of Western society abounds with characters akin to the psychopath. Many of them are pictured as totally villainous and unlovable. On the other hand, the major characters of some novels and plays such as *The Rainmaker, The Music Man* or *One Flew Over the Cuckoo's Nest* are people who, though "afflicted" with the traits of psychopathy, are, nevertheless, alive and exciting. They are people who have the capacity to bring excitement, fun and even love into the lives of others.

Psychiatrists have been aware of this quality and have showed an unusual degree of interest in these troubling people. In his paper on the neurotic character, Alexander describes the fascinating qualities of these individuals in terms that could also be applied to the psychopath.[7] He states:

> The eternal struggle between man and society is exemplified not in elusive intrapsychic processes, but in the visible drama of their own lives. That is why they are born heroes who are predestined to a tragic fate. Their defeat is the victory of society and the spectator who has had some conflict within his breast (and who is without it) is able to live out both the rebellious and the social tendencies of his personality by sympathetically feeling themselves into the lives of the vanquished.

In this dramatic and sensitive description, Alexander has perhaps grasped a major reason for society's fascination with the psychopath.

## A Theoretical Concept of Psychopathy

Throughout this discussion psychopathy will be considered as an abstract state rather than as a definite syndrome. Pure psychopathy is considered to be a state which theoretically exists at one end of a continuum of behavior and personality traits. Certain individuals who are usually labeled psychopaths may sometimes approach this end point, but no one ever reaches it. Stated differently, the pure psychopath does not exist, but there are individuals who are more or less psychopathic.

Using this relativistic frame of reference we can view psychopathy as the repeated efforts of an individual to *search for a painless freedom from object relations.* The word "search" is important because implicit in this concept is the idea that "painless freedom from object relations" can never be found in human interaction and must remain a fiction. The adjective "painless" is included to distinguish psychopathy from autistic withdrawal, a condition in which the individual may seek freedom from object relations but does so only with great anguish.

The psychopath constantly seeks to be free of deep attachments to other people. He perceives the normal ties of affection, dependency, trust and love as fetters or traps which must be avoided at all costs. He seeks a type of freedom in which what he does, who he is and where he goes is independent of the appraisals of others. He perceives all alternatives to his way of life as leading to helplessness. The constant search for painless freedom is a defense against the intolerable experience of helplessness.

This concept is best illustrated by clinical example. The author, like so many other psychiatrists, has long been intrigued with the problem of psychopathy, and for years has searched for the "pure psychopath," the individual who is completely free of guilt, who takes what he wants without discomfort and who seems totally uninterested in relating to others. Such an individual might correspond to Alexander's concept of the "pure criminal" or to Benjamin Karpman's concept of the "idiopathic psychopath" or "anethopath." The patient to be described comes close to fitting this clinical picture.

He was a twenty-two-year-old white male who was seen initially in a staff conference at a state reformatory. He was serving a five-year sentence for fraud and swindling. His family background was similar to that of many delinquents. The father was an inadequate individual, an alcoholic, who absented himself from the home for long periods. The mother was described as a long-suffering, "martyred" type of person who, in spite of her protestation of affection toward the patient, was often irresponsible. She would frequently leave the children alone in order to pursue her extramarital escapades and drinking activities.

Throughout his school years, the patient was well liked by teachers and friends. His academic performance was slightly better than average. He was active in athletics and when he reached adolescence was unusually successful in attracting women. He left high school during his senior year to work in an auto shop. Finding this work too boring, he became a used-car salesman and even at the tender age of eighteen had little difficulty in breaking most of the sales records of his firm. He chose not to linger at this position, however, and moved on to a series of sales jobs. In all of these he repeated a pattern of marked success followed by lack of interest, boredom and moving on to what appeared to be a "greener pasture." During this period he had many heterosexual involvements. For about three years prior to incarceration he had been engaged in a number of "confidence games" designed to swindle the unsuspecting. He was far more successful than most criminals and managed to lead a financially comfortable life until apprehended.

After the staff reviewed his history, the patient was invited into the conference room to be interviewed. He entered with poise and dignity, an unusually handsome individual who, although dressed in prison garb, managed to be neater and better groomed than anyone else in the room. He stated that he was pleased to have the opportunity to talk to a group of intelligent men and throughout the conference showed an ease which disturbed the onlookers. The initial part of the interview focused on his adjustment to prison. He revealed that he had become interested in journalism while at the reformatory and had recently been made editor of the prison newspaper. His success in this role had already led to a promising offer of a position on the town newspaper at the termination of his sentence. His casual observations that he was accepted and respected by guards and other inmates were easily confirmed.

When the author pointed out to him that he seemed to have found quite a comfortable place for himself in the prison setting, he replied, "Why shouldn't I? A man can be happy wherever he is if he has faith in himself, is confident and is interested in life." The author was intrigued with such comments and the next day spent several hours interviewing the patient in private. The patient talked freely and obviously enjoyed conversation with a psychiatrist. In discussing his viewpoint of life he stated: "Most people seem to have to believe in something to survive. Me, I have learned to believe in myself. My goal is to make myself as happy as I possibly can and to experience life to the fullest. To most people this sounds selfish, but to me it makes real sense." He could offer little explanation as to how he had come to adopt this philosophy of life except for the following:

"Life was hard for our family when I was little, and until I was nine years old I was worried and nervous most of the time. Then things really got bad. My father disappeared, and one day when my mother was going out and planning to leave me alone, I felt that I just couldn't stand it any more. I thought to myself that I would cry and plead with her to stay and maybe she wouldn't leave me. Then suddenly it came to me that no matter what I did, no matter how much I cried or pleaded, it wouldn't make any difference, she would leave anyway. At that moment somehow or other, I was a free person. I didn't need her and I didn't need anybody. I stopped worrying and I started having fun. Since that time life has been easy, and I can be happy even though I am in prison."

Two other items of information which the patient revealed are of interest. He admitted that at one time he had sought psychotherapy at the institution, partly "because I was curious" and partly "because people were beginning to suspect I was different from them and I was afraid that if they ever realized what I am like, they would find some way of hurting me. Going into psychotherapy was like masking myself. It was a little bit like going underground. I tried it for several weeks, had some interesting chats with the therapist and then figured that I had had enough."

When asked about situations which made him uncomfortable, he replied, "The only danger I can see for myself is if I ever feel I really need to become involved with others. When I borrow a pack of cigarettes from another inmate, I try to return it as soon as possible so that I don't think I need him for anything." Then he stated, "Sometimes I think I would like to change and be like other people and sometimes I worry that maybe they have something that I don't. Then I start to think that I might lose so much of my strength if I ever become like the others. I have to hold on. I can talk to people, use them and enjoy them, but I can't let them mean anything to me."

This history is, of course, edited in a way that allows us to focus mainly on those issues which are relevant to the thesis of this chapter. If we keep this patient in mind, together with the concept that "psychopathy is a search for painless freedom from object relationships," various aspects of what most psychiatrists would consider psychopathic behavior will begin to take on a new meaning.

The antisocial character of the psychopath can be understood more clearly if we think about him in terms of his apparent lack of need for others. If an individual experiences interpersonal relationships as stultifying and dangerous and if he really strives to deny his involvement in what others might think or say, then for that individual any sort of behavior is permissible. For the person who does not care about the appraisals of others, the concept "antisocial" itself becomes meaningless. Antisocial behavior becomes only that behavior which is defined by law as punishable if one if unfortunate enough to be caught.

The apparent aggressiveness of the psychopath also takes on a different quality. Actually, the psychopath is no more or no less aggressive than any other person. If other people are truly insignificant, there is simply less need to mask aggressiveness through feigned passivity. Similarly, the impulsiveness of the psychopath becomes more understandable. The ability to delay gratification is a strength that is for the most part contingent on having experienced favorable learning experiences with other human beings. Impulses are restrained with the expectation of ultimately receiving greater rewards from others. This obedience to the reality principle can exist only so long as one really wants to gain the love and respect of others. If an individual can approach a state of freedom from caring, the advantages of restraining immediate gratification are certainly less apparent to him.

The inability of the psychopath to form bonds of lasting affection with others should be considered not only as an inability but also as an aversion. To a certain extent the psychopath consciously and unconsciously seeks to avoid relationships. He is a person who has been deeply hurt by others. His inability to maintain relationships based on mutual respect can be visualized in part as an unwillingness to try. He avoids situations which are painful and feels safe in relating to others only when he does not need them.

The psychopath has also been described as a person who does not experience guilt in the same way as other people. This can be understood by considering that he is a basically ahistoric individual for whom the past and the future are meaningless and for whom only the existing moment is important. Milton Miller has described the psychopath as a person who can "walk through snow without leaving footprints."[9] History, however, must be written about people and about meaningful interactions between people. The psychopath, to the extent that he is successful in freeing himself of a need for others, can approach an ahistoric condition. His lack of commitment to people, causes or ideas allows him to slip through life with little impact upon the world. On the other hand, this same lack of commitment provides him with unlimited maneuverability, freedom from guilt and the sometimes enviable quality of being able to experience comfortably a wide variety of situations. Since the psychopath travels lightly, it is possible for him to visit a great deal of the world.

The charm of the psychopath, his bewildering comfort in stressful situations and the observation that we at times envy, admire or even hate him are clarified if we consider his behavior in the light of a search for freedom. Alan Wheelis in his novel *The Seeker* describes the intense feeling of pleasurable release experienced by a man who makes an almost conscious decision to cease to care about others.[10] The major character of the book, a psychoanalyst, finds that he is then able to maintain a lucrative practice, gain professional acclaim through superficial accomplishments, overcome many of his anxieties and experience new success in seducing desirable women. The behavior of the major character is clearly psychopathic. But what fun he has while suffering from this "disease"!

Wheelis recognizes that if a man can disentangle himself from involvement with others he is free to develop qualities in his own personality which are socially useful. Other people will be attracted to the psychopath because he holds out the possibility of sharing his freedom. Women are especially fascinated by his straightforwardness and apparent lack of dependency.

While we may personally deplore the behavior of certain entertainers, business people or even psychiatrists who live excitingly above and beyond the codes most of us hold to be dear, we would be dishonest if we did not consider the possibility that "these people have something." Perhaps it is not, as Alexander suggests, only rebelliousness which explains our fascination with the psychopath. More likely it is his apparent freedom. We can argue that this is an immoral freedom, that it is an unsatisfying freedom or that it is basically an inhuman freedom. It is still a commodity so often lacking in the lives of most of us that it is highly coveted.

Approaching the problem from this frame of reference may explain the defensive urgency of many groups to consider psychopathy as a mental illness, but it also exposes some of the confusion which can arise when deviant behavior is considered as part of a medical model. Psychopathy is an illness, but only in the sense that it seeks a basically inhuman kind of existence which if allowed to prevail in a great number of people would make the continuation of organized society impossible. To the extent that we become more rational in describing and judging psychopathy, we are forced to look at other aspects of psychopathy that would come under the heading of "nonillness." From some frames of references and in some value systems, psychopathy "can't be all bad." Obviously, for the psychopath himself his behavior may be sustaining and gratifying. He is always a little puzzled when society reacts toward him with such great anger.

## Psychopathy and Criminality

In describing the psychopath we have listed a group of traits which are defenses against a subjective feeling of helplessness. The psychopath defends against oppression even when no oppression is present. His personality structure makes it difficult for him to find a conforming or mental-illness adaptation. The psychopath is an activist, who in his efforts to suit the world to his own needs often finds that it is necessary to violate the law.

Two points must, however, be re-emphasized. First, the psychopath is not necessarily a criminal. He certainly need not be an unsuccessful criminal. If a really "pure psychopath" could exist, his success in the world would probably preclude his ever coming to the attention of a psychiatrist. Second, true psychopathy is an abstract state, and it is doubtful if any person could ever achieve a painless freedom from object relations. Even the prisoner we described earlier could not be called a "pure psychopath."

Still, it must be noted that those criminals who the psychiatrist is allowed to examine seem to show a high degree of psychopathic behavior.[11, 12] What is important about this behavior, however, is that it is ineffective.

CLASSIFICATION
CORRECTION

ACCESSION

REPLACE?

pages 10 - 22 missing

DISCARD?

NOT OUR COPY

NOTE:
LINE-OUT THIS SIDE
WHEN FORM IS NO
LONGER NEEDED.
(SEE OTHER SIDE)



or mediocre psychopath. He may
ıt he has great difficulty in finding
vercome his need for the love and
ychopathic behavior for only brief
e often preceded or followed by
dependency.

ıost pure form in adolescent de-
dependent and even worshipful
ıle, however, of sustaining these
closeness and rebel (sometimes
ere so deeply involved).

ly when they accept a certain
lves to receive gratification of
ıal setting. Like the adolescent,
ain his comfort. Relationships
ıelplessness, and the criminal
kes out against the world by
...al act. In so doing he seems to be saying, "I don't really need you people. I don't really need anybody." For most criminals this is a pathetic cry. A temporary state of freedom is obtained, but his inept behavior usually guarantees that he will soon return to a familiar state of dependency.

### Psychopathy, Masochism and Paranoia

The criminal's tendency to vacillate between rebelliousness and a peculiar kind of conforming dependency can be partially clarified by an examination of other psychoanalytic concepts.* There are other behavioral patterns which, like psychopathy, can be seen as efforts to deal with the experiencing of closeness as helplessness. These are also frequently found in the character structure of criminals. One such behavior is masochism, which is a tendency to find pleasure in suffering and pain. Psychiatrists and philosophers have long puzzled over man's diverse capacities to hurt himself, to gain sexual pleasure through pain and to experience uneasiness in the absence of realistic difficulty. There are many complicated classifications and theoretical explanations of these seemingly paradoxical behaviors. Perhaps the simplest is that masochistic behavior represents an attempt on the part of the individual to control the source and timing of anticipated punishment by inflicting it upon himself.

* A good deal of the material of this section is based on concepts developed by Reik,[13] Brenman[14] and Bergler.[15]

Many criminals seem constantly to provoke others until retaliation takes place. Once they are punished, they settle down and become more comfortable. This behavior was described in Freud's classic case, "The Criminal out of a Sense of Guilt." Because of guilt and fear engendered by incestual feelings toward his mother, a young man committed a crime so that he could be punished. Arrest and punishment, which were more or less under his control, were less frightening than fear of harm by his father, which was not under his control.[16] The tendency of many criminals to provoke the environment until punished and then to accept punishment willingly is familiar to psychiatric criminologists. While Freud suggested that such individuals were reacting to an Oedipal struggle, a similar pattern of behavior can be seen in offenders who are dealing with broader and more primitive conflicts. Some of the criminal's search for dependency gratification seems to be mediated by mechanisms which can be considered a form of masochism.

Masochism, like psychopathy, begins with an equating of closeness with helplessness. However, the masochist is unwilling to renounce his needs for others and finds a unique way of approaching them. He makes himself helpless before others but on his own terms. His behavior, although leading to some psychological pain, also provides certain advantages. If the masochist can provoke others into punishing him, he is brought nearer to dependent relationships. Some people seem to be able to enjoy being taken care of only when care is forced upon them and is accompanied by a certain amount of suffering. Psychoanalysts believe that suffering becomes "eroticized" and is a source of pleasure in itself. This would appear to be only one of many factors involved in such behavior. We must also note that the suffering person has the complete attention of his torturers. The prisoner may resent his jailer, but the jailer must assume complete responsibility for the prisoner's existence. He is forced to gratify his prisoner's needs for dependency. Since the masochist engineers the situation so that a helpless state is "forced" upon him, he need not acknowledge his needs for closeness or dependency. At the same time, masochistic behavior allows a person to control the nature and timing of his punishment. It attenuates his degree of helplessness and allows him to retain some feeling of autonomy. While psychopathy combats helplessness through a denial of need for others, masochism combats helplessness by placing it under the individual's own control.

Another trait which is closely related to psychopathy and masochism is paranoia. Paranoia involves the projection of unacceptable motives, inadequacies and responsibilities onto the external environment. This character trait requires that the individual convince himself that it is not he who wishes to do harm, but others; that it is not he who cannot master his problems, but that it is a cruel and depriving world that keeps him from being effective; that it is not he who seeks dependency or punishment, but that it is others who impose it upon him. The paranoid person sees the world as a hostile place in which closeness always leads to danger. His exaggerated ability to see "the mote in his brother's eye" (but not in his own) spares him a great deal of self-blame, guilt and anxiety. At the same time it often leads to belligerent attitudes and behaviors which are inappropriately directed against the external environment. The paranoid person is prone to indulge in criminal activities since he is always responding to more oppression than is actually present.

It is interesting to consider the manner in which the paranoid defense is related to masochism and psychopathy. If one provokes the environment for the goal of self-punishment, he must picture that environment as hostile. Masochistic behavior would be meaningless and ineffective unless the masochist were convinced of the oppressive intentions of others. The masochist is able to say, "It is not I who have hurt myself, but *they* who hurt me. I do not seek dependency gratification, but *they* force it upon me." If one adopts a psychopathic defense and denies his need for others, he creates a picture of a world in which others are malevolent or dangerous. The psychopath is able to say, "I cannot be blamed for avoiding others, for if I trusted *them, they* would destroy me."

There is an obvious linkage between psychopathy, masochism and paranoia. Each is ultimately a defensive reaction to helplessness, and each is an effort to avoid an open, unstructured and uncontrolled relationship with others. The offender who behaves in an unreasonable manner is often a person who repeatedly vacillates between efforts to deny his need for others (psychopathy) and efforts to obtain closeness and gratification of dependency needs upon his own distorted terms (masochism). The paranoid mechanism is implied in either of these maneuvers and sustains them by constantly providing rationalization and cloture.

Throughout much of the literature of psychiatric criminology, there is an inference that the criminal is a masochistic person who unconsciously seeks punishment.[17, 18] It is assumed that the criminal is ineffective because he unconsciously intends to be ineffective. This hypothesis seems to ignore the adaptive value of crime and is only one possible explanation. The criminal's ineffectiveness can also be understood as an inability to free himself from his need for others or as an inability to be a "good psychopath." At the moment a provocative act is committed he may be seeking freedom as well as punishment. There is no way of determining whether his failure resides in an unconscious masochistic wish to fail or whether it is a maladaptive by-product of an ineffectual search for freedom. Both explanations may be partially valid, but the latter explanation is usually not given sufficient consideration.

If we examine maladaptive criminal behavior solely in terms of the ineptness of the psychopathic defense, such behavior can be explained without invoking the difficult concept of masochism. Our explanation need only account for the factors which encourage the criminal to seek the psychopathic defense yet use it so ineffectively. These factors have already been described. The criminal seeks freedom in order to maintain organismic integrity, but he cannot find such freedom because he cares too much about others and needs them too much to be a "good psychopath." If he were really a "good psychopath," he would be able to handle situations of oppressive stress more gracefully. Consider the following grotesque but illuminating clinical vignette.

The author as part of his prison consultation duties was asked to examine a twenty-two-year-old male inmate who had been in solitary confinement for thirty days. This unusual length of stay had been provoked by repeated episodes of verbal and physical aggressiveness directed toward the prison guards. The patient's aggressiveness seemed boundless, and even when physically restrained he would spit and curse. Although his intellectual functions were intact, his obviously self-destructive behavior had aroused the concern of the guards, who were beginning to tire of their struggle with this man. They hoped that he would be sent to the state hospital. The man was in a state of helplessness comparable in some degree with that of the hypothetical prisoner we discussed in Chapter 6. His condition had been brought about, however, largely by a combination of his paranoid attitudes and his inability to seek freedom in a constructive manner.

When interviewed the patient expressed almost global aggression toward his jailers, toward those who had imprisoned him and even toward members of his own family, who he felt had abandoned him. He swore revenge and, though the hopelessness of his struggle was apparent to him, he gave no indication of wishing to call it off. His physical condition was deplorable. He had lost weight, was unshaven, unkempt and had begun to show signs of vitamin deficiency. He nevertheless refused an offer of hospitalization, stating, "I am not crazy, and even if you transfer me out of here, sooner or later I'll come back and I'm going to get these guys." Although overt symptoms of psychosis were not obvious, the patient was transferred (against his wishes) to the state hospital simply on humanitarian grounds. As anticipated, he improved quickly, was returned to the prison and, of course, was soon experiencing further difficulty.

The apparently unresolvable situation of this man while in solitary confinement was similar to that of a helpless child trying to influence a cruel and depriving mother. He was confronted with an authority which was in complete control of his existence, but which was at the same time nongiving, arbitrary and, from his standpoint, cruel. Yet he needed his torturers for they supplied him with food, clothing, cigarettes and on rare occasions even bits of affection. The patient seemed inextricably bound up in a struggle with a rejecting and depriving maternal structure which he could control only in a negative direction; that is, he could induce his captors to punish him, but he could not force them to help him. He would attack and feel relieved while attacking, and then he would be punished.

While interviewing this man, I was preoccupied with alternative solutions by which the patient might handle his grievous situation. The prison authorities had not really been too unfair. They were simply performing their duties as required by prison protocol. It was obvious that the patient's own paranoid attitudes had helped to bring him to his plight. Why couldn't the patient see this? Why couldn't he accept himself as a deviant, aggressive and perhaps bad person and make an effort to live up to the expectations of conformity that others were trying to impose upon him? He was unfortunately too angry and rebellious, and had been too deeply wounded to accept this kind of solution. I then began to wonder why the patient simply didn't "go crazy." Certainly, many neurotic individuals could not have stood for more than a few days the abuse and isolation this individual had endured. When I verbalized this thought, I was met with the reply, "I thought about that, Doc, and I know my behavior seems crazy, but I'm not. I know who I hate, and I hate them too much to ever go crazy." Finally, I hit on what seemed to be the best way out and communicated this thinking to the prisoner. "Why not pretend to conform, why not pretend to go along with these people, do what they want you to do until they leave you alone and then do as you please and live your life as you please from there on in? You don't really have to give a damn about them. Just pretend you like them and then you will be free to do as you please the rest of the time." This suggestion was the first one that both moved and troubled the patient. It also troubled the writer. What had been suggested as the most healthy means of handling a gruesome situation was actually cynical, dishonest and psychopathic.

If we return to our consideration of psychopathy and related traits, we can ask if the depriving or rejecting mother (or world) really offers the growing child many more alternatives than those available to our unfortunate inmate. If mother, parents or authority are consistently visualized as all-powerful, cruel or arbitrary, what behaviors are available to the individual? A direct attack upon parents or upon any authority structure which is perceived as oppressive implies that the attacking individual still cares. At the same time that he seeks freedom, he is hopeful that his behavior will bring him the love and recognition he so desperately craves. But the "healthiest" resolution for the individual exposed to this kind of unfortunate situation would be possible only if he could cease to care. If one really doesn't care about others, he can then "fake it." He can pretend to conform while allowing himself complete freedom to satisfy basic needs. This, of course, would be pure psychopathic behavior.

Our prisoner obviously did not have the strength to behave in a truly psychopathic manner. Whether or not he unconsciously sought the suffering which was imposed upon him is debatable. What is clear, however, is that his quests for freedom took the form of an ineffective and futile rebellion. Actually, he cared too much about the reactions of others to really find the freedom he craved.

Many criminals use the psychopathic defense far more effectively than the prisoner we have been discussing. Yet even they cannot use it consistently. Sooner or later their needs for others lead to rebellious behaviors which have an implied message that they do care for others. At this point their criminal behavior becomes increasingly ineffective. Ultimately, the psychopathic defense does not free the criminal; it only sustains him for brief periods.

*Chapter 9*

# THE STRESSES OF ADOLESCENCE

HAVING argued that certain children enter the teen-age years with a greater predisposition to crime, our efforts throughout this chapter will be to describe the additional crime-favoring stresses of adolescence and particularly those that seem to be generated by the American culture. In our era juvenile crime appears to have superseded adult crime in social importance. The term "delinquency" itself has come to imply an adolescent offender. One of the more important questions of our times is why so many teen-agers are willing and even eager to indulge in antisocial activity. The author believes that it is not possible to respond to this question without considering the ethical and political structure of the Western world. Efforts will therefore be made in the latter part of this chapter to consider broader issues, such as the meaningfulness of the American way of life, the spiritual climate of our country and the problems of adjustment to a society that is changing at an unprecedented rate.

In keeping with a broader approach, our observations will apply to all delinquent behavior rather than selected forms of unreasonable behavior. Historically, society has been far more willing to accept a medical approach toward the juvenile offender than toward the adult offender. Psychiatrists, through their work with community agencies, have familiarized themselves with all types of juvenile delinquents, including many who are never institutionalized or punished. We might also note that a significant portion of the behavior of juvenile delinquents is, in the words of Albert Cohen, "malicious, negativistic and non-utilitarian."[1] As such it has an unreasonable quality which is of immediate interest to the psychiatrist.

Many of the delinquent behaviors of adolescents seem to be totally devoid of a social purpose which could be understood or accepted by adults. Activities such as gang fighting and property destruction are inconsistent with any of the success goals of our society. Even such juvenile delinquencies as burglary or theft often seem to be carried out in such an aimless or hazardous manner that it is doubtful if they are motivated by economic needs. The behavior of the delinquent is incongruent with the goals of the middle classes and can be considered a mockery or perversion of such goals. It is also at times alien to the goals of the lower-class adult population, who are sometimes as disturbed as middle-class adults by the unreasonable nature of juvenile crime. Even the adult criminal is critical of the juvenile delinquent and often looks upon him as "sick," dangerous and as a potential threat to more organized crime.

## The Biological Foundation of Stress

The criminogenic influence of any of the stresses of adolescence is largely dependent upon the expectations of the culture. Each society provides different social roles for its adolescents. The age at which specific attitudes and behaviors are supposed to become "normal" or appropriate is determined by the needs of that society. This means that the stressful aspects of biological or psychological maturation will depend upon the varying social roles which adolescents are asked to assume.

In our country adolescence is regularly described as a period of storminess, unpredictability or chaos. While cultural factors contribute to this volatility, changes in the biological state of the organism form the foundation over which such behavior develops.

A high incidence of criminality during the adolescent years is at least partly related to the fact that this is a period of rapid growth and major biological changes. The preadolescent may experience criminal impulses, but he does not have the biological equipment with which to act upon them. The adolescent, on the other hand, has sufficient physical strength to transform his antisocial wishes into antisocial conduct. For the first time in his life he has the capacity to express his needs through a wide variety of acts, some of which are forbidden by law.

There are other, more subtle biological changes during adolescence. With the onset of puberty and the development of secondary sex characteristics the adolescent must learn to cope with and channelize an increased sexual drive. He must accommodate himself to the fact that his body is changing. These changes influence every aspect of his life, from his eating and sleeping habits to the amount of energy he can mobilize for the performance of routine tasks. As the body changes, patterns of adaptation must change.

Accommodating to changes in body maturation and body image is in itself a formidable task. Further problems develop when physical maturation does not progress at the same rate as psychological maturation. For example, a certain number of girls probably become involved in transgressions of the sexual code because of precocious physical development which is not accompanied by a similar psychological maturity. Such girls are more likely to be targets of seduction and will have gerater difficulty in understanding the social meaning of sexual behavior. Similarly, boys whose physical development proceeds more rapidly are likely to be invited to participate in antisocial activities before they are psychologically equipped to evaluate the consequences of delinquency. This may be one reason for the frequently noted correlation between mesomorphy or muscularity and delinquency.

## The Psychological and Social Stresses of Adolescence

Stressful experiences during adolescence will reinforce criminogenic tendencies in those who are strongly predisposed and may precipitate criminal behavior in those whose predisposition is less intense. The same stresses which play a role in creating predisposition during the earliest years of life also seem to further criminality during adolescence. Even in the absence of stresses of neglect, abuse, inconsistency or overcontrol, momentum toward a delinquent adaptation is frequently created by efforts to resolve sociopsychological problems which are peculiar to the adolescent years.

The adolescent must first come to terms with his sexual drives. To be considered well adjusted to our culture, he must identify himself with the social world of his own sex and must gain a reasonable degree of comfort in his relationship with the opposite sex. The adolescent must also gain some degree of psychological and social independence from his parents. This requires that he prepare himself to live without them and that he find other sources for gratification and support. As a corollary to a need for independence, the adolescent must begin to develop work habits and skills which allow him to find his own way in the world. He is required to grapple with the issue of a future which will be largely determined by his vocational choice.

These problems touch upon the question of identity. To develop a firm image of who he is, the adolescent must find some comfort in his sexual role, must be aware of the extent of his need of others and the extent of his own capacities. The uncertainties he experiences in finding and retaining a consistent sense of self are often manifested in violent emotional upheavals.[2, 3, 4] Some of these upheavals are directed against the environment.

While some development of a firm sexual identity takes place during the Oedipal and latency periods, adolescence is that crucial period during which sexual attitudes and behaviors are either reinforced or partially extinguished. In this sense adolescence is a kind of "second chance," a period in which there is an opportunity to modify some of the disturbances of earlier life. On the other hand, disturbing experiences during adolescence can be severe enough to disrupt seriously a previously adequate personality.

The development of a socially acceptable sexual identity requires the support of a reasonably intact family. The adolescent needs parents who are comfortable with their own sexual roles, who can serve as models for identification. He also needs reassurance that his sexual role is worthwhile and respected.

A large number of adolescents develop grave uncertainties as to their sexual identity. Many factors can encourage doubt, discomfort and turmoil. Perhaps the most common disruptive situation arises when the parents are unable to meet each other's needs and expect the child to provide compensatory gratification, thus forcing the adolescent into social roles which he is ill-equipped to assume.

In our culture many disturbed families are especially prone to use the male child to fulfill roles which properly belong to the father. (Similar patterns occur with female children and, as we shall see later, have some relevance to female delinquency.) As the father abdicates certain responsibilities, the mother turns to the son as her most important love object. When the child is increasingly brought closer to the mother, his sexual wishes toward her may become more conscious and, since they are socially unacceptable, more repugnant. Any male child who is forced into an exploitative closeness to his mother may come to experience an insidious discomfort with masculine roles. The mother or the father may discourage normal maturation because of their unconscious fears that such change could lead to a living out of incestual drives. The child himself has to exert more rigid control of his impulses and is inclined to shun socially acceptable sexual behaviors. As the adolescent comes to realize that his relationship with his mother is based on overcontrol and exploitation, he is likely to generalize and come to fear any kind of sexual closeness to women. Not only does he see all women as dangerous seductresses, but he is also plagued by guilt and fear of retaliation from the father.

There are many other types of familial situations in which closeness to a parent of the opposite sex becomes associated with a feeling of anxiety and helplessness. Such situations lead to an inability to assume an acceptable sexual role and contribute to the development of sexual deviations in which the desired object is not a person of the opposite sex and in which the sexual aim may not be one of mutually gratifying intercourse. Fear of sexual closeness has important implications in understanding the relationship of sexual identity to delinquency.

This is an example of only one mechanism which can lead to an uncertainty as to sexual identification. Similar problems can result when the father is physically absent, emotionally distant or fails to provide an adequate model for his son. The adolescent who is uncertain as to his sexual identity is liable to be deeply preoccupied with fears of being considered a "sissy" or effeminate. Sometimes his fears are aggravated by an awareness of attraction to members of his own sex. This constitutes a new stress since any feeling which the adolescent perceives as being suggestive of homosexual tendencies is vigorously condemned by our culture. One common way in which males are taught to defend themselves against socially unacceptable feelings of sexual uncertainty, femininity or latent homosexuality is by seeking to prove their masculinity through aggressive behavior. This defense has considerable relevance to juvenile delinquency.*

The ideal masculine role in the minds of most adolescents exaggerates the value of aggressive activism. Passivity is often seen as weakness. Unless an adolescent is comfortable with his sexual identity, he will equate conformity with femininity. Delinquency provides an active role which offers the doubting adolescent an opportunity to reassure himself as to his wholeness as a man. A significant portion of male juvenile delinquency can, in fact, be described as "masculine-proving behavior." Juvenile delinquency far more than adult crime is characterized by actions which involve tests of courage and the presence of risks. In resorting to criminality as an adaptive response to the experience of helplessness, many adolescents also find that they are able to retain a more comfortable masculine identity.

Adolescence is also a period when the child is uncertain as to whether he wants to remain in a comfortable but dependent relationship with his

* In addition to the kinds of threats to masculinity which derive from family conflict, we must also note that social stresses such as poverty or ethnic persecution will also diminish the adolescent's capacity to identify with the masculine role. There is evidence, for example, that Negroes have more serious doubts about their masculinity than whites.[5]

parents or to seek the uncertain rewards of greater freedom. He often vacillates between moments of excessive dependence and excessive independence. If he is loved enough and if his parents really want him to be a mature, self-reliant person, he is gradually able to overcome his more infantile dependent needs. He then learns to find gratification in mutual nonoppressive relationships with peers. If these conditions are not met, maladaptive responses invariably occur.

The unloved child may be unwilling or unable to free himself from an excessive dependence upon his parents. A more common situation is that in which the parents cling to, control and overprotect a child who is ready to be more independent. Both of these patterns lead to an excessive concern with identity and status and sometimes culminate in a violent reaction directed against the parents and adult society. In the first instance the child's fear of losing gratification may be overcome only by an inappropriate and angry disavowal of all dependency feeling. In the second situation explosive rebelliousness may be the only behavior through which the child can find a reasonable degree of freedom.

The adolescent's struggle to free himself is complicated by his increased ability to perceive not only his own inadequacies but those of his surrounding world as well. Adolescence is a time in life when intellectual capacities and knowledge are sufficiently developed to allow for objective evaluation of others. The adolescent is in a position to discern what is true and what is not true, who is lying and who is not. In earlier years the child is bombarded with a great number of philosophies, standards and attitudes which may be essential to his peace of mind but which cannot be sustained when exposed to the light of fact and reason. His new-found ability to evaluate rationally ethical precepts or exhortations imposes new stresses upon him.

It is possible that much of the rebelliousness of the adolescent is related to his discovery of fact and truth. A discerning adolescent learns that his parents may have been inconsistent, devious or inadequate. He discovers that much of what has been demanded of him and presented as something he should do for his own good is more likely to be something he has been asked to do simply to satisfy an arbitrary need of others. The adolescent learns to perceive the "double bind," and at this phase in his development he has some ability to break out of it. He becomes particularly sensitive to the issue of "phoniness." Wishing to hold onto the idealism which may have been presented to him in earlier years, he becomes enraged when he discovers that most of the world and particularly his parents do not adhere to their own avowed standards.

The ability to detect phoniness, "double binds" and arbitrary control from others can lead to a number of unfavorable reactions. The adolescent may feel guilty because of an irreverent attitude he senses toward previously loved objects. He may defend against such feelings by denying that they exist. Or he may withdraw from others and particularly from the adult world. A more common reaction is rebelliousness and a premature search for independence. Unfortunately, many adolescents come to this moment before they are capable of making an effective and self-sustained adjustment. In the absence of either sufficient maturity or opportunity to improve their situation, a premature search for independence may be channelized into desperate and ineffective delinquent behavior.

One of the more unfortunate aspects of ineffective rebelliousness is that it drains off energy which should be properly directed toward mastering skills essential for survival in a competitive world. Developing proper study habits and learning a trade or profession require a certain amount of sublimation and a channelizing of energy toward a goal. If the adolescent is preoccupied with bitter struggles with his parents and the rest of the world, he is handicapped in committing his interests and energies toward those areas where mastery is really a possibility. If he does not develop proper work habits and a degree of vocational commitment during this phase of life, he may well lose a sense of who he is and where he is going. He will also lose the ability to compete with his more socially adjusted contemporaries. All these factors militate toward a greater sense of helplessness and a greater propensity to criminality.*

## Delinquency and the Social and Moral Climate

The conduct of the adolescent is determined by the social and moral world in which he lives. The psychiatrist can study and describe the manner by which that world influences the child's development, but in so doing he cannot offer a complete answer to such a question as "Why is juvenile delinquency increasing?" An answer to this question must be sought in the peculiarities of our society. The medically trained practitioner does not find it easy to approach a behavioral problem in terms of ethics or politics. However, if he wishes to investigate the causes of delinquency, he cannot avoid such issues. In this section the author will offer some abbreviated, highly judgmental observations as to how the modern-day American culture encourages delinquent behavior.

While delinquency in America is primarily a lower-class phenomenon,

* The sociologist, David Matza, argues that the adolescent delinquent is in a state of drift between freedom (independence and internal control) and control (parental and social restraint). He believes that the delinquent is characterized by a tendency to postpone commitments to either criminal or conventional norms.[6]

middle-class delinquency is on the rise. Whatever the class status of the delinquent may be, there are so many new oppressive stresses impinging upon our adolescents—emanating either from the society as a whole or from individual families—that heroic attempts at adaptation are often necessary. At the same time outlets for activism and pressures toward law-abiding conformity seem to be decreasing. This is another way of saying that the social and moral direction of our culture favors an increase in both mental illness and delinquency.

One problem that increasingly plagues American adolescents is an inconsistent presentation of value systems. When more and more delinquent adolescents insist that there are too many inconsistencies and double messages in the current environment, we can understand their complaint in one of three ways. They are either correct in their appraisal or more willing to talk about the problem than older generations or far more suspicious and rebellious than older generations. While there is probably some truth in the last two explanations, it is also possible that we live in a society that is peculiarly characterized by inconsistency, self-deceit and paradoxical communication. We can illustrate this point by listing only a few of the double messages that might be received by a lower-class Negro boy growing up in a crowded urban area. He would be repeatedly exposed to inconsistent messages such as the following. On the left-hand side are listed those ethical guidelines he would probably receive in church, in school and from his parents. On the right-hand side are listed those messages which he would learn from his experiences on the street or from observing the actual behavior of his parents and other adults.

| | |
|---|---|
| "Virtue is its own reward." | "Don't be a fool; take what you can get." |
| "Love thy neighbor." | "Don't involve yourself in other people's troubles." |
| "Thou shalt not steal." | "Some kind of stealing is all right, but just don't get caught." |
| "Obey the law always." | "Try to stay out of trouble. Obey those laws that meet your needs." |
| "The meek shall inherit the earth." | "You get what you fight for." |
| "All men are brothers." | "We don't want those niggers moving into our neighborhood." |

| | |
|---|---|
| "Thou shalt not covet thy neighbor's wife." | "Everybody has to cut loose once in a while, but don't let the 'old lady' know." |
| "Ask not what your country can do for you, ask what you can do for your country." | "What do I owe this country? Not a thing." |
| "You must learn to control your sexual impulses." | "You're not a man until you've had it. You're not a queer, are you?" |
| "Everybody in America has the same opportunity." | "Don't get too uppity, black boy." |
| "You can be happy without money." | "Nobody gets in without a ticket." |

The reader can probably think of many more contradictory ethical standards which would be imposed upon this puzzled child. The middle-class adolescent would be exposed to some of the above contradictory messages but would be more likely to hear confusing communications such as the following:

| | |
|---|---|
| "A man's family comes first." | "Don't bother me now, I'm too busy." |
| "Adhere to your principles." | "I'd like to fight this issue, but what will the neighbors think?" |
| "Control your sexual impulses." | "Betty is already thirteen and I worry; she never goes out on dates." |
| "Alcohol is bad for you." | "Don't make so much noise; this hangover is killing me." |
| "We love you for what you are." | "If you disgrace us, we'll never forgive you." |
| "A man should go to church and he should fear God." | "I'd go to church more often but the minister is so dull." |
| "You must help your less fortunate neighbors." | "Taxes, taxes, they ought to crack down on those welfare chiselers." |
| "You are your brother's keeper." | "Keep your nose clean and stay out of other people's troubles." |

We can only speculate as to the impact of such inconsistent messages upon a child who is trying to find codes and ideals. Should he conform to the ideals of his church? Or should he listen to the more cynical values of the street or marketplace? How is he to know what to believe? With whom and with what should he identify himself? Is it possible for him to find a consistent ideology?

The reader may feel that this picture of ethical inconsistency in our society is overdrawn. It might be argued that every culture throughout history has shown some discrepancy between its professed values and the values implied in the actual conduct of its citizens. This is certainly true, but at the same time these discrepancies seem to be more starkly drawn in American society. As older beliefs have lost their power they have not been replaced by new ones which are meaningful. In other eras our citizens, particularly those who belonged to the lower classes, found that conformity was made easier by religious faith. Today, although church attendance is high, few people live by the tenets of their religion and the clergy seems to have little influence in controlling behavior. With regard to some issues such as premarital sex, consensus seems to replace morality and we find the churches being led to revise their attitudes in order to keep up with popular opinion.

Some writers such as Paul Goodman[7] and John H. Scharr[8] have recognized that our society does not provide meaningful ideologies for its citizens. The American adolescent has few consistent social, political or religious ethics with which he can identify. There are a number of possible explanations for this ideological vacuum. One hypothesis is that a wealthy nation such as ours loses sight of older standards when so many economic rewards are readily available. Perhaps people need to have a certain amount of deprivation coming from the environment, a deprivation which provides valid struggles that can be believed in and attacked directly. The recent behavior of university students seems to support this hypothesis. Exposed to a rather comfortable existence, our students seem to be actively searching for any cause that they find meaningful. They seek to be activists, but in the absence of valid struggles often find causes which are mischievous or trivial. When the free-speech movement at the University of California in Berkeley was successful, some of its partisans immediately took up new causes of filthy speech and free sex.

Another explanation is that a generation that has grown up in a time of chaos and incredibly rapid change, a time when friendly nations become enemies and enemy nations become friends within a few years, despairs of believing in anything. When population and technological progress are expanding so rapidly, there is less adaptive value in holding onto anything which is familiar, including ethical codes. Still another way of understanding this problem is that technological improvement in mass communications media provides us with so much new information about the world that it is easier to question and doubt. It is almost impossible to hide anything from our children. The average preteen child, who spends over twenty-five hours per week watching television, learns a great many of the cynical truths about the world at a very tender age. It is not easy for him to accept ethical rules which he knows are often violated with impunity.

However one understands this problem, it must be admitted that our era is characterized by an increasing number of people who feel and admit to themselves that their lives are meaningless. The expression of this feeling varies with social class. The less educated adolescent is unlikely to ask, "What is life about?" He nevertheless demonstrates similar doubts in many of his behaviors and attitudes. When he seaches for "kicks" and "coolness," he implies a lack of commitment to any belief or ideology. It is of interest to note that when any meaningful struggle with which adolescents can identify becomes available the rate of delinquency drops. There is evidence, for example, that Negro children who are associated with the civil rights movement are less likely to be delinquent.[9]

Somewhat related to the issue of ethical confusion and meaninglessness is a breakdown in the sense of responsibility. The forces which are moving us to rapid technological progress and social change seem at times to be practically out of our control. In a mass society the citizen inevitably experiences some sense of futility when he attempts to see himself as a responsible agent who can shape the direction of his life. This is particularly true of the adolescent, who realizes that he will have practically no opportunity to influence the kind of world in which he will eventually live. A feeling of powerlessness diminishes a sense of personal responsibility. The more one feels unable to control his destiny, the less responsibility he wishes to take for his behavior.

Psychiatry and psychoanalysis are repeatedly blamed for having contributed to a breakdown in the ethical standards of our children and for a subsequent rise in juvenile delinquency. It is often argued that the doctrine of permissiveness promulgated by some Freudians has led to the rearing of a generation of untamed, pleasure-seeking delinquents. On two counts this accusation seems farfetched. Permissiveness does not necessarily breed crime, and it is probable that other forces in our society have had a greater influence than psychiatry in spreading this doctrine. Furthermore, it must also be noted that the preaching of permissiveness as interpreted by some represents a gross distortion of Freud's thinking.

A more damning accusation that might be leveled at psychiatry is that our model of mental illness can be used to encourage the notion that people are not responsible for their own behavior. The equation of sickness with nonresponsibility seems to have been generalized to other behaviors, including delinquency. In a society in which people do not feel responsible for their own actions the criminal adaptation is more easily justified and supported. Statements such as "With all my problems, how could I have behaved differently?" are becoming commonplace.

In addition to the dearth of consistent ideologies in American society, certain economic factors seem to be encouraging an increase in delinquency. Juvenile crime tends to go up and adult crime tends to go down during times of prosperity. The problems of adjusting to an affluent society seem to have their greatest impact upon the adolescent. In the presence of relatively easy access to material comfort those who are denied such opportunities are particularly embittered. If we really do have twenty million poor in this country, their plight must be intolerable since it is obvious that the other 160 million are leading a very comfortable life. No poverty-stricken child today can fail to see the evidence of wealth all around him. It is not that there are only a few "lucky ones," but rather that he is one of the few "unlucky ones." He is a member of a minority group who knows that better things are very close and yet very far.

An especially complex problem is created by increased mechanization. There are few jobs left for younger men who are seeking to earn their sustenance through active and meaningful physical labor. As more and more machines do our work for us, there are fewer struggles to be fought with the environment. The trend toward automation implies that vocational success will become increasingly dependent upon intellectual skills and continuing self-education. These are not qualities which characterize the lower-class adolescent. He has been raised with greater emphasis on active than on contemplative skills. In a world where technological evolution has become technological revolution he might be considered a kind of "atavistic throwback." Like the Indian child on the reservation, he has not been raised to deal with a world of disappearing natural resources, inactivity and automation. Perhaps we are unwittingly producing a new Lombrosian criminal type, this time in the form of a primitive child who is completely untrained for quiescent survival in an extraordinarily complicated world.

What to do with increased leisure time has become a problem of fulminating intensity. Again, it is the person who has been trained to enjoy intellectual activity who is capable of making the best use of unstructured time. The rest of the population seems to be succumbing to a lethargical twenty-five hours a week at the television set. Adolescents, who watch less televisioin than any other age group, have needed and have sought additional activity to challenge them. Even for the teen-ager, however, physical outlets for leisure activity are becoming more limited and less gratifying. The adolescent who needs to work off energy, to prove his masculinity or to find some means of combating the insidious boredom of his life finds fewer outlets in our society and certainly none that are as exciting as delinquency.

We have up to this point mainly considered the direct impact of our culture upon the child. Insofar as social and moral problems of our culture influence parents, they will also have an indirect effect upon the adolescent. The parents of the adolescent are usually in the third or fourth decade of their lives. These may be tranquil and gratifying years for some, but they are despairing years for others. By the time a person reaches the age of thirty-five he has a firm idea of his over-all status. He can evaluate the successfulness of his marriage, he is aware of his vocational potentiality, and he has some knowledge of his capacity to endure stress. If he senses realistic limitations on his future and if he cannot accommodate himself to these limitations, he may turn to his children as major sources of hope and gratification. Many parents identify themselves with their children and seek justification and meaning in their own lives through a vicarious enjoyment of their children's lives. Such parents do not allow their children to find independence and maturity. Their expectations of their children create severe problems. A child who is forced into activities which he might not have chosen if left alone will sooner or later rebel.

In our society there seems to be much impetus toward initiating children into courtship behavior as early as possible. Mixed dancing classes for ten-year-olds, "make-out" parties for grade-schoolers and dating before the age of thirteen are becoming an acceptable part of American life. At least a part of this activity is generated by adults who are vicariously attempting to find some excitement to compensate for their own boredom and inadequacy. It must also be noted that parental urgings for children to indulge in all the pleasures they themselves may have missed has a two-edged quality. Hardly a parent today, poverty-stricken or not, has been exposed to the material advantages our children have come to take as a matter of course. Most of us fail to acknowledge to ourselves how jealous we are of our own children. Actually, a certain amount of our pushing and a certain amount of our neglect may both be related to the fact that many of us simply cannot tolerate seeing our children "have it so good."

## The Adolescent Mystique

A lore has grown up in our nation, centered around the unique enigmatic quality of adolescence. The teen-age culture is described almost as if adolescents were an alien people who happen to be living temporarily in our land. Books, records, the mass communications media and the commercial interests treat the teen-ager as a member of a special class—privileged, nonresponsible, fun-seeking and undecipherable. Adolescents are more firmly separated from their parents than ever before. Peer-group ties supersede family ties and peer-group ethics take on more of a guiding influence than adult ethics. More and more, adolescents tend to be looked upon as a separate class of people.

What we have created is an adolescent mystique. There is no reason, psychological, social or historical, why our teen-agers should be so alien to us. They are certainly no more complicated than adults and certainly easier to communicate with than smaller children. Yet the cry, "You can't understand teen-agers," is uneasily and warily phrased by the adolescent and gullibly and unquestioningly accepted by his parents. This assertion leads to many harmful attitudes. We fail to acknowledge our responsibility to our children We fail to exercise proper restraint where restraint is needed. Too often, we throw up our hands in despair and offer our children anything they want as long as they are reasonably docile and unobtrusive.

The adolescent mystique, however, also has another side to it. We indulge, we live through, or we allow a laissez-faire existence to our adolescents only up to a point. When they begin to disappoint us, we cease to be indulgent. It is then that our smoldering resentment, our jealousies over their material advantages, their sexual freedom and their irresponsible way of life begin to gnaw at us. Insofar as they are seen as an alien group it is often easy to hate them, and hate them we do when given the opportunity. While we allow the adolescent many advantages which were denied to ourselves, we also limit his action-oriented activities with increasing stringency. We define as delinquency many actions which would have been called pranks or naughtiness in our own youth. And constantly we maintain attitudes of smoldering resentment which periodically are accentuated by eruptions of gross malice. At those moments when we call for increasingly stern punishments our relish in proposing shameful and humiliating retribution takes on almost sadistic proportions.

Considerable space has been devoted to a discussion of issues which are not usually thought of as having much to do with either psychiatry or criminology. Yet it must be acknowledged that the incidence of mental illness and crime varies with the social and moral climate of the culture. This simple truth seems repeatedly to evade those who discuss solutions to the problem of social deviancy. Many different "cures" are regularly proposed, with the claim that they will either eradicate or substantially diminish the amount of juvenile delinquency in our society. Actually, when any judge, psychiatrist or sociologist proposes a simple solution to the crime problem, he deceives both himself and the public. *We can either have the kind of society we have now with a high rate of delinquency or we can have a different kind of society with a lower rate of delinquency. There are no easy answers. Any significant diminution in delinquency will require a change in the form of the world we have come to know. In the absence of such change all of us are relegated to a role comparable to that of the battle surgeon. We are limited to treating the casualties and not the causes of the social struggle.*

*Chapter 10*

# CRUCIAL ISSUES IN JUVENILE DELINQUENCY

MOST adolescent crime is either a group undertaking or it is activated and sustained by association with fellow delinquents. Adolescence is that time of life when man's tendency to form clubs, cliques and other associations of peers reaches its peak. In our society some adolescent groups are organized around participation in antisocial activity. Although little is known about how gangs are formed or why certain adolescents either accept or reject their norms, a great deal has been learned about the structure of the gang and its activities.[1, 2, 3] This information suggests that the gang is a peculiarly appropriate instrument for temporarily solving the problems of the oppressed adolescent.

The gang satisfies many basic needs. In a neighorhood characterized by a high incidence of violence, it offers some protection from other gangs, the police and individual marauders. Some delinquents living in slum areas insist that their sole purpose in joining a gang is to gain security from physical attack. The gang is also a source of friendship. Loyalty is often intense, and the adolescent who joins such a group is offered some sense of identity and status. The gang may become the focal point for a wide variety of nondelinquent activities. It provides access to recreational activities, to members of the opposite sex, and sometimes to a safe physical shelter where the adolescent can temporarily avoid contact with a disturbing family.

The antisocial activity of the gang provides an outlet for the expression of aggressive energy. This is especially true of lower-class delinquents, who are denied access to more legitimate means of competition and rivalry.

The gang creates many struggles or battles in which masculinity can be proven and creative skills developed. It is a natural outlet for "losers" (those who sense their inability to rise or find an acceptable place in our society) since it provides an outlet for a form of ruthless but exciting play which does not result in the usual frustration and failure these boys experience when they adhere to the more conventional rules of society.

For the child beset by chronic anxiety and depression, the gang offers a means of protection and a vehicle for striking back. It helps to make the enemy visible and allows individual paranoia to be tempered by group justification. It gives to all its members a kind of ideology. Gangs do develop a sense of purpose, even if that purpose may appear to be perversely directed against the norms of the society. Frequently they offer a cynical rationale and philosophy of life that have more meaning to the adolescent than anything offered by his parents or the church. Conventional norms are easily discredited, but the gang's ideology is reinforced by the unpleasant experiences of daily life.

While the gang is most often thought of as a catalyst of crime, it may also be a direct criminogenic influence. It sometimes becomes an unreasonable autonomous force whose behavior is not predictable out of an understanding of its individual members. A group of rebellious youngsters can be stimulated to preform more antisocial acts when together than any individual member would dare to do alone. The gang may therefore mobilize potentials for delinquency which might otherwise lie dormant. Sometimes it calls for "masculine-proving behavior" on the part of its members, behavior which could be alien to the boys' own needs. Those instances in which a boy commits a crime to gain the approval of his group may be exceptional examples of crime as a form of helplessness rather than as a defense against it. It is the group itself which then combats the helplessness of its individual members.

## Symbolic Aspects of Delinquent Behavior

The selection of a criminal act is often dependent upon the symbolic and unconscious meaning of that act to the offender. The crime itself may be a form of substitute gratification which is more acceptable to the criminal than his original unconscious wish. While an understanding of the specific motivations and symbolic meaning of various crimes is helpful, this direction of investigation has received too much emphasis by psychiatrists. There is a tendency to assume that the cause of a crime is understood once the symbolic meaning of that crime is known. The search for a specific motivation can lead to generalizations which do not account for the fact that the dynamic meaning of a crime is relevant only to a given individual and even here as only a partial explanation. Futhermore, as we shall note in a later chapter, understanding the symbolic nature of crime does not help very much in treating the offender. Psychiatrists and other professionals become prematurely disillusioned when they discover that their arduously gained dynamic insights may not be too helpful to the criminal.

With these reservations, it must still be admitted that many types of adolescent (and to a lesser extent adult) crime have a symbolic unconscious meaning to the offender. Through the mechanism of displacement, unacceptable behaviors and attitudes are transferred to substitute objects and lead to substitute actions which may violate the law. This concept can be illustrated by examining selected types of crimes and describing dynamics which are often found to be specifically related. While the reader is cautioned not to look upon these dynamics as general explanations, he is also advised not to consider them too lightly. Often they are amazingly applicable to the individual offender.

Much adolescent crime directed against persons and property is given specific directions by forces outside of the delinquent's awareness. Aggressive feelings originally engendered by frustrating parents may be displaced toward all authority figures. Although destructive behavior has a general adaptive function of its own, the choice of property to be attacked may have symbolic meaning. Some delinquents regularly vandalize schools, churches and other institutions which represent an authority they wish to reject. Sometimes there is an even more specific motivation involved in a crime, as illustrated in the following case.

A fourteen-year-old adolescent boy was arrested for having removed several hundred prized breeding trout from a local fish hatchery and leaving them to die in the woods. This act caused a huge financial loss to the state and set back restocking plans for this particular species for several years. An enraged and confused judicial agency asked for psychiatric consultation before passing sentence. Examination revealed a timid, passive boy who had no history of earlier delinquency. A product of a broken home, he had been raised by an overburdened, despondent and socially inadequate mother. His schoolwork and social maturity were far below par. He saw himself as an isolated, lonely person whose only companion was a mongrel dog. One week before his offense, the dog was killed by an automobile. The boy saw the accident and noted that the driver did not stop. Following this event, he was profoundly depressed and remained in this condition until he committed the crime. During his interview he stated, "I don't know why I did it except that they had destroyed something of mine and I wanted to destroy something of theirs."

In some instances of theft the choice of the object to be stolen or the person to be stolen from is deeply influenced by unconscious factors. Psychoanalysts recognize that when a young child steals from his parents he may be unconsciously seeking their attention or affection. Similarly, the adolescent or adult may steal an object which to him symbolizes affection, erotic love or status. An equation of stealing and love-seeking is obviously oversimplified, and this type of psychoanalytic speculation has been the object of much ridicule. The problem is that such a proposition might be quite relevant for the individual patient but may not be susceptible to generalization. The psychiatrist who finds that two or three people who steal are seeking love is on shaky grounds when he says that all criminals steal for love. Nevertheless, the psychiatrist not infrequently encounters patients such as the following.

A seventeen-year-old girl was referred for psychiatric examination after she had been apprehended for shoplifting. She had stolen only pens and pencils from local bookstores. During her interview she talked quite freely about her problem. Raised by exceedingly strict and religious parents, she had always tried to adhere to her faith to the best of her ability. After having had but few experiences with the opposite sex during high school she entered a large university, where she was greatly stimulated by new opportunities for sexual contact. After a short period of time she began to "go steady" and to engage in heavy petting. She felt both erotic stimulation and affection and was convinced that she wanted to marry her boy friend as soon as possible. Her boy friend did not share her enthusiasm for matrimony. One night she decided to offer herself to the boy, entertaining the secret hope that she would become pregnant and force him into an early marriage.

After several hours of heavy petting she invited her boy friend to have intercourse with her. He refused, stating that he was worried about impregnating her. The patient was frustrated and mortified but said nothing. When she later discussed the incident, she repeatedly said, "I couldn't understand how he could possibly refuse me." The next day she went out on her first pen-and-pencil-stealing expedition. When she stole, she was continually troubled with what seemed to her an absurd thought. She kept thinking she had to take these items and put them in a box. When questioned, she revealed that she recently had learned that the word "box" was a vernacular equivalent to vagina.

This girl's story sounded almost like a caricature of a Freudian case study. The author seriously considered the possibility that she was pulling his leg. Yet her extraordinary naïveté and her obvious frankness testified to her veracity. Futhermore, after a few interpretations of her anger at being rejected and the similarity of phalluses and pens she seemed much relieved. Out of curiosity, the author asked her to come in one year later and found that she was still in school, unmarried but relatively content. She had done no further shoplifting.

## Classification of Delinquency

This author is not impressed with either the accuracy or value of classifications of delinquency. Categorization somethimes provide clarity, but it neglects consideration of the unitary nature of disturbed behavior. A few of the psychiatric classifications of delinquency have gained some prominence in the literature, and these will be briefly reviewed.

All psychiatric classifications separate delinquency which appears to be socially learned behavior from delinquency which is believed to be related to individual psychopathology. Psychiatrists concede that a child who has a stable home life and a relatively well-integrated personality can become a delinquent if he is exposed to a social environment which condones antisociality. Such a child is compared to a soldier in a foreign army who, believing in his cause, may attack the environment simply because he has been trained to do so. There is disagreement as to what percentage of delinquency is primarily socially learned behavior. Richard Jenkins believes that well-integrated or socialized adolescents approximate half of the delinquent population.[4] He distinguishes them from a second major group, the unsocialized delinquent. Socialized delinquency is believed to be determined by parental negligence and exposure to criminal values and is characterized by stealing, truancy and bad companions. Unsocialized delinquency is related to parental rejection and is characterized by poor school adjustment, violence, fighting, destructiveness and incorrigibility. This particular breakdown of delinquent types is largely determined by symptomatology.

Psychoanalytic classifications are dependent upon inference as to the personality structure of the child. Usually three major categories are described: environmental delinquency, based on social factors; neurotic delinquency, based on specific conflicts directly related to the crime; and characterological delinquency, based upon the presence of traits which are usually described as neurotic character, latent delinquency or psychopathy. A comprehensive classification has been offered by David Abrahamsen, who lists six major categories: (1) environmental delinquency or learned delinquency arising from criminal associations; (2) neurotic delinquency arising from intrapsychic conflict; (3) delinquents with character disorders; (4) delinquents who can be considered genuine psychopaths; (5) delinquents who are disturbed enough to be considered psychotic; (6) organically impaired delinquents, including those with a history of encephalitis.[5]

All psychiatric classifications seem to rely upon judgments of the degree of unreasonableness of the delinquent's behavior. Socialized or environmentally determined delinquents are described as behaving in a more reasonable manner than unsocialized delinquents. The conflicts with society to which such delinquents seem to be responding are more starkly drawn and visible than those of the child whose conflicts have a more personal intrapsychic basis. In this sense it is easy for behavioral scientists to convince themselves that they are dealing with significantly different groups. The problem with any classification of delinquency, however, is that it has to be oversimplified beyond the point of validity. Even the most sociologically determined delinquent act is often motivated by wishes which are not ordinarily examined closely enough to determine the extent of their actual "normality." At the same time the emotionally disturbed delinquent will not violate the law unless confronted with certain social conditions. There is so much interrelationship and admixture between artificially defined categories of delinquency that it is difficult to appreciate their meaningfulness or usefulness.

## The Maintenance of Delinquent Patterns

Although the adaptive advantages of the initial criminal act are apparent, it is more difficult to understand the value of repetitive unsuccessful criminality. Yet when we talk of criminals or delinquents, we are generally referring to recidivists as well as first offenders. In many respects causative factors are similar whether we are examining the first, second or tenth offense. Once a person is defined as a delinquent, however, certain social and psychological factors intervene and tend to make the criminal adaptation self-perpetuating and autonomous.

The mere social fact of being labeled a delinquent sets forces in motion that encourage continuing identification with the delinquent role. To begin with, the child who is adjudicated a delinquent is exposed to a social milieu in which his peers are constantly enjoining him to continue an antisocial way of life. Even if he has been a "loner," once apprehended for a delinquent act he may be forced into an environment which supports delinquency. If he is jailed or institutionalized, he will come into contact with other offenders, and if put on probation, he is required to cope with changed attitudes on the part of his parents, his friends and legal authorities. Being under increased surveillance and living with constant reminders of his misbehavior can be a stress in itself. For example, sometimes the rules of parole or probation are so strict that even the normal adolescent would find them intolerable. Such restrictions are especially difficult for the oppressed delinquent. Punishments or reprimands move the child further away from adult standards and closer to identifications with delinquent peers. As he feels increasingly rejected by the adult world, his anger and bitterness find an outlet in further antisocial attitudes and behavior.

Once the child begins to identify himself with the delinquent role, his learning experiences bind him more firmly to that adaptation. Sociologists have focused upon career aspects of delinquency and have described in detail how certain criminal skills are developed in the same manner as the socially adjusted person develops academic or vocational skills.[6, 7] For some adolescents and adults, crime does become a way of life which requires learning the intricate details of such activities as pickpocketing, burglary, hiding out and fighting. We know that some delinquents become extraordinarily adept at such activities. The learning of these skills may completely bind the delinquent's energy and attention so that little is left over for anything else. He becomes an expert in crime and a novice in other areas and is more likely to continue those activities for which he is trained.

Psychiatrists are mainly interested in the manner by which alterations in personality allow the child to sustain a delinquent orientation. The most obvious defense mechanism which the delinquent employs is projection. To justify his rebellious behavior, he usually attributes more of an oppressive quality to the society than is actually present. Other defense mechanisms employed by the delinquent ego are rationalization and denial. The delinquent soon learns to explain and justify illegal behaviors by always thinking about them in a frame of reference which gives them a kind of reasonableness. False major premises are invoked, which then logically lead to conclusions that delinquency was justified. The delinquent also learns to deny unacceptable feelings and behaviors both to himself and others. Often it is extremely difficult to learn whether he is lying or whether he has actually convinced himself that a situation is as he believes it to be. Many offenders, for example, will deny the occurrence of an objectionable act even when the evidence for its having happened is overwhelming and even when confession might actually be to the offender's advantage.

A unusually comprehensive description of delinquency-sustaining mechanisms has been presented by Fritz Redl and David Wineman.[8] They see the delinquent ego as being one that is at least in some areas "hypertrophied," and they argue that the delinquent develops marvelously effective mechanisms for sustaining impulsivity and antisocial behavior. The kinds of mechanisms which Redl and Wineman describe have been given such amusing and cryptic titles that they are almost self-explanatory. Simply listing these mechanisms provides the reader with an interesting description of the delinquent's ego defenses:

I. Tax Evasion

Repression of own intent.
He did it first.
Everybody else does such things anyway.
We were all in on it.
But somebody else did that same thing to me before.
He had it coming to him.
I didn't use the proceeds anyway.
I had to do it or I would have lost face.
But I made up with him afterward.
He is a no-good so-and-so himself.
They are all against me and nobody likes me.
They are always picking on me.
I couldn't have gotten it any other way.

II. Search for Delinquency Support

Ferreting out the "wrong" type of friends.
Affinity toward gang formation and mob psychology.
Seduction toward the initiatory act.
Hankering for delinquency lure.
The exploitation of moods.
Rebel for somebody else's cause.
The cultivation of delinquency-prone ego ideals.
Delusion of exceptionalistic exemption from the laws of cause and effect.
Dependency on delinquency-tied ambitions and skills.

III. Defense Against Change

Confessional constipation.
Escape into virtue.

Group ostracism against those who reform.
Avoidance of delinquency-dangerous personnel.
Refusal to give up delinquency-prone life factors.
Strangulation of love, dependency and activity needs.

IV. Mechanized Warfare with Changed Agents

Diagnostic acuity in battle-relevant areas.
The legalistic mind.
Expertness in the manipulation of people and of chance.
Absurdity of demand.
Anticipatory provocation.
Organized defamation.

## Some Comments on Female Delinquency

If one were to make a case for the maladaptive nature of criminality or the similarity of mental illness behavior and criminal behavior, he could find no better population to study than adolescent female offenders. It is doubtful if most female offenders ever cause harm to anyone but themselves. The two commonest forms of female delinquency, sexual promiscuity and running away from home, frequently offend our sense of propriety, but they are in no sense dangerous to our persons or to our possessions. On the other hand, these activities may cause great harm to the girl herself. Promiscuity leads to a degradation of self-image, guilt, remorse and a gradual alienation from conventional standards. Running away can result in seduction, abuse or hunger. Both of these behaviors are usually carried out in such an unreasonable self-destructive manner that they are as often labeled mental illness as they are crime.

In practice the decision to label female misbehavior as delinquency or illness is largely determined by social class. For a number of years I was privileged to direct a student health psychiatric clinic at a large university and at the same time act as a consultant to a nearby training school for girls. During this period I observed that girls seen at both institutions behaved similarly but were treated differently. In my role as student health psychiatrist, I examined a number of girls who admitted to, or were apprehended for, some type of misconduct. The rate of promiscuity among student patients was about equal to that of the delinquent group. It was unheard of, however, for a college girl to be defined as a delinquent because of sexual misbehavior. Shoplifting and other petty theft occurred with considerable frequency in both groups, but in the college girl was almost always considered to be a sign of emotional disorder. In lower-class girls identical activities led to a label of delinquency. Many kinds of pranks and attitudes of contemptuousness toward authority occurred in both groups, but again they recevied differential treatment. The college girls sometimes flaunted rules and regulations as though they were made to be broken. This was defined as either "healthy" rebelliousness or as a sign of personality disturbance. No such luxury was allowed to lower-class girls, who were more likely to be defined as antisocial or incorrigible.

The author can recall participating in a conference at the training school in which discussion centered about community reaction to a girl who had made several long-distance phone calls and had illegally charged them to local business men. Everyone was convinced that community reaction against this girl was so negative that she could never be paroled to that area. The author found himself sharing this sentiment until he recalled that he had recently sat in on a much more benign and optimistic conference designed to deal with an epidemic of this same behavior at the university.

Middle-class girls, of course, are more careful to test limits of inappropriate behavior. They know when it pays to be respectful and obedient since they have more often been rewarded for such behavior. It is also true that stealing among upper- or middle-class girls has a more apparently unreasonable quality since it is less likely to be governed by economic need. Yet the peculiarities of our society's reaction to female misbehavior are such that in seven years of consulting to a state school for girls the writer has never heard of the commitmnt of an upper-middle- or upper-class girl. During this time a number of serious crimes, including murder, were committed by girls of these classes which received much publicity throughout the state. In every instance the girls were either put on probation or sent to a mental hospital.

This means that punishment is mainly imposed upon those girls who do not have "respectable" homes or access to sufficient resources to protect against institutionalization. Many of the girls who end up in a training school are sent there simply because their families are unwilling or unable to care for them and there is nowhere else to send them. After a period of time, of course, the lower-class girl who is labeled delinquent does become hardened, angry and antisocial. Subcultures form which are dedicated to an attack on middle-class institutions and morality. It is hard to see how these attitudes could fail to develop. The average female delinquent knows she is more of a victim than a miscreant and quickly perceives adult hypocrisy when she is told to "be good" or to reform.

A sizable number of females who regularly participate in rule-breaking behavior (whether they are called delinquent or not) demonstrate a collection of character traits which define what psychiatrists refer to as the hysterical personality.[9] The hysterical personality is typically a girl or woman who is seductive and flirtatious, and often promiscuous. She tends to be histrionic and is adept at dramatizing her own plight. She is prone to periods of deep depression and anxiety, which follow one another with rapidity. Such a person is both superficial and flexible. Acutely aware of the needs of others, she learns to play upon them and accommodate herself to a variety of roles. Her sense of self is poorly developed. She is illness-prone and will develop a bewildering variety of physical and emotional complaints whenever the sick role is available and serves her needs. She is loath to acknowledge responsibility for many of her behaviors and can conveniently repress affects which are troubling. Above all, she is dependent. Her dependency has a demanding, "sticky" quality, and she sometimes reacts aggressively when dependency needs are frustrated.

Women with such personality traits make up a large percentage of the outpatient clientele of the practicing general physician or psychiatrist. This may well be as consistent and frequent a form of behavioral reactions as the physician sees. As with such traits as psychopathy, however, we have problems in deciding whether we should call this behavior a form of illness. Up until recently the diagnosis of hysterical personality was not even included in our official nomenclature. Few dynamic formulations have been offered to explain how these traits come to develop.

It should be apparent that the hysterical personality describes a person who is prone to impulsive actions, a person who can easily become involved in sexual misconduct and delinquency. The reader may also have noted that some of the characteristics of the hysterical personality bear close resemblance to the traits of psychopathy, paranoia and masochism. In the author's opinion, this personality type is probably a reaction to the same type of stresses as those which lead to psychopathic traits but in this case the stresses act upon females, a group confined to social roles which do not hold out the possibilities of unlimited freedom. The oppressed girl, limited in physical strength, in mobility and in access to socially acceptable aggression, fights back by using her best weapons, exaggerated femininity and controlling passivity. She becomes particularly adept at employing the message, "I can't help myself," to manipulate others and control her environment. Such behaviors describe many female delinquents.

It should be noted that while this behavioral pattern is conducive to mental-illness roles, criminal roles seem to be less appropriate. Society has to be deeply troubled and annoyed with hysterical women before it calls them criminals. Even the most "hardened" female offender does not wear the "delinquent" label very well and casting her in this role makes all of us a little uncomfortable. Our reluctance to punish people who can so easily identify themselves as helpless may partially explain low rates of female crime in our society.*

In the histories of female delinquents parental deprivation and abuse seem to occur with even greater frequency than among males. One common dynamic pattern can be described as follows: The child receives inadequate nurturance and insufficient attention from her mother. As she reaches latency she begins to seek these same gratifications from her father. Particularly when the parents do not meet one another's needs, the father is likely to develop an overly close relationship with the child. Erotic impulses intervene and the relationship between daughter and father takes on a latent sexual quality. With the onset of adolescence and sexual maturity this close relationship cannot be maintained without the danger of violating incestual taboos. At this point the father becomes more distant and the daughter turns to other men or boys and seeks their affection and love with a desperate intensity. The price for affection is usually sexual intercourse. The potential delinquent then seeks gratification of basic oral needs through sexual activity, but since she rarely finds what she is looking for she moves through a variety of unsatisfying and frustrating sexual relationships. The dynamic pattern described here is similar to but also different from the pattern we see in normal development. Most healthy girls do have a kind of latent "love affair" with their fathers, but they have received sufficent gratification from their mothers so that their need for the father does not take on a desperate "oral" quality.

There are several variations of this pattern. The erotic component of the relationship with the father often becomes threatening to the child. She fears the incestual consequences of her own impulses and attempts to resolve the problem by leaving the disturbing situation. This encourages such behaviors as running away. Not infrequently the latent sexual relationship between father and daughter leads to overt incestual behavior.[10, 11] A surprisingly large percentage of delinquent girls claim that their first initiation to sexual experience occurred during latency and that their seductor was an older man.[12] The writer estimates that about 15 percent of the total training school population were seduced by their own fathers or step-

* The author recognizes that there are many other reasons for the low rates of female delinquency, including the obvious fact that the greater social restraints females experience and their physical limitations allow them to commit fewer crimes.

fathers. While this estimate may appear to be exaggerated, it is possible that the actual number of such cases could be much higher. Because of fear of punishment, shame or a wish to protect their father many girls are reluctant to report incestual acts. Those girls who have been exposed to incestual experience tend to be plagued with serious behavioral problems throughout adolescence. They show the most exaggerated forms of hysterical personality traits and are often promiscuous, overwhelmingly dependent and subject to transient psychotic episodes.

While we have focused upon the exceptionally self-defeating quality of female delinquency, it must be admitted that some female delinquency is also damaging to others. Recently youth workers have noted that female delinquency is becoming a little more like male delinquency. More and more girls form gangs, steal, drink and fight. This change seems to coincide with the increasing emancipation of women. As girls are given more opportunities and as they are given equal rights, their behavior more nearly approaches that of boys. As the social roles of boys and girls become more alike, their delinquent activities become less distinguishable from one another. Given the directions of our society, we can probably anticipate more serious female crime in the future.

## Chapter 11

# THE STRESSES OF ADULTHOOD

AS AN adult lives his life, as he works and plays, as he relates to those who are close to him and moves among friends, enemies and acquaintances, and as he regards himself living his life, he is normally beset by challenges and stresses of greater or lesser severity. For some adults, the circumstances of their lives may produce stresses which are particularly strong, and which may favor the development and continuation of criminal behavior.

Some stresses may be easily observable, such as poverty, membership in a racial or ethnic group subject to discrimination, lack of job skills or education, a failure to marry or to marry happily, or, finally, an excessive use of, or addiction to, alcohol or other drugs. Other stresses may involve the inner life, as when psychopathy or masochism or paranoia is present, or when the adult has failed to develop religious beliefs, meaningful ideologies and even an adequate sense of self-worth and self-esteem. An important stress may be the existence of criminality in his past.

None of these stresses is in itself a sufficient cause of crime. Each exerts only a relative influence, and many criminogenic factors have a high degree of interrelationship.

We have already considered several of these factors. As we have seen, traits such as psychopathy may lead to patterns of behavior which favor a criminal adaptation. Poverty, lack of vocational skills, lack of education and membership in a minority group are linked together and are usually characteristic of the lower-class status to which most criminals belong. Failure to develop religious beliefs usually leads to weak internal controls, and failure to develop any type of ideology at all removes a possible channel for active release of aggressive energy. Most of these stress conditions imply a lack of something: status, skill or sustaining beliefs. If a man still has such deficits upon reaching adulthood, he is more likely to engage in crime.

Before discussing such stresses as failure to develop an adequate sense of self-worth or esteem, failure to marry or to marry happily, previous criminality in one's past and alcoholism and drug addiction, we must re-emphasize that individuals respond differently to similar stresses. What is meat for one man will be poison for another. Marriage for some men will end a criminal career, but for others it will launch one. Alcoholic intoxication brings some men to aggressive action but puts others to sleep. When we talk about a factor as an important determinant of crime, we are talking about a probability that a given factor will be highly correlated with criminal behavior or we are merely speculating as to how such a factor could be a criminogenic stress for some people.

No one has systematically studied the way in which adult criminals view themselves, although there have been some sociological studies of the self-concepts of delinquent children.[1] There are many indications that, in or out of prison, criminals see themselves as inferior beings, not fully capable of dealing with the problems of the world. The stresses we have discussed in earlier chapters contribute to the development of a self-concept which precludes confidence, optimism or goal-directed aggression. Ultimately, such a poor concept of oneself becomes a stress in itself.

To many people the criminal appears to be a self-satisfied, even a smug individual. Those who work intimately with offenders soon learn that this appearance is a superficial façade. Although the criminal may attempt to deny his own sense of inadequacy to himself and others, his actual behavior is a more accurate gauge of his true feelings. The man who "steals small" can hardly be thought of as a person who has a high value of his own worth. Neither can the man who molests a young child because he is too insecure and frightened to seek sexual contact with a mature woman.

Some criminals betray feelings of self-doubt when they are challenged by vocational, intellectual or recreational activities which are more characteristic of a noncriminal way of life. Offenders frequently have their first exposure to such activities in the prison setting, and they then tend to show one of three responses. They may openly express their fears of participation, they may deny all interest in the activity, or they may approach it with a false and grandiose bravado. This lack of confidence or optimism represents more than just lack of skill. It also implies an attitude of defeatism and inferiority. Even on the athletic field those criminals who may have exceptional physical coordination and strength do not perform up to their capacity. Criminals seem to be "losers." They lose even when they have the natural ability to win.

All the above statements describe an apprehended or incarcerated offender and offer only inferences as to how a depressed self-concept encourages criminality. It is logical to assume, however, that a person with a poor self-concept will have difficulty in meeting the challenges of his world. A diminished sense of self-esteem deprives the individual of assurance that he can effectively change those conditions that oppress him. It pushes him closer to ways of life which are dominated by helplessness and despair. Such a person finds criminal behavior especially attractive. In addition to expressing contempt for a world he feels incapable of joining, criminality holds out at least some hope of self-proving and success. When the criminal pleads that "Crime was the only way out," he is talking about a basic and pervasive inner uncertainty which reflects a lack of confidence in his ability to do anything else.

### Failure to Marry or Unsuccessful Marriage

In a frank and intimate discussion of his experience as a youth worker, Vincent Riccio describes the impact of falling in love upon very disturbed adolescent delinquents.[2] Riccio believes that love and subsequent marriage "cure" more delinquents than all the efforts of psychiatrists and social workers put together. His observations should not be taken lightly. Love has always been an effective antidote to almost any kind of emotional disturbance. It either diverts attention from painful feelings of anxiety, depression or inadequacy or it directly resolves conflicts which produce such effects. Love implies a relationship which is relatively free of oppression. Love also diminishes preoccupation with unrealistic fears. Not surprisingly, it is a powerful crime preventative.

If a man moves through adult life without finding love or marriage, there is a greater likelihood that he will become a criminal. The responsibilities and dependency created by marriage (even without love) have an important socializing effect upon the potential or past offender. Many crimes require a certain amount of geographic mobility, a type of freedom which is almost precluded by matrimony. The marital relationship is also a social system which in itself provides an outlet for gratification of a wide variety of needs. Criminal behavior often is associated with a feeling that dependency gratification is totally unavailable. Once one is married, there are many ways in which dependency upon a wife can be alternately accepted or denied within the relationship. There is less likelihood that the married man will despairingly convince himself that dependency gratification will never be possible. He is, therefore, less likely impulsively to take chances by breaking the law.

Although love and marriage usually discourage crime, there are certain situations in which they have the opposite effect. Feelings of jealousy and possessiveness may temporarily overcome the tranquilizing qualities of mutual affection. The threat of separation from a loved one, particularly when she threatens to leave of her own volition, raises many infantile feelings of rage and omnipotence. Crimes of violence may then be committed by individuals who have never demonstrated antisocial inclinations but whose personalities cannot accommodate to situations in which loved ones play upon their dependency needs. The following case portrays a dynamic pattern which is not uncommon.

The patient was a thirty-year-old white male who had never had a previous criminal record. He was a basically passive individual whose lack of economic success led to a great deal of marital discord. After five years of marriage his wife informed him that she was planning to leave. She chided him for his vocational ineffectiveness and his lack of aggressiveness and hinted that there were other men available who were more adequate than he. For the next few days the patient and his wife argued bitterly each evening. He slept poorly and had difficulty working at his job. One evening he came home with a gun and told his wife that if she didn't stay with him he was going to kill himself. She laughed at him and told him that he "didn't have the guts." With this the patient rushed down to the basement, ruminated for a brief period and finally decided that he would alarm his wife by shooting two bullets into a mattress. When he did this, there was no response from his wife. Enraged at her lack of concern for his apparent suicide attempt, he charged upstairs to find her watching television. She laughingly insisted that she knew all along that he had been bluffing. With this the patient shot her, killing her instantly. He then called the police and when arrested repeatedly said, "I loved her so much, how could I have killed her?"

## Previous Criminality

In an earlier chapter we briefly considered some conditions impinging upon the adolescent delinquent which encouraged repetition of criminal activities. The high rate of recidivism among adult criminals (over half of all the criminals in prison at any given moment have previous records) suggests that here, too, the criminal role is self-perpetuating.

The adult ex-criminal is rejected by those elements in society which might provide access to more legitimate means of survival. He is rarely trusted, is watched carefully and is often treated as a second-class citizen. Under such conditions he finds it difficult to maintain an adequate level of self-esteem. Exposed to physical and psychological deprivations, the ex-criminal is likely to crystallize his paranoid attitudes toward the world and to move even further away from conforming values. Acceptance is found only in association with other criminals, who share his antisocial values.

The necessary but sometimes overzealous attentions of legal officers constitute a formidable burden in themselves. An ex-criminal knows that he is likely to be arrested whenever there is an outbreak of crimes similar to those for which he had been previously convicted. His treatment by police officers is less than respectful. Parole supervision can be an oppression in itself. Many of the rules of parole are so stringent and unreasonable that they create rebellious feelings in the most placid of criminals. Unfortunately, parole officers, just like any other citizens, can sometimes be bigoted, arbitrary or sadistic. Since the officer has an almost unlimited degree of power and control over the ex-criminal, he can become the most significant source of oppression in that offender's life. While intense supervision by parole officers and other legal officers is immensely valuable for some criminals, it could for others provide the additional stress which leads to new criminal acts.

Still another factor which can contribute to a perpetuation of the criminal role is experience with incarceration. The ex-criminal might discover that prison is not so frightening as he thought it was going to be. He learns that he has the capacity to "do time" and survive. For a certain number of criminals, prison might even offer the inviting prospect of complete security, a dependent way of life and limited opportunities for status. For those who have deviant sexual tendencies, there is even a certain amount of erotic adventure. Fear of punishment and incarceration may deter some criminals, but others find prison less frightening than the depressing realities of their lives in a "free" world.

## Alcohol

The relationship of overindulgence in alcoholic beverages to crime has long been of major importance in adult criminology. There are four ways in which alcohol consumption is related to crime.

1. In most communities intoxication in public is defined as a misdemeanor. Drunkenness itself can be a crime.

2. Excessive use of alcohol over a long period of time may diminish

one's capacity to participate effectively in noncriminal activities. A process of psychological and social deterioration alienates the chronic alcoholic from normal channels of gratification. Many crimes are committed by individuals who, though not intoxicated at the time of the offense, have been so incapacitated by chronic alcoholic indulgence that they find that crime is the best they can do.

3. In the early stages of intoxication confusion is not prominent. At this stage the major effect of alcohol is reduction of tension. Aggressive and sexual impulses which are ordinarily repressed are more likely to be consciously experienced. The intoxicated individual's judgment is impaired, and he often is unable to plan his behavior in a rational way or to perceive its consequences. Under such circumstances a wide variety of crimes involving violence, sexual misconduct, auto theft, forgery, robbery or burglary can occur. It is also apparent that moderate to severe intoxication is not conducive to safe operation of a motor vehicle. Drunken driving can lead to major traffic violations.

4. Severe and prolonged intoxication can produce an impairment of brain function characterized by a degree of confusion severe enough to lead to drastic misinterpretations of reality. The psychiatric syndromes of pathological intoxication—acute hallucinosis and delirium tremens—are characterized by a high degree of disorganized behavior. The same is true of severe acute intoxication. During a state of confusion caused by excessive intake of alcohol, assault or other types of antisocial behavior are not uncommon.

The pleasant effects of alcohol are well known to anyone who has ever indulged, and most people find that taken in moderate quantity alcohol is a relaxing substance which allows a certain tranquility and promotes social ease. When taken in excess, however, what starts out as a social blessing often becomes a social menace. Drunkenness, with associated disregard for socially accepted behavior, is one outcome. Alcoholic addiction is another. There are several million people in our country who are dependent upon excessive intake of alcohol to retain a tolerable degree of personal and social comfort. For some people alcohol becomes the most important influence in their lives. They become totally dependent upon this agent, and their addiction has far-reaching social, psychological and biological consequences.

Alcoholics are defined by the World Health Organization of the United Nations as people "whose dependence upon alcohol has attained such a degree that it shows a noticeable mental disturbance or interference with their bodily or mental health, their interpersonal relations, and their smooth social and economic functioning—or who show signs of such development."[3] This definition describes alcoholism as a form of social deviation, and as such it is best understood as an adaptation to stress. Like crime and mental illness, alcoholism seems to be engendered by feelings of helplessness. It is a fairly effective adaptive device for dealing with such feelings since it provides temporary relief from painful affects, and this relief is more or less under the individual's own control. To a certain extent one does not have to conform to or change an oppressive environment if he can modify his perception of that environment, and escape it through temporary intoxication.

There are also many unfavorable aspects to alcoholism as an adaptive device. The alcoholic is usually considered a social misfit. Once alcohol dominates a person's life, he begins to lose the interest or the capacity to earn his own way in the world. Alcoholism cannot be a stable adaptation, because drunkenness does not provide complete tranquilization, and the beneficial effects of alcohol are transient. The drinker experiences considerable physical and psychological discomfort upon withdrawal. In addition, he runs the risk of serious physical deterioration. Very few alcoholics can continuously indulge their addiction for a sustained period. They either learn to abstain, are defined as mentally ill and hospitalized, commit crimes and are institutionalized, or they die.

Society has great difficulty in deciding how to define or treat the alcoholic. He is alternately greeted with attitudes of solicitude and rage. Some people would prefer to see him as mentally ill, in need of medical treatment. Others see him as sinful and believe that society's informal disapproval of excessive drinking should be codified so that alcoholism would become a crime. In practice the alcoholic may be treated as though he were physically ill, as though he were mentally ill or as though he were a criminal. The treatment he receives is dependent upon his social status as well as the attitudes of local judicial and community agencies.

The theories which propose to account for alcoholism reflect the same uncertainties that characterize the study of the criminal. We find the same varieties of biological, sociological and psychological theories.[4] The biologists have invoked nutritional deficiencies, inheritance, glandular disturbances and even constitution as causes of alcoholism. Sociologists have focused upon social drinking patterns as they vary with class, neighborhood and ethnic groupings. Psychiatrists have stressed conflicts between dependency needs and aggressive drives, and psychoanalysts have emphasized self-destructive tendencies, oral fixations and latent homosexuality.

The writer prefers to look upon alcoholism as a complex form of adaptation which influences both the external and the internal environment, by allowing the individual to break the rules of society (an alloplastic adaptation) and by allowing the individual to diminish temporarily the painful aspects of unpleasant affects (an autoplastic adaptation). As with criminality, there are no consistent data or even theories to account for why a person "chooses" this particular form of adaptation.

The most important criminogenic effects of persistent drinking or chronic alcoholism are psychological and social deterioration. The chronic alcoholic eventually fails to maintain gratifying interpersonal relationships. He becomes isolated from friends and family. His self-concept (when he is sober) deteriorates, and he experiences many moments of despair in which he punishes himself vigorously. As his social effectiveness diminishes, the chronic alcoholic gradually finds himself in a pitiful state of poverty and physical neglect. For such a person, crime can serve many purposes. Sometimes stealing is necessary to sustain the drinking habit. In a moment of remorse the chronic alcoholic may commit a crime with the conscious hope of punishment, or in order to force someone else to take over his problems or to coercively deprive him of access to alcohol. When deterioration is exceptionally severe, violation of laws, which is followed by institutionalization, may be the only means by which the alcoholic can find food and shelter.[5]

Moving away from the problem of chronic alcoholism, we find that the most interesting and important relationship of alcohol to crime is associated with the state of acute alcoholic intoxication. Again, assessing the importance of drunkenness as a factor in crime is extremely difficult. It is not easy to discover which criminals were intoxicated at the time of their crimes and what role this condition played in their behavior. The limited amount of data which attempts to deal with this question is usually obtained from studies of incarcerated offenders.

The study which is quoted most frequently was made almost twenty-five years ago by the well-known psychiatric criminologist, Ralph Banay.[6] Banay interviewed offenders at Sing Sing Prison and was able to estimate the percentage of crimes which seemed to be related to heavy drinking. He noted an incidence of acute intoxication of 19.7 percent in 1938-39 and 24.2 percent in 1939-40.* When he related his data to the type of crime committed, he found significant variations. Alcoholic intoxication or a history of excessive indulgence was more prominent in sex offenses, assault and burglary than in homicide, robbery or grand larceny.

* Banay also noted an even larger percentage of offenders who had been heavy drinkers (1938-39: 25 percent; 1939-40: 27.8 percent) but assumed that their alcoholism did not have a direct relationship to the criminal act.

Other studies have also suggested that a significant proportion of crimes is committed while the offender is in an intoxicated state. The percentages reported, however, are inconsistent. McDonald has summarized the findings of nine authorities who studied the relationship of alcohol to homicide.[7] The percentage of offenders who had taken alcohol prior to the offense varied between 19 and 83 percent.

Studies such as these, plus the subjective impression of many correctional workers, suggest that a high percentage of crimes are committed while the offender is intoxicated. The data, however, have serious limitations. Most studies rely on information obtained from the incarcerated offender, and there is some tendency for the subject to exaggerate the degree of his intoxication in order to rationalize behavior which he or others might find unacceptable. A certain number of criminals deny responsibility for their behavior in the sense that they maintain, "It was the liquor that made me behave that way." On the other hand there are some criminals who are ashamed of their drinking and will falsely minimize its extent. A more accurate assessment of the causal influence of alcoholic intoxication would require objective information as to the degree of intoxication at the time of the offense.

An interesting means of obtaining such information was employed by the Columbus, Ohio, Police Department. Beginning in 1943 they began to study the level of alcohol in the urine of criminals arrested immediately after the commission of any type of felony. In 1954 L. M. Shupe reported on the findings in 882 such cases and noted a level of significant intoxication in 70 percent.[8] While this is certainly a much more objective means of studying the relationship of alcohol to crime, Shupe recognized that the percentage of intoxicated offenders was quite high and that his population was not truly representative of all felons. The very fact that his cases were caught so soon could have been due to the effects of alcohol, and certainly many criminal types (such as the forger, who is ordinarily apprehended many days after his offense) could not be adequately represented. Nevertheless, this kind of research is intriguing and suggests a quite important relationship between alcoholic intoxication and crime.

Even if we assume that a large population of apprehended criminals are intoxicated at the time of the crime, we cannot be sure of the causal influence of the alcohol. In any given crime associated with alcohol we do not know whether the threshold of restraint was so low to begin with that criminality might have arisen anyway. We must consider such questions as: Did the individual deliberately use alcohol in order to free himself to commit a crime or "to get his courage up"? Can we be sure that the criminal really experienced the psychological effects of intoxication simply because he claims to have been drunk or because laboratory tests indicate that he was pharmacologically intoxicated? How are we to explain the fact that so many millions of Americans regularly become heavily intoxicated and yet do not commit crimes? And, most importantly, if intoxication is a factor in crime, how does it exert its influence?

The first three questions cannot be answered unless we know a great deal about each individual criminal. We can, however, speculate as to the manner in which alcoholic intoxication exerts a general criminogenic influence as follows: Pharmacologically, alcohol acts as a cerebral depressant which encourages certain psychological changes during the early stages of intoxication. Its most important effect is a diminution of tension and fear. This change, even when minimal, has a profound effect upon the intoxicated person's perception of the world. He sees himself as different and he sees the people around him as different. There is an increased tendency to perceive feelings and events with greater sensitivity and at the same time a greater tendency to misinterpret the intentions of others.

Offhand, it might be thought that a diminution of anxiety would discourage criminal behavior. For the person who is on the threshold of committing a crime, however, alcohol could provide exactly the right amount of calmness, courage and resolution that would be needed for action. In addition, alcohol tends to diminish realistic fears. Many people experience antisocial feelings close to or at a level of consciousness but never express them because of realistic fears of punishment. If these fears are attenuated, crime is a more likely occurrence. And furthermore, diminished anxiety or fear undoubtedly contributes to the ease with which intoxicated criminals are apprehended, because the inebriate often does not bother to take the reasonable precautions which a more anxious or fearful man would find prudent.

Alcohol also diminishes the drinker's fear of punishment from his own conscience or superego. The intoxicated person experiences considerable freedom from guilt feelings. Impulses which he ordinarily regards with shame and guilt may begin to feel acceptable, and hence are more likely to be expressed. Any person who has had the experience of being drunk is familiar with the great remorse which may occur on the following day. Much of the suffering of the hangover has psychological rather than physiological meaning. The hangover victim knows that in his freedom from guilt on the previous night he may have experienced or expressed feelings which he would ordinarily have kept out of consciousness. While everyone worries about what he might have done while drunk, most of us manage to control ourselves. A person who is struggling with overwhelming feelings of helplessness could, however, experience antisocial impulses which, depending upon social circumstances, could be expressed in the form of a law violation.

In spite of the attenuation of disturbing feelings of tension and guilt, the intoxicated state is not entirely blissful. Alcohol is not a completely effective tranquilizer. The inebriated person may remain painfully aware of his own inadequacies. The chronically unsuccessful and socially downtrodden individual is ordinarily able to repress or deny his unhappiness and discontent. But alcohol, while lifting other repressions, can also make an individual more painfully aware of the meaninglessness of his life. The inebriate is always a little uneasy. He is aware of a need to think more highly of himself, and this is reflected in his search for proof of his worthwhileness. In our society, "showing off," exaggerated interest in sex, bragging and "masculine proving" are characteristic of the drunken male. It is as though he comes close to feeling a sense of sureness, of dignity or of autonomy, discovers how badly he wants it and must find a way to obtain it. In this condition he is likely to seek behaviors which demonstrate his own strength and importance. The world, which has deprived him of a sense of his own value, may be attacked. Sometimes it is only through commitment of a deviant act that the intoxicated person can reassure himself as to his wholeness as a person.

We have noted that many offenders are intoxicated at the time of the criminal act and have suggested some mechanisms by which intoxication could encourage criminality. It seems to the author that criminology has not given sufficient attention to the problem of alcohol. There was a time when many believed that excessive use of alcohol was a direct cause of most crimes. Later studies such as Banay's suggested that this factor was not so important as had been previously believed. The emergence of a relativistic multiple-factor approach tended to further diminish interest in intoxication as a cause of crime. Today it is difficult to find a criminology text which devotes more than a page or two to the subject. Yet every study that has been made suggests that no less than 19 percent of imprisoned offenders have been intoxicated when they committed their crimes, and in most studies this figure is significantly larger. Furthermore, there is some objective evidence that the majority of criminals apprehended during or shortly after an offense are drunk. Granted that we must reject any naïve concepts of causality, this evidence is impressive and should not be ignored. Alcoholic intoxication can at least be defined and measured in a somewhat objective manner, and it may turn out to be as important a factor in adult crime as we are capable of studying.

## DRUG ADDICTION

Excessive use of narcotic drugs, particularly of heroin, has become a major social problem in America. As more and more teen-agers have become drug users, public alarm has grown. Many lay people see a close and frightening relationship between drug addiction and crime, particularly crime which involves violence. Actually, if we discount the fact that narcotic usage itself is usually defined as a crime, this relationship is far less pronounced than is generally imagined. Studies of the incidence of crimes in neighborhoods in which the rate of addiction has risen suggest that there is no concomitant increase in crime.[9] In fact, crimes of violence tend to decrease when users confine themselves to the most seriously addicting drug, heroin.

While sociologists argue that drug addiction is a socially learned phenomenon,[10, 11] It seems quite unlikely that such a self-destructive behavior could develop and be sustained in people who are not deeply troubled. In our country the greatest rate of addiction is seen in Negroes and Puerto Ricans, groups that are poor and subject to discrimination. Psychiatrists have noted that the chronic drug addict is usually an immature person who seeks refuge from his problems through artificial tranquillity.[12, 13] (Sociologists have been critical of psychiatric interpretations of narcotic addicts' personalities. They argue that psychiatrists do not have an opportunity to examine the drug user until the user is already addicted. Both sociologists and psychiatrists recognize that addiction drastically alters the personality, but psychiatrists suspect that a large percentage of addicts were disturbed to begin with.[14]) In this sense he possesses many qualities that are similar to the alcoholic's. The subculture of the addict, however, sustains his maladjustment by providing him with group justification and a relatively nonresponsible way of life.

Drugs are used to find not only tranquillity but also excitement. Some drugs like Benzedrine, marijuana, LSD, psilocybin and mescaline are often taken because they provide stimulation or new experiences. On the other hand, addiction to other drugs such as barbiturates or opiates is more likely to develop out of a search for tranquillity and escape from the troubles of an oppressive world. The relationship of drug usage or drug addiction to crime is dependent upon the drug used and the degree of addiction. Excessive dosages of a drug such as Seconal or Benzedrine (even without addiction) can produce states of disturbed consciousness during which impulses which are ordinarily controlled are expressed.

Such drugs may be used by teen-agers or other criminals to provide courage prior to a criminal escapade.

The most addicting and most socially alarming drug, heroin, has certain paradoxical and unusual influences on criminal behavior. Unlike alcohol, heroin is an almost perfect tranquilizer. When under its influence the addict has no wish to mobilize sexual or aggressive energy. He is more likely to be inactive and completely passive. In such a condition he is not likely to seek criminal activity. Stories of crazed addicts committing brutal crimes while under the influence of heroin have little basis in reality.

On the other hand, heroin is an expensive drug, and the user builds up a tolerance which requires increasing dosages to maintain the desired effect. The average addict is not in a financial position to support his habit. He is often a socially oppressed person to begin with, and even if he is not, his addiction takes him further and further away from successful living. All this means that the heroin addict must find a means to support his ever-increasing need for narcotization. Eventually he turns to crime. It is interesting to note that the crime of a heroin addict tends to be less unreasonable and more purposeful than those of many other criminals.[15] The addict is desperately and devotedly interested in only one thing, obtaining more heroin. He steals, pimps or prostitutes primarily to obtain enough money to support his addiction. Unlike the alcoholic, the heroin addict commits crimes which are more likely to be utilitarian.

## Illness and Crime

For the most part, illness during the adult years is not linked to criminality. Illness roles and criminal roles are often antagonistic. If a person is considered to be unable to help himself, he is capable of modifying his environment without resorting to criminal action. In addition, illness tends to impede the learning of skills which might be used to carry out a criminal act.

It must be clearly understood, however, that states of adaptation are always temporary and subject to constant change. Illness itself is a stress, and under certain conditions it can further the development of new adaptive mechanisms. Mental-illness behavior can become so incapacitating, so ineffectual and so maladaptive that alternative means may be chosen to alter the environment. When the adoption of a mental-illness role leads to even greater oppression from the family and society (rather than attitudes of kindness and conciliation), it may create a need for a more potent attack upon the environment.

Irrespective of the stresses which allow mental illness to be sustained over a long period of time, it is usually true that chronicity eventually produces deterioration in social and psychological functioning. This deterioration is similar to that which we have described in the alcoholic. The chronically disturbed person becomes increasingly more isolated from others and eventually loses many of the intellectual skills and emphatic responses which are essential for survival. When this happens, his community is likely to treat him harshly.

Chronicity also implies greater susceptibility to hospitalization. Sociologists have recently begun to examine the oppressive nature of mental hospitals.[16, 17] Hospitals have a disturbing tendency to encourage perpetuation of deviant behaviors. The individual who is unfortunate enough to spend a long period of time in a mental hospital may learn to become dependent on institutional life and may become progressively alienated from the rest of society. These events and the attitudes which they engender increase the subjective experience of helplessness. They sometimes encourage a shift in adaptational devices in the direction of criminality. Thus, for some, the secondary social effects of mental illness can become a criminogenic stress.

### Crime and Aging

The majority of adult criminals arrested and convicted fall between the ages of twenty and thirty. These ten years are often referred to as the "hazardous decade."[18] Criminal behavior decreases sharply after the age of thirty. There are many possible explanations for this phenomenon.

We have noted earlier that crime requires a certain amount of mobility and physical strength. Both of these qualities diminish with age. Perhaps even more important, however, is the difficulty an individual experiences in maintaining an aimless, uncommitted and self-indulging existence as he grows older. As one reaches his thirties, it is extremely difficult to seek or to maintain any kind of "painless freedom from object relations." The greater susceptibility to physical illness, the realization of approaching infirmity and the omnipresent awareness of death increasingly push one toward commitment. As a person commits himself to other people or to ideals, he takes on obligations which discourage either a psychopathic or a criminal existence. We know that many criminals and psychopaths "burn out" as they grow older.[19] Nonconformity is rare after the age of thirty-five. This is most likely related to an increased awareness of dependency needs which cannot be stifled, rationalized or denied.

Of course, for some individuals aging may be accompanied by unusual stress. The later years of life are sometimes characterized by an oppressive environment which may drive even the most conforming individual to a more active adaptation. Social and psychological deterioration are not uncommon. Physical deterioration which influences intellectual and emotional processes may constitute a superimposed stress. With the onset of senility or arteriosclerotic brain disease, a certain number of individuals experience an impairment of previously adequate control mechanisms. All these conditions can favor certain types of antisocial behavior.[20] Most commonly, however, when this behavior is associated with processes or diseases of aging, society defines the offender as mentally ill rather than as criminal.

*Chapter 12*

# CRIME AS REACTION

SOMETIMES the stresses of life are so overwhelming that the organism ceases to function in even a minimally effective manner. Breakdown in ego function is usually accompanied by great anxiety and an inability to distinguish between stimuli which arise from the outer world and those which arise from within. Capacities to perceive, to integrate or to test reality are so damaged that even compromise maladaptive behaviors fail to stem the tide of anxiety. Ordinarily repressed impulses are experienced and acted upon in a chaotic manner. When such actions result in law violation, the criminal act appears to be especially purposeless and meaningless.

Although it is convenient to speak of a breakdown in ego function, it must be clearly understood that the ego is not a concrete entity which can be dissolved and rendered entirely ineffectual. Even under conditions which promote maximum disorganization some adaptive capacity is retained by the organism. It would perhaps be better to talk about partial ego breakdown, although we must recognize that in the states we are about to discuss the degree of ego failure is far more significant than in most other forms of maladaptation.

Although the number of crimes committed as a direct or indirect response to overwhelming stress is probably not large, they are of obvious interest to the psychiatrist. Unfortunately, most of the psychiatric literature concerned with these crimes focuses upon the legal responsibility of the offender. Although the pursuit of the question of responsibility is required by our legal system, the writer is convinced that this issue seriously interferes with a rational evaluation of any cause of crime. With regard to the relationship of overwhelming stress to crime, preoccupation with the question of responsibility leads to "all or none" errors in two different directions. If we decide an individual's mental disorder makes him nonresponsible for his criminal act, we frequently imply a degree of total causation which cannot be justified by the data. At the same time, if we consider the offender fully responsible, there is a tendency to reject the importance of factors which have probably had at least some causal influence. As in earlier sections, we will find it useful to discuss the subject matter of this chapter in a neutral frame of reference, which requires that we ignore the question of the offender's responsibility.

Conditions of ego failure are most conveniently considered under the headings of disturbances of consciousness, panic states, excited states, delusional states and severe depression.

## Disturbances of Consciousness

Disturbances of consciousness vary in degree from a slight absence of "clear-mindedness," "awareness" or "attentiveness" to much deeper disturbances which are characterized as delirium or stupor. The degree of impairment of consciousness which must be present before antisocial impulses are expressed varies with the individual and his immediate environment. For most people, however, if there is to be a breakdown in controls with subsequent expression of primitive antisocial impulses, there must be a sufficient clouding of consciousness to produce a state of confusion. Confusion has been defined by Alfred Noyes as "a disturbance of consciousness characterized by impairment of the sensorium, by difficulty of grasp and by bewilderment, perplexity, disorientation, disturbance of associative functions and poverty of ideas."[1] Confusion may also be accompanied by overwhelming anxiety, perceptual distortions and marked incoherence. The confused individual has difficulty in interpreting the source or meaning of signals from his environment. He cannot effectively mediate between his drives and the demands of the external world.

A number of physical stresses, including infection, intoxication (from an agent such as alcohol), trauma, circulatory inadequacy, metabolic disturbance or tumors, may cause sufficient impairment of brain tissue function to produce confusion. For the most part, confusional states based on organic brain damage tend to be reversible. In formal classification they are known as acute brain syndromes. When brain damage is irreversible, we speak of a chronic brain syndrome.

Because the confused person may be disoriented and because he cannot accurately identify the intentions of those people who happen to be with him, he is more likely to act in an unconventional or antisocial manner. When such a person commits an illegal act, the decision to label him sick or criminal depends upon our knowledge of his emotional disturbance. Most people suffering from chronic brain syndromes, for example, have been behaving in a peculiar manner for long periods of time. Their unreasonable behavior both before and after a criminal act usually leads to diagnosis of mental illness. It is somewhat more difficult to detect the influence of confusion in acute brain syndromes. This is because the patient may not have been noted to have been behaving unreasonably before an offense. By the time he is apprehended his confused state may have disappeared. When the confusional state associated with an acute brain syndrome is not recognized, the disturbed person is likely to be defined as a criminal.

It is interesting to consider the extent to which an individual's premorbid personality influences his behavior during a confusional episode. Most of us have at some time or another experienced confusion (caused, for example, by high fever, use of anesthetics in surgery or overindulgence in alcohol) and yet few of us become aggressive or antisocial. Many people, in fact, react by becoming more quiet and withdrawn. Obviously, the behavior of a confused person cannot be considered independent of his personality. The confused state does not cause criminal behavior but rather contributes to a general weakening of psychological strength so that the threshold for expression of antisocial behavior is lowered. Stated differently, confusion is not a cause of crime, but predisposed individuals are much more likely to commit crimes when they are confused.

Similar considerations are relevant to the perceptual distortions which take place during the confused state. The delirious man who sees the familiar pink elephants attacking him, or who sees the hospital attendant as a vicious assassin, may act to defend himself against his misperceived enemies. Is this man a "victim" of his confusion or is he reacting to something within his own personality? The psychiatrist's answer is that the confused person may truly misinterpret reality but that the direction of his distortions is determined by his own personality. The false reality which he creates is determined by his own conscious and unconscious motivations which he projects onto his perceptual world. Similarly, his failure to perceive some aspects of the real world is selective and is determined by his own needs. No two confused people behave exactly the same. If we give a group of normal people an hallucinogenic drug, each person will experience a unique hallucination.

In considering the relationship of acute confusional states to crime, David Abrahamsen's so-called second law of criminal behavior is helpful.[2] According to Abrahamsen, a criminal act is the sum of a person's criminalistic tendencies plus his total situation divided by the amount of his resistance. This may be expressed by the formula $C = (T + S)/R$. The acute confusional state does not alter the individual's "criminalistic tendencies" since it cannot influence the past physical, psychological or social experiences of the individual. It can, however, alter his perception of the total situation so that he may perceive a benevolent situation as one which is dangerous. It can also lower his resistance to the expression of certain impulses by limiting restraining adaptations. The organic confusional state enhances the possibility of an individual committing a crime by influencing two of the terms of Abrahamsen's equation.

Crimes committed during confused states related to trauma, tumor, infection or systemic disease are quite rare. Fortunately, individuals who experience these conditions usually develop some signs of physical illness early enough in the course of their disturbance so that they are placed under medical treatment before they find themselves in trouble. For practical purposes, the most important confusional states associated with crime are related to excessive indulgence in alcohol and to convulsive disorders. Although the major criminogenic influence of alcohol takes place before a confused state is actually reached, intoxication to the point of confusion and chronic alcoholic brain damage which produces confusion are frequently important factors. Confused behaviors associated with excessive alcoholic intake are similar to those seen in confusion associated with any organic brain syndrome. The crime-favoring qualities of brain syndromes in general have already been discussed. Understanding the relationship of epilepsy to crime requires examination of a special type of confused state, which will be described in greater detail.

Interest in the relationship of epilepsy to crime goes back to the nineteenth century. As early as 1806 Pinel noted that the dementia which frequently followed a seizure could result in violence.[3] Lombroso felt that there were distinct similarities between so-called epileptic and criminal types.[4] In our own country case reports of crimes believed to have been committed during a convulsive or postconvulsive state have appeared since 1854. In recent years physicians have continued to note that seizure activity is often associated with aggressive or antisocial behavior.[5]

In spite of these observations there is no evidence that epileptics commit more crimes than other people. Whenever they have been studied, crime rates of epileptics have turned out to be almost identical with those of the general population.[6] The relationship of convulsive disorders to crime must be understood in terms of the effect of this stress upon a given individual.

The relative importance of epilepsy as a factor in crime is exaggerated by its prominence as a legal issue. Before, during or after an attack the epileptic may be confused and may suffer an impairment in his ability to assess reality. An antisocial act can occur during any of these periods. Offenders, their attorneys and many psychiatrists have directed their attentions to determining the extent to which the epileptic condition could be looked upon as a necessary and sufficient cause of such crimes. As we shall see, it is almost impossible to prove such a relationship. What we do know about the relationship of convulsive disorders to crime can be summarized as follows.

During the actual convulsion the patient is usually unconscious and incapable of committing a crime. Furthermore, whether the experience of repeatedly being exposed to convulsions has any direct relationship to crime is questionable. The only stresses associated with chronic epilepsy that seem to be criminogenic are secondary effects, namely, the attitudes which society takes toward the diseased person. Since Biblical times most societies have treated the epileptic badly. He is denied access to many legitimate opportunities for success, and is subjected to discrimination and isolation which may lead to serious social and psychological difficulties.

It is possible for a crime to occur during an epileptic aura (the preseizure phase, which is sometimes characterized by strange affective states, hallucinations or confusion) or during the postconvulsive state. Even when a crime occurs in such close temporal relationship to a seizure, it is still difficult to evaluate the influence of other factors such as motivation or social role. Some epileptics behave strangely before a seizure and others behave normally. In the postseizure phase some awake calmly while others awake violently. Aggressiveness either before or after a seizure is probably associated with a previously formed personality trait which is activated by physiological change.

There is a type of convulsive disorder known as psychomotor epilepsy, which is characterized by automatic behavior. During such seizures the patient may engage in behaviors which seem to have no reasonable meaning or purpose. The seizure may last from a half-minute to two minutes and is correlated with electroencephalographic findings of abnormal discharges from the temporal area. Following the attack the patient may have no recollection of his actions. These automatic actions are thought of as being totally split off or dissociated from the patient's ordinary behavior. It is, of course, possible for a man to commit a crime during one of these seizures. Whether we can say that the seizure is the cause of the crime is another matter, which must be explored more fully.

In adolescence there is some evidence that crimes of violence are more likely to be committed by children who are subject to thalamic or hypothalamic seizures (the "6 and 14 syndrome"). Here again the seizure does not appear to be a sufficient cause of the criminal act.

Aggressive behaviors occurring during the confusion which precedes or follows a *grand mal* convulsion are rare, and the possibility of their leading to criminal acts is even more unlikely. Several interesting cases, however, have been reported. In 1872, for example, A. O. Kellogg reported the case of a forty-year-old man who had a convulsion early in the morning and was put to bed by his mother and two sisters.[7] Shortly afterward he seized a fire shovel and beat his sisters over the head. He then slashed one girl's throat with a razor. After ten or twelve days of violence he had another series of convulsions, after which he finally quieted down. When he learned of his assault upon his sisters, he was acutely distressed and surprised.

The relationship of psychomotor epilepsy to crime is far more important. In this type of epilepsy the patient may suddenly develop a "spell" and behave inappropriately for a brief period of time. He might carry out an organized but inappropriate act (such as taking off and putting on his shoes) or he might suddenly become irritable or enraged. There has been a number of cases in which ordinary docile individuals have suddenly behaved in a brutal manner while experiencing a psychomotor seizure. Earl Walker reports the case of a law-abiding man, apparently in love with his wife, who one night inexplicably stabbed her to death.[8] When committed to a mental hospital, he reportedly told the physicians, "The other patients tell me that my wife is dead, that I killed her, but I couldn't have. She is the dearest thing that God ever gave a man. I just couldn't have killed her." He was completely amnesic for the event. It was noted that he had had epileptic spells three or four times a day and that during some of these attacks he was likely to become quite hostile and aggressive. An abnormal electroencephalogram was suggestive of psychomotor epilepsy. In this particular case surgery was recommended, and the patient gained some relief following a left temporal lobectomy.

While the diagnosis of psychomotor epilepsy can be made with some precison through careful history-taking and confirmatory electroencephalographic evidence, it is much more difficult to relate a specific crime to this disorder. The following three case abstracts illustrate the complexity of the problem.

A forty-three-year-old man who had always been considered a respectable citizen was arrested for exhibiting himself. He had been walking along the lake front of a large city when he suddenly stopped and began to undress publicly. When brought to the police station, he could not remember what he had done and did not know why he had been arrested. He was sent to a mental hospital for a pretrial examination, where an electroencephalogram revealed an abnormal discharge from the left temporal area. Further neurological study suggested the presence of a brain tumor.

A twenty-five-year-old man had a long-standing history of assaultiveness. These actions took place mainly in bars and were associated with heavy drinking. Afterward he could never recall any details of his violence. He eventually became embroiled in an altercation in which he mercilously assaulted and killed another man. Upon arrest he denied any recollection of the crime. Electroencephalographic study showed a seizure discharge in the temporal area.

A thirty-year-old man, apparently happily married, was arrested for attempting to force sexual attentions upon a ten-year-old boy. There was some indication that this behavior had occurred previously. During the offense his actions seemed carefully designed to avoid apprehension. He had a vague recollection of his behavior, was sure that he had done something illegal but could not give a rational explanation for his actions. An electroencephalographic study was suggestive of psychomotor epilepsy.

It is not difficult to appreciate the role of epilepsy as a causal factor in the first case. The patient's history plus the purposelessness of his actions supports the relevance of epilepsy as a necessary cause. In the second case, however, there would be some question as to whether assaultiveness always occurred together with the seizures. Even if this could be ascertained, there would still be a question as to the degree to which the organic disorder influenced the disturbed behavior. We would wonder how low this man's threshold for assaultive behavior might have been and if such behavior would have occurred even without seizures. In the third case the apparent goal-directedness of the patient's actions and his partial recall of his behavior would make us skeptical of the importance of epilepsy as a factor. Yet we can never be certain that his behavior, like that of Case I, might have been restrained if there had not been a cerebral abnormality.

The neurosurgeon, Earl Walker, has established six criteria which he suggests can be utilized by attorneys and physicians in attributing a crime of violence to an epileptic condition.[9] Walker's concern is with criminal responsibility, but his criteria are equally relevant to assessing the importance of the epileptic attack as a causal factor in the crime. These criteria are:

1. It must be proven that the patient is subject to bona-fide epileptic attacks.

2. The kind of epileptic attack that is alleged to have occurred during the criminal act must be similar to other attacks which can be observed or described in that individual at different times.

3. It must be proven that the period of loss of awareness alleged to have been present during the crime is commensurate with the type of epileptic attack the individual has experienced.

4. It must be proven that the degree of his assumed unconsciousness during the epileptic attack which resulted in criminality is commensurate with the degree of unconsciousness the patient had demonstrated in previous attacks.

5. It must be proven that the EEG findings are compatible with the type of clinical disorder assumed to be present, that is, if the individual is assumed to have temporal lobe epilepsy, a spike should be demonstrated in leads from that area.

6. It must be established that the circumstances of the crime enhance the assumption that the individual was not aware of what he was doing at the time of the crime. There must be evidence of irrational motives, unnecessary violence or failure to attempt to avoid apprehension.

In recent years neurologists have discovered an abnormal electroencephalographic pattern in some adolescents who have committed apparently senseless and brutal crimes such as murder, sexual assault or fire-setting. This pattern appears in about 3 percent of the general population but in about 60 to 70 percent of teen-agers confined to institutions because of behavioral disturbances.[10] The pattern is referred to as "14 and 6 per second positive spiking," and the behavioral disturbance is referred to as the "6 and 14 syndrome." F. A. and E. L. Gibbs believe that the electroencephalographic abnormality is evidence of hypothalamic or thalamic epilepsy.[11] Violent acts committed by adolescents who may demonstrate this abnormality presumably represent an unrestrained expression of primitive autonomic drives triggered by a seizure discharge. While the existence of the "6 and 14 syndrome" is not fully accepted by all neurologists and psychiatrists, most agree that there is some correlation between this electroenchephalographic finding and a tendency toward primitive-rage reactions.

It must be noted, however, that the "6 and 14" abnormality can be found in many children who never commit crimes. Sherwin Woods has emphasized the importances of earlier psychological disturbance in crimes associated with this "syndrome." In reporting on two adolescents who demonstrated positive spiking and who had committed brutal, purposeless crimes, Woods pointed out the existence of severe pre-existing emotional disturbances in each case. Current views of the relative influence of this type of neurological factor in producing criminal acts are well summarized by Gilbert Glaser as follows:

> Our own laboratory experience suggests that traits of positive spiking might be regarded as a neurophysiological handicap, the importance of which varies as a function of the environment of the patient. A child subjected to the dual stress of 6 and 14/sec. positive spiking and a poor behavioral environment may well react with an unacceptable clinical response that would not be elicited if he lived in a less stressful situation.[13]

While the number of crimes committed before, during or following any kind of epileptic seizure probably is small, convulsive disorders should not be neglected as a causal factor in the study of crime. Epilepsy may be a necessary cause of a certain number of violent and purposeless crimes. From a practical standpoint, it is especially important to identify every possible linkage of epilepsy to crime. Some types of seizures can be controlled with drugs or surgery. It is also likely that new and better treatments will soon be discovered for each type of epilepsy. Pharmacological agents, which are not often useful in criminology, may be quite useful in treating the relatively uncommon epileptic offender.

## Panic

There are some stressful situations which create so much anxiety that control of impulses becomes extremely difficult. Some anxious individuals become disorganized to the point of panic. The panic-stricken individual may resort to antisocial behavior because he sees it as the only hope for survival. Where overwhelming stress is apparent and coming from external and visible agents, this phenomenon is easily understandable. There are many examples of otherwise law-abiding individuals who, during wartime or under the threat of natural disaster, behave in a criminal manner. We are more concerned here with panicky behavior which arises even when external dangers are not apparent. In these conditions the individual responds to severe internal conflicts which make him overwhelmingly anxious and cause him to misinterpret his environment. Such panic can be looked upon as a type of confusion in which the individual sees the world as far more oppressive and dangerous than it actually is. Crime may result when the disturbed person acts to alter a misperceived environment.[14]

While panic can be engendered by a wide variety of conflicts, the most important relationship of panic to crime is found in situations where masculinity is threatened. In our society most young males tend to defend themselves desperately against homosexual or "feminine" feelings. A combination of intense latent homosexual tendencies and restrictive cultural standards often leads to a state of conflict which can generate overwhelming anxiety. The conflicted individual may suddenly become aware of unconscious homosexual tendencies (usually because of some circumstances such as restriction to an all-male environment, severe intoxication or an overture by an overt homosexual) and seek to preserve psychological equilibrium by resorting to defense mechanisms which distort reality. The degree of anxiety may be so great that even paranoid mechanisms will not suffice to allow a tolerable state of comfort.

"Homosexual panics" are most often seen in environments where men live closely together and particularly when they are deprived of regular contacts with the opposite sex. Although not listed as a formal diagnostic category in official nomenclature, this syndrome is well known to psychiatrists who have worked with the armed services, merchant seamen, prisoners or any group in a closed institution. It probably occurs with more frequency than is generally acknowledged and plays an important role in many crimes of violence. The patient who is experiencing a homosexual panic is exquisitely anxious, may have hallucinations and delusions and is physically agitated. The direction of his hallucinations and delusions suggests fears of castration and fears of being homosexually seduced or assaulted. Both unacceptable sexual and aggressive impulses are projected onto the environment so that the panicky individual often reacts violently to free himself from dangers which do not exist.

Homosexual panics are most likely to occur in individuals with maladaptive personality traits. The person who is most likely to develop a homosexual panic is typically uncertain as to his masculinity, is identified with lower-class values, is rigid and more or less ineffective and retiring in his personal relations. The following case is typical of a crime of violence engendered by homosexual panic.

The patient was a nineteen-year-old youth who had recently joined the United States Coast Guard. He had never been away from home before, and he immediately encountered great difficulty in adjusting to the service. An essentially shy and unsophisticated person, he was embarrassed by the intimacy of barracks life. He could not accustom himself to open nudity, shared toilet facilities or any kind of earthy or vulgar masculine behavior. For two weeks prior to the offense he had been experiencing strange and disturbing feelings. These began when he was assigned to a bunk next to a man who made frequent suggestive remarks about the patient's attractiveness. The patient felt vague, erotic stirrings which in turn made him feel extremely guilty. One night, a week before the offense, the patient dreamed that he was kissing this man and awoke to find that he was sexually excited. After this he became even more withdrawn and kept to himself as much as possible. He began to experience feelings of uneasiness which he could not relate to any concrete problem in his daily life. Each night he had nightmares in which animals were chasing him. Two days before the offense he thought that he had heard a soft voice from somewhere behind him calling him a "queer." When he turned, no one was present. The next two days were characterized by extreme anxiety. Although he managed to continue working, he felt that people were making derogatory remarks about him and believed they could detect that his body was becoming more feminine.

On the night of the offense the patient was feeling distraught and nervous. He readily accepted an invitation to spend a weekend leave on a proposed drinking spree with some of his acquaintances. This group included the man who had made suggestive proposals. After several hours of heavy drinking this man suggested to the patient that they find a hotel room and spend the night together. The patient felt both temptation and guilt and almost in a dazed condition accepted this proposal. When they were settled in the hotel room, the friend began to embrace him in an erotic manner. At this point the patient "went berserk." He grabbed a heavy lamp and bludgeoned his companion to death. Several hours later the patient was found by the police wandering along a city street in a confused state. When they tried to question him, he became assaultive. Several officers were required to subdue him. He seemed both terrified and enraged and continually shouted that he wasn't going to let anyone "f--k" him. At the jail he shouted and insisted that his life was in great danger. He accused the police of ridiculing him and had to be forcibly restrained. The patient was taken to a prison hospital, where he remained in a disorganized state for another twenty-four hours. As he gradually calmed down, he was able to relate some of the details of his offense. Most of the above information was not obtained, however, until many months of pretrial hospitalization had passed.

## Excited States

There are other behavior disorders which are characterized by such severe disorganization that the symptoms themselves become an overwhelming social stress. We will briefly consider excited states which are associated with catatonia and mania. Excited behavior is obviously detrimental to smooth functioning in our society. Fortunately, the excited person is often defined as ill and is hospitalized before he causes trouble. If he does not receive medical treatment, however, he may be driven to make a definitive attack upon his environment which may result in his being treated as a criminal. Because of the obvious disturbance of these people, psychiatrists and others often assume that their antisocial actions are accidental by-products of an illness. Again, however, if we accept the adaptational approach, we will recognize that the illness behaviors arise as efforts to alter an oppressive environment and contain within them a potentiality for criminal action.

Catatonia is a behavior characterized by massive disorganization of the personality accompanied by unreasonable and uncoordinated efforts to change the environment. The catatonic is a person who is gravely handicapped in his ability to relate to others. He adapts to this handicap either by frantically searching for interpersonal contact or by totally withdrawing from others. In the excited phase the patient is typically agitated, incoherent and so motorically driven that he is capable of exhausting himself to the point of death.

Fortunately, the ready availability of tranquilizing drugs has made this condition quite rare. We still see cases of catatonic stupor (total withdrawal from the environment, often accompanied by immobility), but true catatonic excitement is rarely seen in communities where psychiatric care is available. When it does occur, however, excited behavior often takes the form of violent attacks upon others.

The behavior disorder known as manic excitement occurs with more regularity, and since it develops in a gradual, insidious manner, antisocial acts may be committed before the patient is designated as mentally ill. Manic behavior is best thought of as a release phenomenon or a breaking away from superego restrictions. It is characterized by excessive motoric activity, garrulosity and a constant search for pleasure. In psychodynamic terms, the manic is a person who frantically seeks release from the oppression of guilt feelings. To sustain his temporary freedom, he behaves in an overactive, overvoluble and apparently self-satisfied manner, as if his "motor" were running too fast and could not be stopped. Such people behave as though a personified "depression" were chasing them, as if any cessation of activity would envelope them in despair.[15] Often serious feelings of depression precede, alternate with or intermix with the more alloplastic manic behavior.

The manic patient may experience many degrees of apparent freedom and good feeling. He may be mildly elated, quite euphoric or wildly excited. Unlike the catatonic, however, there is far less disorganization of the personality. The manic is "tuned in" with his environment, and although his actions may be abnoxious, their purpose and direction are usually clear. Since he feels driven to a frantic demonstration of his freedom from guilt, he is likely to perform many acts which are antisocial. His desperate need to sustain a sense of well-being may overcome his previously learned standards of conformity.

The layman has considerable difficulty in accepting the notion that the manic, who can be so obnoxious (and who superficially seems to be having so much fun), could actually be a disturbed person. Particularly when excitement is not severe, he is likely to be treated as a criminal. Generally, however, the manic is an extremely unreasonable criminal. His antisocial behavior serves no utilitarian purpose. The following case illustrates some of the behavior and psychological mechanisms of the manic reaction.

The patient, a forty-five-year-old married woman, was known in her community as an aggressive and ruthless business person. She and her husband ran a large hardware business, and although her husband was titular head, everyone in town knew that she was the "boss." She worked fourteen hours a day and never took a vacation. About one month prior to the onset of her antisocial behavior she began to experience severe headaches. She consulted a physician, who referred her to a psychiatrist. The psychiatrist noted that she was quite depressed. She expressed many feelings of discontent with her life, repeatedly maintaining that she felt "hemmed in" and guilty without knowing why. Psychotherapy was recommended, but after two sessions the patient decided to terminate, stating that she was suddenly relieved and felt marvelously improved. During the next few weeks she became more hyperactive. She slept only two or three hours a night and began to make totally unrealistic plans for a massive expansion of her business. Great quantities of merchandise were bought which never could have been sold. She became flirtatious with several of her male acquaintances and, although she had always been a staunchly moralistic person, offered to have affairs with them. She also filed false quarterly income tax reports, heavily withdrew from her checking account and when the banks refused to cash her checks attempted to forge securities. Eventually, she was arrested and released on bail.

While she was awaiting trial, her family was completely ineffective in controlling her manic behavior. She continued to be euphoric and grandiose, and it was only with the aid of community police officers that they were finally able to persuade her to enter a psychiatric hospital. On the hospital ward her behavior deteriorated. She became wildly excited, incessantly active, profane and uncontrollable. This behavior reached a point where it was endangering her health, and she was given electroconvulsive treatment. After several therapeutic convulsions her manic behavior subsided and her old behavior patterns reappeared.

This lady's excited behavior is best understood as an effort to find release from an unpleasant, conscience-ridden existence. Once she began a frantic effort to combat the internal pressures of her own conscience (and, to some extent, the real external pressures in her life), she was unable to give up an unreasonable but self-sustaining attack upon the environment. Antisociality in this case was only one of many inappropriate efforts to find peace and freedom by altering the environment.

## Paranoid States

Sometimes a person can become so overwhelmed by anxiety and feelings of worthlessness that preservation of personal integrity and a tolerable level of comfort are made possible only at the expense of grave distortions of reality. Feelings of worthwhileness and justification are maintained only by altering personal belief systems so that the individual can convince himself that he is very important and that others are attacking him or are allied against him. Unacceptable, aggressive and sexual feelings are projected and the world is seen as a frightening place.

We have previously noted that many criminals utilize projective devices to justify and sustain antisocial tendencies. What we are referring to here, however, is a degree of distortion of reality which is poorly rationalized and which is totally inconsistent with readily observable facts. The lower-class delinquent may believe that the world is against him, but there is some likelihood that he could defend the reality of his perceptions. On the other hand, the person who believes that he has been given magical powers by a sun god or that his wife is having a clandestine affair with Fidel Castro is clearly out of touch with any reality but his own. We speak of him as delusional—that is, he holds to false beliefs which are not shared by others and which cannot be rationally explained or validated.

Delusions of exaggerated importance (grandiosity), delusions of jealousy and delusions of persecution are extravagant and desperate efforts to sustain ego integrity. Once held and acted upon, they lead to such adverse reactions from the environment that they can become severe and overwhelming stresses in themselves. The person who is ridiculed for his grandiosity may be impelled to commit a dramatic act to justify his position. He may also commit a variety of crimes, from robbery to murder, in an effort to demonstrate his importance and his immunity from ordinary punishment. The delusionally jealous person may drive his loved ones even further away so that jealousy is increased and more desperate actions seem to be required. The person who feels persecuted may seek justification of his beliefs by provoking his environment to attack him. This will lead to an increase in his own aggressive feelings, and as these are in turn projected onto others, his sense of persecution increases. Frequently, paranoid feelings escalate until a direct attack is made against the perceived "aggressors."[16]

Crimes committed by extremely paranoid persons are likely to be colorful and sensational. The victim is usually a person with whom the paranoid individual has been intimately involved, but occasionally an innocent bystander is attacked. There are probably many offenders who have been tried, convicted and incarcerated without anyone even suspecting that their crime was a direct response to a delusion. Quite often the offender keeps his delusions to himself, and if his superficial behavior after the crime is not too unreasonable he may be treated as a criminal. Another complicating factor is that after the crime the offender may feel so justified and fulfilled that his new level of comfort allows him to behave like a "more normal" person.

Sometimes society is unwilling to believe a criminal is delusional even when he discusses his false beliefs openly. We are often suspicious as to whether delusions were actually present at the time of the crime or whether delusional thinking developed as a *post hoc* adaptive device. It is possible for a jealous husband to murder his wife and if he is then unable to tolerate his guilt or acknowledge his responsibility he might easily convince himself that a voice told him to do it. Such behavior, of course, is encouraged by the possibility of raising the plea of not guilty by reason of insanity. While society may question the motivations of individuals who seem to be inventing delusions, most psychiatrists believe that delusional ideas are not usually voiced unless they are believed. It is also likely that offenders who are delusional immediately after committing a crime were also struggling with delusional thoughts at the time of the criminal act.

The following three case abstracts describe crimes in which a causal relationship between delusional thinking and the offense is apparent.

A twenty-four-year-old salesman was convinced that his wife was "cheating on him." His wife was a relatively unattractive woman who, according to her own statements and reports of others, was completely faithful. Nevertheless, the patient was relentless in his pursuit of evidence of her infidelity. He spied on her, hired detectives to follow her and would not allow her to leave the house alone. She was subjected to endless hours of grilling which were designed to make her confess earlier indiscretions. Finally one night, after many hours of questioning, she "confessed" that several years before her marriage she had engaged in heavy petting with a suitor. The patient was convinced that she was not telling all of the story and was still in love with the man (although she hadn't seen him for several years). After days of brooding he devised a crude time bomb which was sent to the suspected lover through the mail. It was detected, and the patient was arrested.

Another patient had been hospitalized at a VA hospital two years before the crime because of inappropriate behavior, anxiety and delusions of persecution. During the early part of his hospitalization he accused one of the doctors of deliberately trying to influence him through secret hypnotic methods. In the following two months he improved markedly, seemed to have abandoned all delusional thinking and was discharged as cured. He left the hospital and returned home but experienced repeated failures in both work and marriage. One day almost a year and a half after his discharge he returned to the hospital, sought out his old doctor and shot and killed him. He stated afterward that he knew he would never be free of "evil influence" until the doctor was dead. Although the plea of not guilty by reason of insanity was raised at his trial, he was found guilty of murder and sentenced to life imprisonment. After two weeks in prison he was noted to be grossly disturbed. He was seen by a psychiatrist, who recommended his transfer to a hospital for the criminally insane.

In the final case, a man wandered into a tavern in a large Midwestern city and began shooting a gun wildly in all directions. Fortunately, no one was killed. When arrested he stated that he was a Westerner, that the Sioux Indians had killed many of his ancestors and that he thought he had seen some Indians at the bar. The patient had been drinking but was not intoxicated at the time of the crime. Strangely enough, the issue of insanity was not raised. He was convicted of assault with a deadly weapon, and he arrived at the state prison in a deluded and disorganized condition. There was no evidence of organic disorder. The patient could give little information as to his past life. He was transferred to the state hospital for the criminally insane, where he now lives an extremely withdrawn existence and continues to express an occasional fear of Indians.

## Severe Depression

Depression is a persistent affect of sadness which varies from mild downheartedness to hopeless despair. Some psychiatrists believe that serious depression precedes most criminal acts and postulate that crime may be a means of combating this unpleasant affect.[17] There are many similarities between what we have previously called helplessness and depression. It is not difficult, therefore, to comprehend how criminal action could serve to alleviate feelings of depression. Our more limited concern here is with that kind of depression which is too severe to be tolerated and which leads to suicide attempts or other desperate attempts to alter the environment. (There is much doubt in our society as to how suicide should be treated. It is obviously a drastic effort to change a situation through a violation of community standards. While considered a crime in most communities, it so often seems like such an unreasonable act that we usually define the unsuccessful suicide subject as a patient.)

Psychiatrists believe that the seriously depressed person is an angry person. Suicide can be thought of as a form of self-murder which expresses a repressed component of murderous feelings directed toward others.[18] The person who is struggling with thoughts of self-destruction is in a nascent psychological state in which aggressive feelings can easily be directed outward. If he has reached the point of seriously considering leaving this world, socially ordained rules of conduct lose much of their meaning. In addition to the indirect damage he causes to family and friends by hurting himself, the suicidal patient may directly injure others.[19] Sometimes loved ones, particularly children, are destroyed because "There will be no one left to take care of them when I'm gone." Not infrequently, a suicidal attempt injures innocent bystanders. The well-known cartoon of the rich man saying to his chauffeur, "James, I'm tired of living, drive off the cliff," has a certain grim appropriateness. We have no way of knowing how many fatal auto accidents which involve several people are related to conscious self-destructive wishes on the part of one person. If other people are intentionally or inadvertently injured during the course of an unsuccessful suicide attempt, the self-destructive person is likely to be treated as a criminal.

Severe depression may also be accompanied by delusional thinking. The commonest delusion of the psychotically depressed person is related to feelings of personal worthlessness. Such a delusion can be thought of as a delusion of grandeur in reverse. To consider oneself the most worthless person on earth really implies a belief in one's own specialness. The depressed person may also experience delusions of persecution. He may attack others not only for "their own good" but also because he is responding to paranoid thinking and is seeking an escape from helplessness through his attacks on imagined aggressors.

The following case illustrates the relationship of depression, suicidal tendencies and delusional thinking in a criminal act. The patient, a twenty-five-year-old mother of two young children, was subject to frequent attacks of nervousness and depression. One year prior to the crime her husband left her for another woman. The patient was forced to assume responsibility for complete management of her household. Her parents were unable to assist her, she had few friends and she lacked the maturity or skill to overcome her serious financial burdens. As she was progressively overwhelmed by her responsibilities, her physical and psychological condition deteriorated. She lost weight, slept poorly and gave up caring for her appearance. Shortly before the offense a neighbor recalls her having remarked that "God was punishing her and the children because she was such an evil person." On the night of the crime the patient put the children to bed, poured herself a "stiff" drink and turned on the gas oven jets. A neighbor in the adjoining apartment happened to pass by a short while later, smelled gas and gained entrance in time to save the patient and her oldest child. The one-year-old infant, however, died. The patient told the police that she had been considering suicide for some time. She argued that she had to take the children with her because they were all contaminated with her "evilness" and would suffer and bring harm to others if they survived.

## *Chapter 13*

# SEX CRIMES AND DEVIATION

IN Western society many individuals are designated criminals because they transgress against acceptable standards of sexual behavior. The sex deviate who violates the law, however, is not usually thought of as a normal criminal. His illegal acts seem so alien or so unreasonable that they are readily defined as a psychiatric problem. The more bizarre the sexual offense, the more it is assumed that the offender cannot help himself. While the sex offender is often looked upon as a sick person, he is rarely treated kindly. In fact, because his behavior threatens and angers us, we more often than not treat him as harshly as any other criminal.

Unfortunately, the problem of sex crimes and sexual deviation is almost incomprehensibly muddled by value judgments, conflicting concepts of normality and a general aura of secrecy that surrounds sexual matters in our society. The laws which define illegal sexual conduct are even more arbitrary than those which define other forms of criminal behavior. There is also a large gap between what society looks upon as abnormal and what the law defines as illegal. In all but ten states, for example, sexual intercourse occurring out of wedlock is a punishable crime. In many states participation in oral-genital relations is defined as a crime even when such acts are performed by people who are married to one another. Legal definitions of minority status usually bear little relationship to the extent of sexual maturity. In the writer's home state of Wisconsin, for example, a twenty-one-year-old boy who fondled the breasts of his seventen-year-old girl friend could technically be imprisoned for taking indecent liberties with a minor. Similarly, if an eighteen-year-old girl petted with her seventeen-year-old boy friend, she could be considered a sex offender. Every American has probably violated a sex-crimes statute at some time in his life and could have been called a sex offender.

Statutes which define sex crimes are obviously not enforced with regularity. When they are enforced, punitive action is likely to be directed mainly against lower-class people who are concurrently experiencing other difficulties in their community. Aberrant sexual behavior is then invoked as sufficient cause for ridding the community of a "troublesome" person. We have previously noted the tendency of our society to institutionalize lower-class girls who have had sexual intercourse with one or more males. Sometimes lower-class boys are also punished for this same "crime." It is practically unheard of, however, for a middle- or upper-class adolescent or adult to be punished for consenting heterosexual activities. Differential treatment according to class is also apparent when other types of sexual behavior are discovered. Any kind of deviant or nongenital sexual practice is liable to be treated more harshly if it is found in lower-class individuals. It is generally true that our society is inclined to treat sexual deviation as a form of illness or immaturity if it occurs in middle- or upper-class people and as a crime if it occurs in lower-class people.

## Normal vs. Abnormal Sexual Behavior

Many, but not all, sex crimes are defined as such because they are believed to represent deviated or perverted behavior. These terms imply a deviation from a socially defined standard of normality. For practically all socioeconomic groups, sexual behavior is considered normal if its aim is mutually gratifying sexual intercourse and its object is a consenting and mature member of the opposite sex. (We must add the qualification that this definition would hold only when such proper sexual objects are available. Some would argue, for example, that homosexuality might be more "normal" than abstinence in a closed institution such as a prison where access to the opposite sex is denied.) Some segments of our society take a moderately tolerant attitude toward deviations in the sexual aim if these behaviors take place between consenting adults and do not become the primary source of sexual gratification. Many upper- or middle-class people would consider oral-genital relations, some exhibiting and looking and a certain amount of sadomasochistic activity as normal. These activities are much more likely to be looked upon as "queer" and offensive by the less sophisticated lower-class person. Deviations in the choice of sexual object are taken seriously by all classes of society and are invariably considered to be abnormal and objectionable.

Our definition of normal sexuality does not exclude the possibility of criminality. Almost any society might define sexual intercourse out of wedlock and some other varieties of sexual behavior as immoral or illegal but would not necessarily think of such activities as abnormal. Thus one can be given the legal status of sex offender without being designated a sex deviate or sex pervert.

Actually, any judgments as to normality are made on shaky grounds. Almost any kind of sexual behavior which humans can think of has some phylogenetic and ontogenetic basis. Animals masturbate, they are incestual, they suck one another's genitals and they attempt copulation with members of the same sex. Infants, if not restrained, will demonstrate similar tendencies. What we consider normal and what we consider abnormal are entirely dependent upon social, not biological, criteria. In defending the "correctness" of social definitions of sexual normality, however, we might note three facts. (1) The kind of sexual behavior we have defined as normal is predominant in every culture known to man. The overwhelming majority of the human race seeks sexual intercourse with a consenting and mature member of the opposite sex as the preferred means of gratification. A few cultures have been far more permissive than ours with regard to homosexuality. No major culture, however, has looked upon homosexuality as the preferred method of sexual gratification. (2) The kind of behavior we have defined as normal has one biological advantage over any other kind of sexual activity. It helps to perpetuate the species. (3) All other forms of sexual behavior when occurring in individuals who utilize them as a primary source of gratification seem to be accompanied by a certain amount of immaturity or emotional disturbance.

As measured against social definitions of sexual normality, the following kinds of behavior which occur with regularity and which are consciously and repeatedly sought as the primary source of gratification are considered abnormal: homosexuality, transvestism, sexual relations with children (pedophilia), sexual relations with animals (bestiality), fetishism, sadism, masochism, voyeurism and exhibitionism. Any of these behaviors are defined as crimes when society believes they will lead to physical or psychological harm to another person, or when they are performed in a manner which is offensive to public taste. At the same time many of these "abnormal" sexual behaviors do not trouble the community if they are carried on discreetly or with consent.

We must also note that for every person who participates in, or is arrested for, a deviated sexual act there are a great number of other people who experience intense motivations to perform the same act but do not indulge their wishes. Two people, for example, may have equally strong drives to exhibit themselves, yet whether or not one or both will actually perform the act is determined by many factors. Ultimately, such a decision depends upon the adaptive value of such action at a given moment. Some individuals with deviant tendencies find sufficient gratification in fantasy; others may have to deal more directly with the environment.

## Some General Explanations of Sexual Deviation

Although motivation will not fully explain any crime, a knowledge of motivation is crucial to understanding sexual offenses. If we ask, "What drives a man to forsake the 'normal' or acceptable sexual standards of his community?," our answer must begin with a study of motivations which are common not only to sex offenders but to many other individuals as well. To discuss sexual deviation objectively, it will be helpful temporarily to ignore legal issues and the question of behavioral choice and focus only on motivation. The following explanations of deviated motivation, therefore, do not distinguish between the offender and the deviated individual who has not acted on his motivations.

Although classifications of deviation made on the sole basis of motivation have some usefulness, they must also be examined critically. The personality of the person who indulges his deviation is likely to be quite different from that of the person who limits himself to gratification in fantasy. Unfortunately, some psychiatrists place both groups in similar diagnostic categories, and these categories frequently have great social and legal meaning. We will note in a later chapter how diagnosis made on the basis of motivation alone, rather than motivation plus actual behavior, can lead to coercive measures against people who have never committed a crime.

There are three major types of theoretical explanations which have been applied to the general problem of deviant sexual motivation. The first is that deviation is the result of a sensitizing event, which may either reinforce socially aberrant tendencies or create fears of heterosexual behavior. A second maintains that deviation is the result of distorted parental relationships which create a fear of normal heterosexual intercourse. The third position sees deviation as a result of a desire to do something which is forbidden and therefore more stimulating. Closely allied to this type of explanation are those which view sexual perversions as resulting from a need for variety which is believed to be characteristic of the human species.

Those theories which relate deviation to specific sensitizing or traumatizing events are consistent with both a psychoanalytic and a learning theory frame of reference. They postulate that at some early phase in the deviated person's life he was exposed to deviant but meaningful sexual experiences which sensitized him to seek similar experiences in adult life. According to this explanation, the child who is seduced by a member of his own sex might have a tendency to seek homosexual contacts in later life. Similarly, the child who is exposed to the primal scene or other kinds of nudity might be stimulated constantly to seek repetition of this experience and become a voyeur. The possibility of developing a sexual disturbance would be increased if the deviant experience were repeated. One obvious inadequacy of this type of theory is that there are many children who are exposed to repeated traumatic events but who grow up to have perfectly normal sexual interests.

The best way to evaluate the influence of sensitizing events is to also consider the emotional state of the child at the time that the events occurred. Everything we know from psychoanalysis and learning theory suggests that if the child is in a state of great need and is exposed to a behavior which is gratifying, he will tend to seek that kind of behavior in the future.[1] This inference is generally confirmed by clinical experience. Psychiatrists believe that a child who enjoys a gratifying and healthy relationship with his parents will not be permanently influenced by a sensitizing deviant experience.[2,3] On the other hand, the child who is in great need at these moments may learn to desire deviated acts.

There are other kinds of sensitizing events which have a clearly traumatic quality and are believed to foster deviation by creating a fear of normal sexuality. The child who is exposed to the primal scene, who is explicitly threatened with castration or who is vigorously punished for any kind of sexual expression may come to fear his more normal tendencies. Psychiatrists, and particularly psychoanalysts, believe that such a child could seek deviant outlets because of unpleasant affects which come to be associated with normal sexual activity. This kind of explanation of sexual deviancy is closely related to and can also be considered a part of more general theories of deviation as a fear of heterosexuality.

While acknowledging the importance of sensitizing or traumatic events, many psychiatrists believe that the most useful explanation of sexual deviancy can be formulated in terms of a fear of heterosexuality which is based on repeated exposure to disturbing family relationships.[4,5] The male child who develops an overly close, erotically tinged relationship to his mother and who does not develop an adequate relationship with his father may come to fear that he will be punished for his incestual feelings. The threat of castration can be great enough so that he will later repress his desire for all females. Similarly, the female child who is overly intimate with her father could come to fear punishment and might avoid sexual attachments to all men in later life.

Explanations which center around maladaptive resolutions of the Oedipus complex are perhaps the most seriously held psychiatric theories of deviant sexual behavior. Such explanations posit that the person who learns to fear normal heterosexual activity can move in one of two directions. He can either seek gratification with a different object (e.g., homosexuality) or he can seek a symbolic kind of gratification through an activity which is a partial and distorted substitute of his original need (he may become a fetishist and feel safer if he values the clothing of the loved object more highly than the object herself, or he may become involved in the issue of looking at or exhibiting himself to an object whom he fears to contact more directly). Since he often sees the parent of the opposite sex as frustrating and depriving, his feelings toward other persons of that sex may be contaminated with great rage and anger, affects which are then expressed in sadomasochistic behavior.

If sexual deviation is seen as a displacement of drive energy, it follows that the intensity of drive which is channeled into the deviant act will be as great as that which might ordinarily be reserved for the normal sexual act. Another way of looking at this is that for some people expression of love may not be possible except through a deviant sexual act. Thus, paradoxical as it may appear, the sadist who mercilessly beats his victim or the voyeur who must spy upon his sexual object may at the same time be seeking an outlet for deep feelings of affection. Either person may find fulfillment and realization of his needs for closeness only through his deviation. Many deviated individuals report that they feel whole and complete only at those moments at which they live out their perversion. The perversion becomes the most important element in their lives and in some cases the major reason for their existence.[6]

A person who seeks a deviant sexual aim or object is aware of the fact that his motivations are seriously condemned by the remainder of society. His desired act is forbidden and always carries with it possible punishment, guilt and shame. Some observers have argued that the forbidden nature of deviant sexual behavior accounts for much of its attractiveness.[7] The degree of excitation seen in some perversions, an excitement which often supersedes that which "more normal" individuals report experiencing during heterosexual intercourse, is believed to be related to the experiencing of something that is forbidden and dangerous. Those who hold to this view believe that man is deeply stimulated by any kind of dangerous behavior. Another way of looking upon this phenomenon is that freedom and a sense of autonomy may be so completely denied to some oppressed people that it can be found only in the unconventional and offensive. It is sometimes argued that sexual excitement is greater if the sexual act is not only unconventional but is also considered disgusting. To wallow in "degrading and puerile" acts might indeed create a sense of ultimate freedom from the dictates of others which could enhance the erotic quality of the perversion. This phenomenon is perhaps best depicted in literature and especially well in Genêt's *Our Lady of the Flowers.*[8]

It is also true that a certain amount of guilt always accompanies a deviant sexual act. It appears that this guilt, while contributing to some suffering, can also be transformed into pleasure. The existence of a mechanism by which pain is transformed into pleasure is presumed by psychoanalytic theory.[9] There seems little doubt from clinical experience that the shame, suffering and anguish associated with a forbidden sexual act can make that act "sweeter."

The incidence of perverse sexual behavior is strikingly higher in males. Females are rarely convicted of committing sexual offenses.[10] There are many possible explanations for this fact. It is possible that women are simply more adept at keeping their sexual problems to themselves and are less likely either to admit to deviant thoughts or to be caught in any kind of deviant behavior. Another possibility is that the more rigid sexual prohibitions which are imposed upon women lead to greater repression and less awareness of perverse sexual material. It is also true that our society does not take female sexual deviation very seriously. Male homosexuality, for example, frequently arouses disgust in both sexes. Female homosexuality is more likely to arouse curiosity. Many other double standards seem to have become incorporated into our laws. For instance, the woman who undresses with her shade up is not likely to be labeled an exhibitionist, while a man who does the same thing could very well be arrested. On the other hand, a man who watches a woman undress could be arrested as a "Peeping Tom," while the woman who watches a man undress may be defined as a victim.

The reason for society's tolerance of female deviancy may lie in the fact that women are a physically weaker sex and are less likely to force themselves upon others. One of society's omnipresent fears of the male deviate (even if he does no more than peek or exhibit) is that he will forcibly rape.*

* A great deal has been written about the sex offender. The exhaustive studies of the Kinsey group,[11] Benjamin Karpman,[12] Manfred Guttmacher,[13] George Henry[14] and Irving Bieber *et al.*[15] are especially useful. Phenomenological insights are also important in this complicated area, and fortunately the fictional and autobiographical

In almost every community in the United States participation in homosexual activities is a legal offense. This is true even when such acts are confined to mutually consenting relations between two adults. In practice the most rigid enforcement of laws is directed against those who aggressively seduce others or against the adult homosexual who seeks out partners who are minors. Consenting adult homosexuals are likely to be arrested only when their behavior takes place in public facilities such as rest rooms. As with other deviant behaviors, the most rigid enforcement of the law is reserved for members of the lower class. The lower-class homosexual usually cannot afford to pursue his activities with sufficient discretion. When he is apprehended, he does not have the same access to legal aid or to the mental-illness role as does the middle- or upper-class homosexual.

Homosexuality is a deviation in the object of the sexual drive wherein a person seeks a member of his own sex for gratification. A single homosexual act can, of course, occur under unusual circumstances in relatively "normal" individuals. There are also individuals who are able to participate with equal enjoyment in both heterosexual and homosexual relationships. Our concern in this section will be primarly with those people who regularly and consciously experience greater attraction to members of their own sex.

Many efforts have been made to classify homosexuals in terms of their behavior during the sex act. It is assumed that there are differences in the motivations or personalities between those who take a feminine and those who take a masculine role and between those who take an active and those who take a passive role. Classifications of homosexuality have some general validity, but these is so much variation, shifting of roles and combinations of roles that we cannot expect to clearly categorize any given individual. At the same time, there is some consistency in the sexual behavioral patterns of a given homosexual individual. Some homosexuals seek one type of gratification exclusively, and there may be slight but consistent differences in the personalities of those who seek different means of gratification.

Male homosexuals most often gratify one another in one of three ways. They engage in either mutual masturbation, oral-genital relations or rectal sodomy. Mutual masturbation implies an equal degree of activity or passivity in both partners. There are some individuals, however, who always prefer to be masturbated while others always prefer to do the masturbating.

---

literature is rich. Some of the most useful insights have been presented by writers who would not be considered behavioral scientists, such as John Rechy,[16] Ann Aldrich[17] and Jean Genêt.[18]

Oral-genital relationships imply that one person will actively suck the penis (fellatio) while the other will be the passive supplier of the organ. In such a situation the issue of passivity and activity becomes confused with femininity and masculinity. Although the passive partner takes the inserter role, which is usually associated with the male, he also demonstrates a passivity which is ordinarily associated with the female. It is also true that many homosexuals will switch roles and that some will attempt to gratify one another simultaneously. In rectal sodomy the man who inserts his penis into another man's rectum (buggery) is taking an aggressive and active role, which is usually associated with masculinity. The individual who offers his rectum as an orifice for gratification takes on a passive role more commonly associated with femininity. Again, however, it is not uncommon for two partners to switch roles.

There are also many variations in the nonsexual aspects of the homosexual's behavior. Many homosexuals who prefer exclusively to take the passive role in rectal sodomy or the active role in fellatio tend to identify with the feminine role in other aspects of life and will assume feminine mannerisms, affectations and dress. On the other hand, many other individuals who are interested in the same kind of sexual activity have a completely masculine appearance and disdain any pretense of femininity. Those who attempt to detect a homosexual by his appearance and mannerisms are easily misled. There are many effeminate men who are totally uninterested in homosexual activity, just as there are many masculine-appearing men who are confirmed homosexuals.

Many of these same generalizations are applicable to the female homosexual. Gratification in this case is usually brought about by mutual masturbation or by oral-genital contact (cunnilingus). There are many female homosexuals who will assume only one role, just as there are many who will assume a variety of roles during the homoerotic act. Again, some female homosexuals tend to assume masculine dress and demeanor. Others remain quite feminine.

In addition to the three general theories of sensitizing events, fear of heterosexuality and attraction to forbidden activities, a number of other explanations of homosexuality have been offered.

It is sometimes maintained that homosexuals have a physical defect which makes them more prone to adopt a deviant role. Advocates of this theory believe that hereditary or acquired physical abnormalities, particularly endocrine dysfunctions, are the causes of homosexuality. Up to this point no substantive evidence which would support this position has been presented.[19] Most students of sexual deviation believe that homosexuality is a learned behavior. Of course, the person who comes into this world with feminine physical characteristics will be more likely to be put into a social role that is conducive to homosexuality. The fat chubby boy or the frail asthenic boy will not excel in athletics, will be more likely to be "babied" and will find less acceptance in activities usually associated with the masculine role. He is perhaps more susceptible to developing a homosexual orientation than his more masculine-appearing contemporary.

Homosexuality is sometimes described as a confusion in sexual identity.[20] Some homosexuals consciously wish to be identified with the opposite sex and on rare occasions seek surgical procedures in the hope that this fantasy will become an anatomical reality. In other individuals confusion of sexual identity has more of an unconscious basis. Psychiatrists relate such confusion to growing up in a disturbed family situation. Parents who desire a girl instead of a boy and who continually stifle a son's masculinity may encourage a feminine identification. And, of course, fear of heterosexuality can also discourage masculine identification. In some families it is apparent to the child that the sibling of the opposite sex is treated far more lovingly than himself. He may equate the capacity to obtain love and gratification with being of a different sex and may identify with that role in an effort to make himself more lovable.

Sometimes homosexuality is described as a search for love from a member of the same sex. The male homosexual often has a father who is distant, detached or frequently absent.[21] Homosexual activity in such cases can be interpreted as a striving for closeness and love from a male, a gratification which was lacking at a time in life when it was desperately needed. A similar dynamic has been noted in the female.

A search for the love of a parent of the same sex usually has an ambivalent quality. If that parent has frustrated the child's needs, hostility as well as love will be displaced into sexual behavior. We do find that homosexuals have an ambivalent attitude toward their partners. Although they are for the most part affectionate, they also tend to hurt each other and are more prone to violent and stormy disagreements than heterosexual partners. Homosexual relationships are notoriously short-lived and ephemeral.

Psychoanalysts maintain that the homosexual is likely to be an immature and self-centered individual.[22] It is sometimes argued that he is far more deeply in love with himself than with others. He seeks an object that is more like himself because he has never been loved enough to be able to give to others. Certainly, clinical observations suggest that most homosexuals are far more narcissistic, egocentric and immature than those whom we consider normal.

There are certain cultural factors in our society which encourage and sustain a homosexual way of life for those who are unable to master the more difficult aspects of existence. This is particularly true for the male. The passive male need not fear rejection and humiliation quite so much if he seeks another male. Once he learns the courting signals of the homosexual world, he can be reasonably certain as to who will accept him as a sexual partner. He also finds that in a homosexual relationship he can be catered to and taken care of in a way which is not at all possible with women. Our society usually encourages the male to care for the material and dependency needs of the female. In a homosexual relationship this responsibility can be put aside.

The homosexual's subculture may therefore be characterized by a carefree, unplanned and stress-avoiding existence. This in itself is a potent force for sustaining a deviant way of life. The person who leads the "gay life" finds a comfortable, nondemanding intimacy, a certain amount of fun and a kind of aimless freedom. The "gay life" represents the essence of nonresponsibility, easy mobility, lack of meaningful attachment to others and unwillingness to assume a mature role in our society. It ignores the most important existential issues by encouraging a life in which commitment to one person or one cause is unlikely. It is perhaps for this reason that many homosexuals "burn out" as they grow older. As the homosexual ages, he finds that he may not be so attractive to other homosexuals as he used to be. He also discovers that he cannot avoid the issues of illness and death. These are all-powerful forces which drive him toward more commitment, which frequently means a "more normal" way of life. The "gay life" is primarily for the young.

Transvestism, or a desire to dress in the clothes of the opposite sex, sometimes leads to law violation and usually causes public concern. Many homosexuals are also transvestites. Some are notoriously adept at disguising their appearance, even managing at times to earn their living as female impersonators. An interest in wearing the clothes of the opposite sex is also found in some individuals (particularly men) who are not homosexuals. Such cross-dressing may lead to erotic stimulation. The nonhomosexual transvestite tends to be less exhibitionistic and more secretive with regard to his perversion.[23] For this reason he rarely comes into conflict with the law.

Nonexhibitionistic transvestism is best looked upon as a fear of intimate contact with a member of either the opposite or the same sex. The transvestite wishes to have close contact with a woman but is also fearful of such closeness. When he dresses as a woman, he himself can be the object of his own impulses, an object which is capable of assuming the role of a member of the opposite sex. As he observes himself in the mirror, the transvestite is in a sense in complete control of a "woman" who will do his bidding and who is incapable of rejecting or depriving him in any way. This kind of transvestism is frequently seen in young adolescents who are aroused by females but are also frightened of their sexual impulses. Although transvestism in adolescents creates a great deal of alarm among adults, this behavior usually disappears as the child's increasing maturity makes it possible for him to develop a gratifying relationship with a member of the opposite sex.

Perhaps the most serious kind of sexual perversion from the standpoint of the law is that in which the offender seeks to gain gratification from an immature object of the same or opposite sex. We must note, however, that there may be marked differences between the laws of our land and the definitions of sexual normality which are implied in the practices of various subcultures. Many thirteen- and fourteen-year-old girls are biologically mature sexual objects, and in some cultures their involvement with older men is not looked upon as particularly abnormal. In our country we assume that even if such a child consents to a sexual relationship with an older man she is being psychologically exploited and victimized.

Some of the men who actively seek sexual activity with adolescent girls rather than with available and psychologically mature women might be responding to deviant motivations. More often their behavior represents a serious defect in judgment. And, of course, many adult males who seduce adolescent girls simply belong to a cultural group which condones such behavior. Our concern here is with those individuals whose major sexual interest is directed toward biologically immature females. We will also briefly consider the homosexual who is interested in younger boys. Both these groups are technically referred to as pedophiliacs.

Pedophilia is commonly explained as a fear of approaching a mature woman. The pedophiliac prefers little girls because they are more helpless, more easily controlled and less capable of humiliating or rejecting him. In many instances, however, the child molester is specifically attracted to little children, and his deviation must be understood as more than a simple aversion to the adult. Such a person may be searching for a repetition of earlier childhood experiences. Many heterosexual pedophiles have been exposed to earlier sexual contact with a sister and may have been sensitized by such events.[24]

The pedophile is also likely to be a very immature person who even in nonsexual areas is more comfortable with children than with adults. His attitude toward his victim is sometimes characterized by a great deal of affection or love. The victim is more often than not cooperative and is likely to be a relative or person well known to the offender.[25]

Still another possible explanation of pedophilia is that the child molester is a person who was exposed to seductive parental attitudes in his own childhood and that he is seeking to "turn the tables" or to become the predator rather than the prey. This pattern is often seen in cases of father-daughter incest where the father often is a person who was exposed to intense closeness and erotic stimulation by his own mother. Such offenders describe a sense of mastery which accompanies their sexual activities with the child.

Homosexual pedophiles seem to have many of the same conflicts characteristic of homosexuals in general. Often, however, they are far more immature, demonstrate more confusion in sexual identification and are unable to develop sustaining relationships with any adults, male or female. In this sense they also share many of the traits of the heterosexual pedophile.

The tendency of young males growing up in a rural environment occasionally to indulge in sexual experimentation with animals (bestiality) is well known. For the most part these are transitory behaviors which disappear and do not recur as the youth becomes more comfortable with other sexual outlets. Occasionally we see physically mature adults who in a drunken or disturbed moment will attempt to have intercouse with an animal. This behavior is quite rare, and the involved individual is likely to be seriously emotionally disturbed. Even more rare are those instances in which a man or woman becomes deeply attracted to a pet or farm animal and indulges in some kind of regular sexual activity with that animal (zoophilia). Such a situation occurs only when the disturbed person is drastically isolated (on either a geographical or a psychological basis) from other individuals. The deviated person who has created his own isolation is, of course, likely to be a person who also has serious difficulties in nonsexual aspects of his behavior.

A tendency to derive sexual excitement or gratification by touching, fondling or fantasizing an object that is not a person but usually an article of clothing associated with a person is called fetishism. Fetishists are almost always of the male sex. Their disturbance represents a deviation in both the object and the aim of sexual gratification. Frequently, the fetishistic object has a fairly clear relationship to a conventional sexual object (women's underwear, shoes or a lock of hair), but sometimes the fetishistic object does not have an apparent relationship to sexual intimacy (raincoats and umbrellas have been known to be highly coveted by fetishists).

While all the general explanations of sexual deviation are valid for the fetishist, additional attempts have been made to explain this unusual behavior in terms of the symbolic meaning of the desired object. Freud originally postulated that the fetish always symbolized the penis. Later psychoanalysts specuated that it could represent some part of the female body. More general theories hold that the fetish originally stands for the body of the mother and that the fetishist is attempting to gain a symbolic fusion with the maternal body.[26]

For the most part fetishists indulge their sexual needs privately and are unlikely to come into conflict with the law. Sometimes, however, they steal the fetishistic object and become lawbreakers. Quite frequently considerable hostility toward women underlies the fetishistic deviation. The author has seen a few cases in which confirmed fetishists have made violent sexual attacks upon others. These are likely to occur at moments when the fetishist is trying to overcome his deviation. His efforts to reach people on a real rather than a symbolic basis unfortunately takes the form of expressing the negative aspect of his ambivalence upon a frustrating love object.

Sadism refers to the tendency to experience sexual excitement and pleasure through inflicting physical or psychological pain upon others, and masochism (when alluding to sexual behavior) describes a tendency to derive excitement and pleasure from being hurt or humiliated. Both are considered deviations of the sexual aim. In his *Three Contributions to the Theory of Sex,* Freud saw both of these deviations as arising from a fusion of aggressive instincts with the basic sexual drive.[27] He postulated that the child's interest in pain and suffering would manifest itself in later life in the foreplay characteristic of normal adults. Most behavioral scientists consider a certain amount of enjoyment of pain to be normal for the female and a certain amount of pleasure in inflicting pain as normal for the male.

Since both sadism and masochism may occur at different times in the same person, we often speak of sadomasochistic behavior rather than sadism or masochism per se. The person who enjoys being hurt will often find equal gratification in taking on the sadistic role.

Sadomasochistic activity is common in the lives of many people who are never defined as sex deviates. Quite often men and women with complementary sadomasochistic conflicts will discover mutually gratifying activities which continue throughout their marriage. Some married women cannot enjoy sexual intercourse with their husbands unless they have first been humiliated or physically abused. They may even seek flagellation or other physical torment. A woman may also be incapable of enjoying the sexual act unless she can first inflict some pain or humiliation upon her sexual partner. Similar disturbances occur in the male. There are probably a great many men who are identified as perfectly normal citizens who are deeply preoccupied with fantasies of humiliating, flagellating, tying, gagging and torturing women. The large number of periodicals which cater to these tastes and the existence of firms which do a thriving business in the sale of whips, handcuffs and other such objects are testimonial to the prevalence of such deviations. There are, of course, also men who suffer from an inability to enjoy sexual intercourse unless similar abuses are first inflicted upon them.

The essence of the sadomasochistic perversion is a preoccupation with helplessness and control. The sadist cannot enjoy his partner unless he is convinced that she is incapable of hurting him in any way. She must be a person deprived of choice. Her pain and humiliation insure the sadist that he is in complete control of their relationship and that expression of sexual interest or love is safe. Many individuals who are preoccupied with sadistic fantasies were subjected to extreme sexual provocation by their own mothers, which left them feeling humiliated and helpless. Sadism both expresses the rage which was felt in that situation and enables the deviated person to find a sexual outlet in which the "tables are turned," an outlet in which he can feel perfectly safe. Masochism can be viewed as a reversal of this phenomenon, a temporary surrendering to the feeling of helplessness. At a certain point the feeling of being totally controlled and helpless can become intense and painful enough to be transformed into erotic stimulation.

From a legal standpoint masochistic behavior is of little concern. Sadism is important, however, when it results in the infliction of humiliation or pain upon an unwilling partner. We have previously noted that normal motivations may lead some adults to seek intercourse with cooperative, underage partners. The adult partner may then be convicted of statutory rape. Some mention should also be made of that behavior which involves forcing of sexual intercourse upon an unwilling partner. This kind of rape often has an intense sadistic component in which the issue of hurting and humiliating the woman can take on more meaning than sexual intercourse itself.

Forcible rape is defined as a crime in every stable society. Fear of rape underlies most of the fears and unrealistic concerns which govern our attitudes toward sex offenders. There is, of course, much more than sadism involved in rape. Many rapists are individuals who are plagued with doubts as to their own masculinity, and some are deeply troubled by latent homosexual conflicts. Quite frequently in our society latent homosexual fears are associated with paranoid attitudes toward the world and particularly toward females, who threaten the deviate's masculine image. The rapist tends to see all women as seductive, depriving and dangerous .He frequently vacillates between perceiving them as frightening giantesses or as lesser beings. In his attacks upon women he both conquers his fears and confirms their inferiority.

It must also be noted, of course, that in many crimes of rape in our society the question of the willingness of the victim is extremely difficult to discern. Given a culture in which most women feel that they always have the right to "say no" and in which many men feel that once a woman is willing to "pet" she is willing to have intercourse, many misunderstandings can result. It is sometimes difficult to know how much of a sadistic or deviant component is associated with those instances of rape in which the woman is well known to the offender and has encouraged his sexual intentions.

Other sadistic crimes occur in which the aim of the offender is not even superficially disguised as a desire for sexual intercourse. Sometimes the direct goal is the infliction of humiliation and pain. Sexual gratification and excitement through forcibly undressing a woman, humiliating her, tying her, beating her and even murdering her are not uncommon. Frequently these offenders are so dominated by aggressive and paranoid feelings toward the world that they are considered to be psychotic.

The voyeur is a person who seeks excitement and gratification primarily through observing the desired object in a state of undress. Voyeurs are almost always men. To a certain extent masculine interest in nudity is considered normal in our society. Both looking and exhibiting are sexually stimulating for all people and are an important part of the foreplay of normal sexual intercourse. The prevalance of interest in nudity is also evidenced by the great number of magazines which depend on provocative photographs to maintain circulation and by such entertainments as burlesque or strip-tease shows. For some individuals, however, looking at the nude sexual object becomes more important than sexual intimacy. These people may spend many hours of their lives prowling about seeking a favorable position from which they can view a female in a state of undress. Such activity is accompanied by great sexual stimulation and sometimes by orgasm.

One of the interesting aspects of voyeurism is that pleasurable stimulation is far greater when the observed object is unaware of the voyeur's presence. The voyeur must believe that the woman would be reluctant to exhibit herself under normal circumstances. Many voyeurs do not experience arousal when viewing a strip-tease show, probably because the woman is willingly showing herself. This implies that a sadistic element is also present in this disturbance. It may also mean that greater exictement is possible when there is a sense of danger, a sense of the forbidden and a possibility of being apprehended and shamed. The sadistic element sometimes becomes manifest. Although most statistical studies indicate that sex offenders do not progress from minor to major offenses,[28] and although most voyeurs are not seeking sexual intercourse, under certain circumstances the voyeur may attack his victim. It is also important to note that society is justified in taking the window peeper seriously. There is no way of knowing whether a prowler wishes to steal, to rape or to look.

In addition to the usual explanations of deviation, psychoanalytic explanations of voyeurism specifically relate this disturbance to maladaptive efforts to deal with castration anxiety.[29] The voyeur may have an unconscious wish to discover that the woman he is observing does have a penis and has not herself been "castrated." The repeated disappointment of the voyeur and his fantasy of being scorned and frustrated by the woman he observes have also been suggested as factors which explain the repetitive nature of his behavior.[30]

The exhibitionist gains excitement and gratification from showing his penis to the female. He usually confronts unsuspecting women or girls and exposes his flaccid or erect penis, sometimes masturbating at the same time. Rarely does he do anything more than attempt to invite the woman's attention. The exhibitionist may repeat this kind of behavior many, many times before he is eventually apprehended.

A common psychoanalytic explanation of exhibitionism is that it is a denial of castration anxiety.[31] The exhibitionist hopes that the women who observes his penis will be impressed and perhaps even fearful of his organ so that he can be reassured that it is a real and potent weapon. Sometimes the exhibitionist will show himself only to younger girls rather than mature women in the hope that the inexperienced child will be more impressed with his penis.

This mechanism may explain the adaptive or anxiety-relieving functions of exhibitionistic behavior, but it does not really help very much in understanding why it is so erotically stimulating. It is also likely that there is a sadistic component involved. The exhibitionist unconsciously may desire to frighten, hurt and impress the woman with his power.

Exhibitionism is at the same time the most easily performed deviant act and the most risky. The exhibitionistic act is almost always perpetrated in daylight. This means that the risks of apprehension are quite real. More than in any other form of deviation, accompanying feelings of danger and excitement are easily generated, and these feelings may contribute to the over-all erotic effect.

### The Relationship of Conscious Sexual Motivations to Other Crimes

There is a considerable psychoanalytic literature which attempts to relate many varieties of stealing and aggressive behavior to efforts to gratify unconscious sexual drives. Some of the psychological mechanisms involved in such crimes have already been described in earlier chapters. Sometimes, however, an apparently nonsexual criminal act may be closely related to conscious sexual motivations. Two kinds of relationships can be described. In some instances a criminal act results almost coincidentally from an effort to seek deviant sexual gratification. In other instances a criminal behavior which is not ordinarily thought of as having much to do with sex may be consciouisly erotic and gratifying.

Many crimes can accidentally arise once the offender begins his search for forbidden sexual gratification. The voyeur, for example, is frequently a trespasser. The fetishist may be driven to steal undergarments. The homosexual may become involved in a subculture which condones certain kinds of delinquent activities. He is also prone to blackmail and could indulge in criminal activity under duress.

Quite often the deviated person will be so ashamed of his disturbance that he will prefer to appear, both to himself and to others, as an ordinary criminal. He might then disguise his sexual activity by also acting in a manner that is more likely to be associated with "normal" offenders. Thus a window peeper sometimes steals from the home he has trespassed and might be arrested for theft, burglary of breaking and entering. The fetishist may steal a number of other items in order to cover up his interest in the fetishistic object. A much more serious type of crime related to sexual deviancy occurs when the person who is observed in a deviant act so fears public humiliation that he impulsively attacks his victim.

There are some offenders who receive conscious sexual stimulation by engaging in certain types of criminal activities. Occasionally burglars report an orgasmic experience upon simply entering a strange house. In this case the act of entering can symbolize a more direct but forbidden kind of sexual activity. One crime which is often accompanied by conscious sexual gratification is arson. Setting and putting out fires is a not uncommon masturbation fantasy of some disturbed persons. A sizable percentage of arsonists report great sexual arousal in starting a fire, watching a building burn or in watching firemen extinguish a blaze. Some psychoanalysts have speculated that this excitement is related to urethral eroticism, or a sexual pleasure associated with urination.[32] The arsonist is believed to be responding to an unconscious fantasy of obtaining gratification through urinating on the fire. While this is certainly a speculative, and perhaps to those who are skeptical of psychoanalytic theory a farfetched, observation, there does seem to be some correlation between fire-setting and urinary problems. Many individuals who are arsonists and who experience some sexual gratification through setting fires are also people who experienced enuresis in their earlier lives.

## The Living Out of the Sexual Impulse

We have emphasized earlier in this chapter that there are many more people who have deep inclinations toward deviant sexual behavior than there are people who indulge in such behavior. Every psychiatrist sees individuals in his noninstitutional practice who are as driven by deviant sexual wishes as sex offenders. Yet these people maintain an acceptable social adjustiment. The psychiatric criminologist must ask why some people indulge in forbidden sexual activities while others with an equal or greater deviant fantasy life restrain themselves. Another interesting question is why some sexual deviates indulge their aberration in a manner which regularly leads to their being apprehended while others manage to continue performing deviant acts for many years and retain their identifications as normal and law-abiding citizens.

The strength of the erotic drive probably has less to do with whether the deviated act takes place than is generally thought. It is unlikely that the homosexual's needs for genital gratification are any greater than the heterosexual's. Even the person with normal sexual motivations is constantly tempted to indulge himself in ways that could lead to law violation. Deviant motivation obviously is not a sufficient explanation of sexual misconduct. All the factors that we have invoked in earlier chapters must also play a crucial role in determining whether a sex crime is actually committed. Any factor which shifts the organism's equilibrium in the direction of weakening of control mechanisms is important. A sizable number of sex offenders are intoxicated at the time of their offense. Sex offenses also occur with greater frequency among people who have already had some experience with the criminal role. The occurrence of a sex crime is especially dependent upon immediate environmental circumstances. Most sex crimes cannot take place unless the desired object is present and behaves in a particular way.

Ultimately, the occurrence or nonoccurrence of a deviant sexual act must be understood in terms of the immediate adaptive value of that behavior to a given individual. For some people, repression or gratification in fantasy is sufficiently adaptive so long as other favorable circumstances are present. Sex offenders are most likely to commit a deviant act when oppression increases and alternative adaptations are unavailable. Thus many sexual offenses take place shortly after a rejection by a significant person, a vocational failure or a humiliation which leads to some lowering of status. The precrime milieu is frequently associated with depression and feelings of helplessness. Organismic needs which are far more complex than a simple need for erotic gratification eventually drive the deviated person to act upon impulses which have been present but repressed or restrained for years. In fact a sizable portion of sex offenders never carry their crimes to the point of orgasm. This is often true even after the victim has ceased to resist. It seems that the sex offender, like many other criminals, is more interested in an action which frees him from feelings of helplessness and hopelessness than in any specific gratification. Many offenders begin to experience a sense of power and wholeness from the moment that they realize that they are actually going to violate a social code.

While certain sex crimes are more readily detectable than others, it is also true that many sex criminals are far more adept at avoiding apprehension than others. This seems to be partly a matter of social class or intelligence. Many sex offenders, however, seem to go out of their way to be apprehended. Much like other maladapted criminals, these offenders seek to have dependency gratification imposed upon them. The sex offender is likely to be even less adept at using the psychopathic mechanism than the average criminal. His deviation in itself represents a failure to achieve a painless freedom from object relations, and his increased use of more overt masochistic mechanisms is often easy to detect. The high level of guilt associated with many sex offenses can lead to an almost conscious wish for punishment. Many sex offenders take surprisingly few precautions to avoid apprehension and others simply turn themselves in. The author has always been amazed at the ease with which many sex offenders confess. It is very difficult to prove the occurrence of most sex offenses, and often a little judicious lying would guarantee the offender's freedom. Guilt, shame and perhaps a wish for punishment seem to overcome his need to remain a free man.

# Chapter 14

# THE CHOICE OF CRIME

IN Chapter 6 we attempted to develop a conceptual framework or model which would help to intergrate the biological, psychological and sociological perspectives of crime. It must be understood, however, that we have not presented a comprehensive theory of crime. Our model does not clearly specify which variables must be present before crime is chosen ahead of other adaptations. It is also limited insofar as it deals only with stresses that can be defined as oppressive and insofar as it is primarily useful in understanding maladaptive or unreasonable criminal behavior. Before concluding the first section of this book let us briefly review some possible explanations of adaptational choice and comment upon the extent to which our model is useful in understanding more reasonable criminal behavior.

## The Problem of Adaptational Choice

The criminologist must explain why two people exposed to similar stresses and motivated by similar forces behave in different ways. This problem is not unique to criminology but is characteristic of all sciences of human behavior. The internist or psychosomaticist, for example, engages with the issue of why some people develop ulcers and other people develop hypertension, even when the genetic experiences and life situations of both groups may be quite similar. In studying mental illness, the psychiatrist grapples with the problem of why some of his patients may react to an oppressive stress by developing a phobia, while others will be incapacitated with obsessive or hysterical behavior. In the frame of reference we have developed here, we must ask why some people choose conformity, others activism, others mental illness and others crime.

Any criminological theorist would be unlikely to assume that the choice of crime is entirely determined by stressful circumstances in the immediate environment. It is difficult to imagine a stress which could be adapted to in only one way. Even the most criminogenic stress would not produce antisocial conduct in every man. A theory of crime must look beyond immediate stresses in the environment and also attempt to describe conditions or traits which predispose a person to criminal behavior. To talk about predisposition without also attempting to explain how that predisposition came about would be begging the question. The theorist must also provide an explanation of how predisposition develops.

The physician has traditionally sought answers to the question of predisposition by examining the constitutional differences of individuals. This approach does not mean that constitution is automatically equated with cause. It is simply a way of saying that many differential responses to stress are genetically determined. Some physical illnesses have a well-established genetic linkage, and many others are highly correlated with constitutional features. The psychosomaticist often leans toward constitution to explain why people exposed to similar stresses develop different diseases or why people exposed to different stresses develop the same disease. Psychiatrists, too, have attempted to invoke constitution as an explanation of symptom choice. It has often been assumed, for example, that the tendency to develop schizophrenia is inherited and that the schizophrenic is biochemically and physiologically different from the normal. Similar kinds of speculations have been made with regard to choice of neurotic symptoms. It is not surprising, therefore, that behavioral scientists have also looked to constitutional factors as possible determinants of criminal deviations in social behavior.

In an earlier chapter we reviewed some of the constitutional and hereditary theories of crime and considered their deficiences. Although such theories have been looked upon with skepticism, it must be noted that minor constitutional differences could play a crucial role in determining behavior choice. It is not too difficult to envision how the child who is born with an exceptional need for motoric activity could encounter greater difficulty in maintaining a conforming adaptation. Other minor types of neurological defects could favor criminality by interfering with ability to learn from experience. It is also possible that congenital variations in the structure of certain parts of the brain, such as the rhinencephalon or thalamus, could make some people more susceptible to intense rage or anger reactions.

Eysenck has proposed a unique and interesting constitutional theory of crime, which emphasizes inborn deficiencies in learning abilities.[1] He argues that the criminal or psychopath is likely to be a person who responds poorly to conditioning. Such a theory has great appeal since many aspects of conditioning are readily testable and can be studied in the laboratory. It must be noted, however, that poor conditioning ability could also interfere with the learning of those techniques that are essential to criminality. If we accept any of the sociological propositions which argue that criminality is a learned behavior, we also have to assume that the person who conditioned poorly would have as much difficulty in learning crime as in learning anything else. Any constitutional theory is likely to be heavily contaminated with value judgments, which begin with the notion that criminality is some sort of defect and is always "bad."

Both psychoanalysis and learning theory attempt to explain predisposition in terms of the specific sensitizing experiences which an individual encounters throughout his life (although it must be admitted that the psychoanalyst frequently falls back upon constitutional theories). For the psychoanalyst, predisposition is primarily determined by the kinds of relationships the child develops with his parents. It is assumed that the child comes into the world with an amorphous mass of drive tendencies and that these are molded into potentialities by the attitudes and experiences he encounters in the first few years of life. Thus psychoanalysts have attempted to isolate and study specific kinds of parent-child relationships which would predispose the child to criminal behavior.[2, 3, 4]

The learning theorists present a less complicated model. They visualize criminal behaviors as habit tendencies and believe that predisposition develops as a response to the total spectrum of training and experiences which the person encounters with many different people throughout all his life. One learning-theory approach to crime is concerned with aggressive responses to frustration.[5, 6] The criminally inclined person is believed to have been exposed to learning experiences which encourage him to react more impulsively to frustration and to see more frustration in his environment than is actually present. Another kind of learning theory, differential association, is less concerned with the mechanisms by which certain behaviors are learned but rather seeks to understand criminality in terms of the frequency, duration, priority and intensity of exposure to criminal associations.[7]

Still another approach which relates crime to learned experience is that provided by role theory. Some sociologists argue that at least some criminal behavior, that of juvenile delinquents, is intimately related to the roles which are learned in the delinquent subculture. According to these writers, such roles are not always chosen but are sometimes forced upon people.

Once a person finds himself in circumstances in which a certain kind of behavior is called for, he has little choice but to perform within that role.[8]

Most theories of crime which deal with predisposition assume the presence of unfavorable circumstances of constitution, geography, race or social class. These are measurable variables which can be defined with some consistency. Moving away from the question of predisposition, we find that the environmental circumstances which are present at the moment of a crime are equally important determinants but are much more difficult to describe or measure. It is almost impossible to examine critically the total network of interpersonal relations and circumstances which characterize the precrime milieu. Yet even the most predisposed person will not commit a crime unless certain circumstances are present.

Specific and highly variable situational elements are often necessary causes of crime.[9, 10, 11] This is particularly true of crimes against persons. The murderer cannot kill unless there is a suitable victim. The circumstances under which his victim may goad him to the point of assault may be so special as to have precluded prediction. Sex crimes are more often than not unplanned. Similar considerations are often relevant to crimes against property.

A truly comprehensive theory of crime must consider both predisposition and immediate criminogenic circumstances. Perhaps the only means of relating these two elements would be to study what actually goes on in the mind of the criminal before and during the time he is planning or committing a crime. The author's attempt to consider the phenomenological world of the criminal is a crude beginning in this direction. Viewing the criminal as a person who seeks to free himself from painful feelings of helplessness sheds some light on the maladaptive or unreasonable aspects of crime. Hopefully, other students of behavior may be able to present more refined and more useful descriptions of the criminal's perception of his world. Studies of the phenomenological world of the criminal may ultimately have great value in helping the criminologist formulate explanations as to why some people choose criminality rather than other adaptations. In the meantime, this approach has immediate value to those who wish to understand and work with the offender.

## The Problem of "Reasonable" or "Normal" Criminal Behavior

Our model suggests that crime develops as a response to unusual stress, but obviously some criminal behavior occurs even where there is little or no oppression. Greed, lust and aggression may be natural tendencies of man. It is erroneous to assume that every offender must experience unusual stress before he will violate the law. In some situations crime could be the most advantageous and reasonable adaptation the offender could seek. It is possible, therefore, that crime could be chosen even where other adaptations are available simply because the criminal knows that his act provides maximum gain for minimal expenditure of energy. If the criminal also has some assurance that he will not be punished and if he believes that he can deal with his conscience, the adaptive value of crime becomes even greater. Crime obviously does pay well for some. It is difficult to argue that the white-collar criminal who defrauds his government or his firm with impunity is behaving in an unreasonable manner. His actions might be deplorable on moral grounds, but if evaluated in terms of the success goals of our society, he would be looked upon as a rational man.

Yet it is tempting to speculate about the personality of the "normal criminal." To what extent might he be responding to stresses which are unusual or different from those experienced by his more law-abiding contemporary? Unfortunately, the study of rational crime is usually based on the assumption that profit or status motives are the only driving forces behind criminal behavior. Nobody really knows what goes on in the mind of the white-collar criminal or the syndicate racketeer. We do not know if either of these individuals is driven by unconscious motivations, irrational fears of inadequacy or an oppressive family situation. Nobody has examined enough syndicate murderers to determine whether their behavior is an effort to do a business-like job or whether there is, indeed, some abnormal sadistic component to their personalities. It is probable that if we studied any of these groups intensively we would discover that some of their members were reacting to misperceived oppression or were motivated by tendencies which if publicly acknowledged would be seen as bizarre and unreasonable. Nevertheless, at this moment such speculations cannot be supported, and we must acknowledge that there are probably many criminals who by any criteria of social judgment should be called normal or rational.

In attempting to relate what has been said about unreasonable criminal behavior to more "normal" criminal behavior, the following two propositions would seem to be relevant. (1) The more the offender's behavior is a response to severe oppressive stress, the more unreasonable is his criminality likely to be. (2) The more indirect or unrealistic the oppression to which the offender is responding, the more unreasonable will his criminality be.

The first proposition is based upon the observation that the person who reacts to oppression by performing a criminal act is using such behavior to resolve a conflict. He is involved in a struggle, a struggle which has become more meaningful to him than anything else. Where one is engaged in struggles for control or for survival, unreasonable criminal actions will occur simply because they help to relieve an uncomfortable state of psychological tension. Success or status goals may become secondary to the organism's need to find the most economical route to a state of equilibrium.

Proposition 2 implies that the more unrealistic or indirect the oppression a person is responding to, the less likely is he to be concerned with the utility of his criminal behavior. If one is attempting to change a situation which he cannot define, or which may not actually exist, there are few effective ways in which he can accomplish this task. His efforts are likely to be inappropriate and ineffective. Although his criminal behavior may enable him to survive with comfort, it will rarely advance or sustain him in those roles which his society has judged to be desirable or praiseworthy.

We cannot go beyond these general statements in any discussion which includes all classes of criminals. All crime is adaptive, but some criminal acts are quite reasonable and useful adaptations. There is nevertheless great social usefulness in trying to define the unreasonable qualities in any criminal act. The more unreasonable the criminal's behavior, the greater is the likelihood that he will inflict harm on himself and others. An unreasonable man is a puzzling and unpredictable man. Since he is more concerned with personalized needs for survival than with generally accepted success goals, he is unlikely to respond to techniques of punishment or treatment that would be suitable for more rational men.

In the naïve assumption that most law violators are rational men, we have developed a system of correctional justice which fails to rehabilitate the majority of criminals. Society's response to criminal acts is almost as unreasonable as some of the acts themselves. Our methods of punishment are crude, sometimes barbarous; our methods of treatment are primitive. In the second part of this book I will examine current practices in the administration of correctional justices in the United States. Much of the picture will be discouraging and depressing. Psychiatric skills in particular have been neglected or misused. The psychiatrist currently is able to make some substantial contributions to correctional justice, but a truly humanistic and rational criminology still awaits drastic changes in our attitudes and institutions.

# PART II

## PSYCHIATRY AND THE PROTOCOL OF REVENGE

## Chapter 15

# THE PSYCHIATRIST AND THE LEGAL PROCESS*

UNLIKE most other medical specialists, the psychiatrist has not restricted himself to the treatment of those who seek his services but has sustained a deep involvement in the legal and social problems of controlling disturbed people. We have noted that one of the major functions of the nineteenth-century psychiatrist was to assist judicial authorities in making decisions as to who was to be punished and who was to be treated as a mental patient. Yet psychiatry's commitment to assist in the control of those who represent a potential danger to society has an even longer tradition. Historically, the psychiatrist did not approach his patients with great confidence in his curative powers. His initial purpose was to classify, isolate and control disturbed people. The "alienist" was an agent of social control, not a healer. Although there were some noteworthy exceptions, psychiatry as a therapeutic specialty did not emerge until Sigmund Freud presented us with psychoanalytic insights which created a belief in the treatability of the mentally ill.

Psychiatry's interest in the law and its involvement in problems of social control are intimately related insofar as legal decisions often determine the direction of control of deviant behavior. For better or worse, psychiatric criminology begins in the courtroom with the problem of separating the "insane" criminal from the "normal" criminal. Up to this point the author has repeatedly stressed that psychiatric involvement in the issue of criminal responsibility is neither socially useful nor, as presently conducted, rational.

* A slightly different version of this chapter was published in the *Wisconsin Law Review*, 1966, pp. 379–401, under the title "A Critique of Current Psychiatric Roles in the Legal Process."

As a prelude to examining the psychiatrist's more useful activities in the control and treatment of criminal behavior, however, we must first describe in some detail the role of the psychiatrist in the criminal trial.

So much has been written about the relationship of psychiatry to the problems of criminal responsibility that it would be presumptuous to offer a comprehensive summary in one brief chapter. Instead, let us attempt to describe a few of the basic principles and theoretical orientations which underlie psychiatric involvement in the criminal trial and present a critical view of current practices.

## Punishment and Responsibility

To understand the role of psychiatry in criminal court proceedings, we must first realize that psychiatric involvement is intimately linked to the question of punishment. If our society did not wish to punish those who have transgressed against it, there would be less urgency for the psychiatrist to enter the courtroom. It is not essential that we review the historical origins of punishment or attempt to document the extent to which punitive measures are directed against the criminal in American society. At this point we are speaking of punishment for punishment's sake alone and not including that punishment which must coexist with any effort at social control. Control implies deprivation of liberty, and this is certainly a kind of punishment for most people. The intention of the judicial agency which invokes social control, however, is more likely to be protective than punitive.

Punishment in America is severe. Our prison sentences are longer than those imposed in most of the other countries. Our correctional techniques are relatively harsh. And, most discouragingly, we probably execute more people for nontreasonous behavior than any other nation in the world.

There are three reasons why society might choose to punish its offenders. It is sometimes assumed that punishment helps to rehabilitate the offender. Penitence is believed to be good for people. It hopefully cleanses them of their sins and makes them recognize and cling to "good" instead of "evil." A second reason for punishment is retribution. The society which has been attacked has some need to retaliate. Vengeance is a powerful motivation, and the psychological need of society to punish its criminals is strong. A third reason for punishing criminals is the belief that punishment has a deterrent value. It is hoped that the person who is disciplined will not be inclined to commit a similar crime. It is also believed that he will serve as an example to the rest of the population, who will be encouraged to resist temptation. If the commission of a criminal act is always associated with a threat of punishment, we assume that most rational people would be less inclined to behave in an antisocial manner.

In spite of the many questions that could be raised as to the utilitarian or moral value of punitive attitudes toward the criminal, punishment for antisocial behavior has been with us since the dawn of history, is especially characteristic of American criminology and very likely will be with us for many generations to come. Punishment of offenders in our society is, however, flexible. If society would simply agree to punish any person who committed an antisocial act irrespective of his intent, his age, his mental status or his socioeconomic class, there would be less need for psychiatric testimony. But this obviously cannot be. A democratic society is guided by the principle that "Our collective conscience does not allow punishment where it cannot impose blame."[1] As Western society has moved to temper cruelty or indiscriminate punishment, humanitarian sentiments have become inextricably interwoven with punitive goals. Since the nineteenth century, for example, few civilized nations have punished children under the age of seven. People who commit crimes under duress or under reasonable apprehension of immediate danger of death or grievous bodily harm (self-defense) are not likely to be punished harshly. Similarly, the person who accidentally injures another (such as in an auto wreck) is not likely to be subjected to stern measures. The guiding principle in determining who should be punished has been that those who of their own free will and with evil intent (sometimes called *mens rea*) commit acts which violate the law shall be criminally responsible for such acts.[2] Presumably, the child under seven or the person who accidentally violates the law or violates the law under duress does not have criminal intent.

As early as the seventeenth century, English jurists such as Coke and Hale proposed that mental illness could totally or partially preclude the possibility of an individual having felonious intent.[3] Over the past three centuries jurists and psychiatrists have continued to examine the proper punishability of a criminal offender who is adjudged to be mentally ill. The extent to which mental illness has been thought to preclude criminal intent has been greatest at those times when humanistic principles have been in ascendancy. It is tempting and not too difficult to convince ourselves that a person who is intoxicated or organically confused cannot have evil intent when he commits a criminal act. If we can believe that a mentally ill person is under duress, is compelled to commit a criminal act or cannot help himself, we are less inclined to punish him.

Another way of looking upon our legal codes is to note that punishability is equated with the criminals responsibility for his actions. This implies a highly restrictive and legalistic definition of responsibility. As applied to the (allegedly) mentally ill offender, it directs the psychiatrist toward the specific task of examining the emotional status of that person and assisting the court in determining whether or not he can be held responsible for his actions. If the offender is judged to have been too emotionally disturbed at the time of the crime to have possessed evil intent (or sometimes if the evil intent is based on a presumption of severe mental illness), he is not responsible and not punishable. Without commenting—for the moment—on the social practicability of this arrangement, let us examine some positions that have taken on the issue of criminal responsibility and ask, "Does the psychiatrist possess any special knowledge or skills which enable him to judge an individual's responsibility for a given act?"

The extent to which a man can be considered responsible for his behavior is a broad philosophical question which transcends legalistic considerations. If a person is assumed to be morally, personally, religiously or legally responsible for his behavior, it must be assumed that he has some freedom of choice. Whether a man's behavior is completely determined by hereditary and environmental circumstances beyond his control or whether he actually possesses "choice" or "free will" is a question which has preoccupied theologians, philosophers and other scholars for centuries. There is clearly much variation between scientific and legalistic or theological viewpoints. The behavioral scientist most often is a "hard" determinist. He believes that all behavior is determined by an interaction of hereditary traits with uncontrollable environmental experiences.[4] If he were to be consistent, he might argue that ultimately no person is responsible for his behavior.

Yet it is difficult to imagine the existence of a society which did not hold its citizens responsible for their actions. By simply creating a legal code, society implies that a man must be held accountable for his actions. All theology teaches us that man has choice. Indeed, it seems impossible for man to survive without some belief in his capacity to exercise free will. The "hard" determinist may argue that social change and the fullest kind of human development could take place in a society which denied the existence of free will, but it is nevertheless important that man not totally abandon his belief in free will.[5]

For most of us the absence of free will implies a degraded or subhuman condition. If we argue that the child under seven, the lunatic and the imbecile cannot be held responsible for their behavior, we also seem to be saying that they cannot be looked upon as real people. It is of interest to note that even those individuals who are defined as having minor forms of mental illness (such as neurotics who claim to be unable to help themselves) are usually looked down upon by the rest of society when they imply that they are not responsible for their behavior. To communicate that one does not have choice (in the absence of measurable interfering factors such as a clearly defined physical illness) admits weakness and requires an abdication of one's status as a first-class citizen.

We have argued that it is society's need to punish which brings psychiatry face to face with the philosophical question of man's responsibility and his capacity to exercise free will. But where the death penalty is involved, the criminal's life may depend upon the psychiatrist's assessment of his responsibility. Nevertheless, any definitive statement which the psychiatrist offers as to the responsibility of the offender must have a certain inconsistency. If he argues that a man is responsible for his behavior, he begins to compromise certain tenets of scientific determinism. If he argues that a man is not responsible, he speaks against ethical codes and traditions which seem to have always been necessary to preserve a smoothly functioning society. The existence of this dilemma is too frequently ignored. Many psychiatrists have convinced themselves that psychiatric examinations and certain psychiatric concepts help to clarify decisions as to man's responsibility. Western society, unfortunately, encourages the psychiatrist to participate in such decisions by setting up legal rules which have been proposed to test the degree of man's responsibility in terms of his mental status.

## Responsibility and Mental Illness

Perhaps the earliest measure which psychiatrists utilized to assess responsibility was the degree of unreasonableness of the offender's behavior. A criminal act which seems totally alien to any goal that a rational man would pursue has traditionally been looked upon as a sign of illness. Both psychiatry and the culture as a whole are often willing to assume that the unreasonable man is a sick man and that a sick man is not responsible for his actions. Depending upon prevailing concepts of mental illness, a characterization of unreasonableness as sickness has often led to an assumption that unreasonable behavior is determined by external and mysterious agents. In eras when mental illness was approached from a more theological standpoint efforts were made to place the responsibility for sick behavior onto external "devils" such as incubi or succubi.[6] With the advent of Kraepelinian psychiatry, responsibility for behavior was placed upon physical disease. Mental illness was thought of as being caused by hereditary or acquired organic impairment. It was the structural defect that was held responsible for such an individual's unreasonable behavior.[7] Even today unreasonable behavior is often blandly described as mental illness, and that illness is characterized as a separate and pernicious external agent.[8,9] We have repeatedly noted that such a demonological concept of mental illness has never been supported by scientific data and is antithetical to an adaptational or homeostatic viewpoint.

With the growth of psychoanalytic knowledge many psychiatrists have sought answers to the degree of man's responsibility in terms of the unconscious component in human behavior. They argue that if an individual behaves in an unreasonable manner because of motivations that are out of his awareness he cannot really help himself and should not be held responsible for his actions. Thus some psychoanalytic observers have argued that free will exists only to the extent that a person is aware of his motivations. According to this viewpoint, choice is available in inverse proportion to the amount of behavior or thinking which is dominated by unconscious processes.[10, 11, 12]

While the author is deeply impressed with the role of the unconscious in determining behavior, he can see little value in utilizing this concept to clarify the problem of responsibility or free will. First of all, the degree to which motivation is unconscious is always relative. We have devised no means of measuring the degree to which a person is aware of his own motivations and must admit that every act carries with it a mixture of conscious and unconscious elements. We are therefore on highly tenuous grounds when we use this criterion to say that a man is responsible for one of his acts but not for another. Furthermore, the belief that out-of-awareness forces should mitigate responsibility subtly personifies the unconscious and relegates it to the role of a dangerous and unpredictable external agent. Used in this sense, it is as though the unconscious were a lurking shadow hidden somewhere in the soul of each individual, waiting only for the opportunity to commit some heinous act. This kind of thinking might lead to regrettable statements such as "It was not I who committed this offensive act but my unconscious mind." Such a notion assumes that a person's unconscious motivations are not a part of the individual in the same sense as his conscious motivations. It is in effect a denial of the existence of the person as an integrated unit.

Another way of looking at the psychoanalytic viewpoint is that an individual should not be held responsible for his actions if he is responding to internalized conflicts or misperceived oppression. While this at first glance appears to be a humanitarian notion, it could in practice grossly discriminate against the offender who is responding to more readily observable stress. Actually, the person whose criminal behavior is primarily engendered by poverty or persecution may be motivated by forces which are just as powerful and unrelenting as those which motivate the emotionally disturbed offender. Crime may be necessary for survival in either case. If the psychiatrist can be persuaded to argue than an offender should not be held responsible for behavior which is largely determined by unconscious factors, then perhaps the sociologist should be required to argue that poverty, discrimination and delinquent associations would also make the offender nonresponsible. Either approach would be compatible with a deterministic viewpoint.

Paradoxically, the psychiatrist who would excuse the criminal from responsibility for his unconscious motivations cannot allow the same luxury to those patients he hopes to treat. Psychotherapy requires the patient to adhere to a code of responsibility. Responsibility in this sense may be divorced from the issue of punishment and can be thought of more accurately as personal accountability. The psychiatrist expects each of his patients to be willing to account for his behavior, to try to explain why he acts in a given way, to accept the praise of others when he acts favorably and to accept the censure or disapproval of others when he is offensive. Although the patient is sometimes reassured by his therapist that he cannot help himself, he is more frequently told that his eventual cure or rehabilitation lies within himself. Psychiatrists regularly remind their patients that getting well is dependent upon how determined they are to change, how willing they are to work on their problems or, ultimately, how much responsibility they assume for their own behavior.

The psychoanalytic movement is dominated by the values of individualism, freedom and maturity. It attempts to do away with the vision of gargantuan forces moving man and attempts to teach the patient that he is capable of conrolling his behavior. No psychoanalyst would allow a patient to disavow responsibility for an aggressive or erotic thought or act. Even in a classical psychoanalytic situation the patient is taught that his unconsious wishes are his own productions and that they are not the visitations of an external devil.

Freud at one time stated:

> Obviously one must hold oneself responsible for the evil impulses of one's dreams. What else is one to do with them? Unless the content of the dream (rightly understood) is inspired by alien spirits it is a part of my own being. If I seek to classify the impulses that are present in me according to social standards into good and bad I must assume responsibility for both sorts; and

if in defense I say that what is unknown, unconscious and repressed in me is not my "ego" then I shall not be basing my position upon psychoanalysis.[13]

The psychoanalytic movement is not alone in holding to such beliefs. Existential schools of therapy are similarly concerned with the needs of the patient to recognize and "be at one" with his feelings and impulses.[14, 15] Progress is measured by such therapists in terms of their patients' movement toward fully knowing, accepting and taking responsibility for their thoughts and actions. This applies to the most disturbed patients, those labeled as psychotic, as well as to those who are better integrated.

When psychiatrists enter the courtroom and testify that certain mentally ill people are not responsible for their behavior, they speak against philosophies which many of them feel are essential to therapeutic effectiveness. This inconsistency or "effort to have it both ways" is confusing and illogical.

## Courtroom Tests of Responsibility

A familiarity with the dynamics of unreasonable behavior or of the unconscious does not endow the psychiatrist with any special insights into the determinism-vs.-free-will controversy. In fact, the psychiatrist's statements in court are often inconsistent with his practice in the consultation room or hospital. Unfortunately, the rules by which he is allowed to present his information to the court confuse the whole issue even further.

In most jurisdictions the rule by which a mentally ill person is adjudged legally responsible or not responsible is derived from nineteenth-century English law. This rule, enunciated in the M'Naghton case over one hundred years ago, states that "To establish a defense on the ground of insanity it must be clearly proved that at the time of committing of the act, the party accused was laboring under such a defect of reason, from disease of the mind, as not to know the nature and quality of the act he was doing; or if he did know it that he did not know he was doing what was wrong."[16] The psychiatrist who testifies in a case in which the plea of insanity has been raised is asked to give his opinion as to whether at the time of the crime the offender knew the nature and quality of the act and knew that it was wrong. There are minor variations of this so-called "right or wrong" test in various jurisdictions, but for the most part if the patient is presumed to know the nature and quality of his act and recognizes its wrongness, he is presumed to be responsible. If the psychiatrist answers these questions negatively, there is a possibility that the offender will not be held responsible for his behavior. Although the final decision is made by a judge or jury, the psychiatrist who responds to the M'Naghton test (whether he is the witness of the defendant or the state) is really asked to make a judgment as to the responsibility and hence the guilt or innocence of the offender.

The M'Naghton rule has been a subject of almost endless controversy.[17, 18, 19, 20, 21] Since it deals with the question of intent, it has a great deal of appeal to attorneys. It is, however, so alien to current concepts of human behavior that it has been vigorously attacked by psychiatrists. An obvious difficulty with the M'Naghton rule is that practically everyone, regardless of the degree of his criminal disturbance, knows the nature and quality and rightness or wrongness of what he is doing. Stated differently, almost any offender knows what he is doing when he commits a criminal act, and although he may feel that he is without choice, he also knows that his fellow citizens will be critical of his actions. Efforts have been made to extend the limits of meaning of the word "know" so that emotional as well as intellectual aspects of behavior can be introduced into the psychiatrist's testimony.* Psychiatrists, however, have rightly pointed out that it is almost impossible for them to testify honestly under this rule. Bernard Diamond has stated:

> Whenever a psychiatrist is called to testify upon the M'Naghton rule of a knowledge of right and wrong as to the sanity or insanity of the defendant, the psychiatrist must either renounce his own values with all their medical humanistic implications, thereby becoming a puppet doctor used by the law to further the punitive and vengeful goals demanded by our society; or he must commit perjury if he accepts the literal definition of the M'Naghton rule. If he tells the truth—stating on the witness stand that just about every defendant no matter how mentally ill, no mater how far advanced his psychosis, knows the difference between right and wrong in the literal sense of the phrase—he becomes an expediter to the gallows or gas chamber.[22]

In 1954 a different rule was enunciated by Judge Bazelon, Chief Justice of the United States Court of Appeals in the District of Columbia. In ruling on the case of Monte Durham, the Court of Appeals said:

> The rule we now hold is simply that an accused is not criminally responsible if his unlawful act was the product of mental disease or mental defect. We use "disease" in the sense of a condition which is considered capable of improving or deteriorating. We use "defect" in the sense of a condition which is not considered capable of either improving or deteriorating and which may be congenital or the result of injury or the residual effect of a physical or mental disease.[23]

* Efforts to tamper with the meaning of the word "know" bring us deeper and deeper into the realm of arbitrariness. The author has made it a practice to question inmates at a hospital for the criminally insane as to the rightness or wrongness of their criminal acts. A few (as do many criminals) will insist that their act was justified, but even the most deluded are able to verbalize that they have always known that their act was illegal and would lead to punishment.

The Durham ruling is quite similar to that which has been applied in New Hampshire since 1869. Many psychiatrists at first welcomed this ruling as a forward movement in the enlightened treatment of the criminal. It was believed that the Durham rule would simplify psychiatric testimony and would allow for rational utilization of psychiatric knowledge. There has, however, been much disillusionment. Initially, the Durham rule was criticized mainly by attorneys, [24, 25] but more recently psychiatrists as well have become skeptical of its value.[26, 27] In spite of many efforts to extend it to other jurisdictions, its usage has been almost entirely confined to the District of Columbia.

Among the major criticisms directed against the Durham rule have been these:

Durham is not concerned with the issue of *mens rea* or intent. It replaces a rule that can be understood and debated by laymen with a more nefarious and professionalized concept. As such it may present the psychiatrist with too much power to decide who is going to be punished or not punished.[28]

Durham reifies mental illness as a distinct condition and seems to assume that it can be readily defined. If the psychiatrist testifies that a crime is a product of mental illness, this implies that mental illness is in itself a distinct force which can exert a direct influence upon the organism. Such a notion is not consistent with current concepts of mental illness.[29]

There is a danger of circularity in the Durham rule. If an offender is defined as mentally ill, this designation is often based upon an observation of his unreasonable behavior during the crime. Both crime and mental illness are forms of adaptation, if the same behavior is used to diagnose both conditions and if we then argue that one condition causes the other, we are in a logically absurd position.

Although the Durham decision has been hailed as a humanitarian achievement, it also makes a very sharp distinction between those criminals who are mentally ill and those who are not. It expresses little or no concern for the disturbed offender who may not be seen as mentally ill. In a sense it condones punishment of the ordinary offender and may distract from a humanitarian concern for the overwhelming majority of offenders.[30]

The Durham decision opens the possibility of keeping people in mental hospitals for long periods of time even though they have not demonstrated evidence of social dangerousness or social violence. Some legal experts have argued that the Durham decision is so concerned with the interests of psychiatry that it neglects the humanitarian needs of offenders and can encourage serious abridgements of civil liberties.[31, 32]

There are a number of other rules for determining criminal responsibility which have had sporadic usage or have been recommended by interested agencies.[33] We will merely list some of these and note that all rules for determining responsibility can be subjected to the same criticisms that have been leveled against either M'Naghton or Durham.

Irresistible impulse is sometimes added to M'Naghton as a test of responsibility. In the federal statement a defendant is not criminally responsible if "his reasoning powers were so far dethroned by his diseased mental condition as to deprive him of the will power to resist the insane impulse to perpetrate the deed, though knowing it to be wrong."

Chief Judge Biggs of the Third Circuit Court of Appeals of the United States wrote a decision in the Currens case holding that to be considered not responsible "the jury must be satisfied that at the time of committing the prohibited act the defendant as a result of mental disease or defect lacked substantial capacity to conform his conduct to the requirements of the law which he is alleged to have violated."

The American Law Institute in drafting a penal code has proposed the following statutes with regard to determining criminal responsibility:

> 1) A person is not responsible for criminal conduct if at the time of such conduct as a result of mental disease or defect he lacked substantial capacity either to appreciate the criminality (wrongfulness) of his conduct or to conform to the requirements of the law.
>
> 2) As used in this article the terms mental disease or defect do not include an abnormality manifested only by repeated criminal or otherwise antisocial conduct.

Some have advocated the use of a concept of "diminished responsibility," and this thinking was partially accepted in the Gorshen decision in California.

We have criticized the theoretical basis of psychiatric testimony and have emphasized the deficiencies of any legal test of criminal responsibility. It must also be noted that many practical inconsistencies and injustices can arise through psychiatric involvement in the courtroom. Specifically, we wish to emphasize three points: (1) For any form of criminal justice to be effective it must be consistently applied to all men regardless of race, social or economic status. We will note that the issue of criminal responsibility is raised with unusual selectivity. (2) Implied in any legal determination of the criminal's responsibility is an assumption that to find a man not guilty by reason of insanity and to send him to a state hospital is a merciful and humane act. In practice this is a highly questionable assumption. (3) Effective utilization of the plea of criminal insanity implies that psychiatrists will come to eventual agreement on a workable definition of terms such as psychosis or mental illness. The writer contends that this is unlikely. Psychiatric studies of the offender provide useful insights which help us to understand his behavior but rarely reach agreement as to the precise nature of the illness involved. The meaning of most psychiatric terms is constantly shifting, and consensus as to definitions is quite rare.

### Inconsistencies in Raising the Insanity Plea

The use of psychiatric testimony to determine criminal responsibility is greatest in those states which have capital punishment. It should be noted, however, that not every emotionally disturbed offender who is on trial for his life uses this defense. Many factors other than the degree of emotional disturbance enter into the introduction of the insanity plea. Much depends on the circumstances of the crime, the availability of forensic psychiatrists, the laws of the state, the attitude of the community and the offender's socioeconomic class. In many jurisdictions, for example, it would be quite unlikely that an uneducated Negro offender would plead insanity, and even more unlikely that he would be found not guilty by reason of insanity.

The guilt or innocence of an emotionally disturbed offender may become highly dependent upon the skills of the defendant's psychiatrist. The psychiatrist's manner of presentation, his personality and his credentials may have as much influence upon the jury as his scientific data. In this sense having a good psychiatrist becomes quite similar to having a good defense attorney. Unfortunately, good psychiatrists like good attorneys cost money. In many jurisdictions it is extremely difficult for a poor person to find competent psychiatric assistance.

It is only fair to note also that some jurisdictions do provide psychiatric assistance for the offender who wishes to plead insanity. In some states an impartial panel of psychiatrists may provide testimony as to the defendant's sanity. The state of Massachusetts goes even further, and under the Brigg's law anyone charged with a capital offense and most felons are automatically examined to determine their sanity.

Even in states which do not have a death penalty the plea of not guilty by reason of insanity is not invoked in a consistent manner. In the author's home state of Wisconsin there are at the present time eleven inmates confined to the state hospital for the criminally insane who have been found not guilty by reason of insanity. Of this number eight are murderers. There are probably no more than ten to twenty individuals who are currently free (most of whom have spent many years in a mental hospital) who have been acquitted by reason of insanity. This is a very small group when compared with the total number of offenders in the state, and is made up mainly of individuals who have murdered or committed other violent crimes. What is important to note here is that the plea of insanity is practically never raised unless there has been violence. If some murderers are not responsible for their behavior, then it is difficult to understand why there are not forgers, burglars, car thieves and sex offenders who are similarly nonresponsible. The explanation must be that the plea of insanity is raised only when there is a possibility of a long prison sentence.

Several years ago the author and a colleague, Dr. Richard Thurrell, studied a group of offenders who were at that time committed to the Wisconsin State Hospital for the Criminally Insane after having been transferred from the Wisconsin State Prison. The issue of insanity had *never* been raised during the trials of these offenders, but they had nevertheless been too emotionally disturbed to remain in a prison. At the time of the study there were sixty such inmates living at the state hospital. Offhand, it might be assumed that these were relatively normal men who broke down under the stress of incarceration. However, this was not the case. Over half of the total number studied had a history of having spent time in a mental hospital before the commission of a criminal act. An additional 20 percent, although not having a history of previous hospitalization, had demonstrated such peculiar behavior that the issue of insanity had been raised in the probation officer's presentence report. A number of these men had to be transferred to the state hospital almost immediately after their arrival at the prison.

It must be repeated that the emotional state of these men was never raised as a legal issue. Although even the most cursory examination would have revealed the presence of what most psychiatrists would call mental illness, nobody even wondered if these men were responsible for their acts. Since Wisconsin is an enlightened state which has an excellent tradition of social welfare, it is difficult to rationalize the cavalier disposition of these cases. Obviously, factors other than the degree of emotional disturbance preceding the criminal act must operate in the selection of those who plead insanity. It seems that this selection is just as likely to be based upon factors such as the economic status of the offender, the type of crime he commits, his race, the attitude of local psychiatrists, the type of negotiated plea which is made with the district attorney or the whim of the community.

If it were argued that although these men were defined as criminals they eventually ended up in the appropriate institution anyway, it would be difficult to disagree. The point is that if only a few offenders are found nonresponsible, and if other disturbed offenders must find a circuitous route to the hospital, there is reason to be skeptical as to the value of psychiatry's humanitarian contribution in the courtroom. Psychiatrists should be troubled by the possibility that the majority of emotionally disturbed offenders are never given an opportunity to plead insanity. The noble victories for humanism claimed when an occasional offender is found not guilty by reason of insanity pale in comparison to the grim indifference which is accorded to most offenders.

At the conclusion of a recent widely publicized trial in the state of Wisconsin[34] some of the author's colleagues were jubilant over what they perceived to be a victory for the forces of social welfare and righteousness. In this case a man had been found not guilty of the crime of murder by reason of insanity, and he was committed to the state hospital for the criminally insane. In spite of the enthusiasm which so many psychiatrists show for this kind of decision, there is reason to be skeptical of its humanitarian value. This particular offender had already spent several years at the hospital for the criminally insane, having been legally confined until he had shown sufficient psychological improvement to be legally competent to stand trial. He was returning to an institution where he would continue to be deprived of freedom.

It is difficult to see what advantages are offered to the man who is committed to a hospital for the criminally insane. In the state of Wisconsin (which has one of the best of such hospitals), he is still sent to a heavy-security institution. His cell is located behind several formidable locked doors, and he is rarely allowed to leave the hospital grounds. Opportunities for receiving help are limited because the institution is chronically understaffed. At the time of the trial and commitment of the particular case we are referring to, the state prison had approximately three times the amount of psychiatric and psychological help available as the state hospital. Many of the men who are sent to the state hospital are retained for as long a period or longer than they would have been if given a criminal commitment.

It is true that punitive elements are less emphatically stressed at hospitals for the criminally insane than in prisons. Both types of institutions, however, are theoretically devoted to a program of rehabilitation. It is also true that in our society there may be punitive aspects to commitment to a state hospital in the form of social attitudes which may be more devastating than legally codified punishment. For many, the stigma of the mental hospital is more feared than the restraints of prison. Even seriously disturbed prison inmates may be reluctant to be transferred to a hospital setting. The mental-illness role is resisted on the basis that dignity, self-esteem and chances for an earlier release would be seriously compromised. Prison inmates sense that confinement to a hospital for the criminally insane is not an evasion of punishment or a "soft touch" and that continued loss of freedom and confinement to an understaffed institution is a grim prospect whether it is called punishment or treatment.

## THE PROBLEM OF DIAGNOSING MENTAL ILLNESS

In an early part of this book we devoted almost an entire chapter to some of the theoretical difficulties of responding to the question, "Which criminals are mentally ill?" At that time we argued for a relativistic viewpoint which looked upon mental illness as a socially defined set of behaviors which represent a temporary adaptation. In this section we must re-emphasize some of the excruciating difficulties and inconsistencies psychiatry encounters when it attempts to relate its relativistic concept of mental illness to concrete social decisions.

Terms such as "insanity," "mental illness," "psychosis" and "neurosis" may be definable for purposes of professional communication, but they can never be refined so that they describe absolute categories. Value judgments invariably enter into any categorization of the individual patient, and although there are criteria which help to separate the mentally ill from the normal, or the psychotic from the neurotic, these criteria are necessarily vague and equivocal. They serve best in separating obvious disorders. They are of little value when applied to borderline cases.

Criminal offenders tend to have personality disorders which are not readily classifiable.[35] The psychiatrist rarely sees offenders who are either overtly disorganized or who are in good psychological health. Because of his propensity for action and because he is exposed to so many different kinds of environments, the criminal patient will show unusual variation in his mental status. It is not uncommon, for example, to find an offender who is grossly disorganized while awaiting trial, who is then fully coherent during court proceedings, who then decompensates at the prison and who still later appears to reintegrate his personality when transferred to the state hospital. In cases such as this the diagnosis of psychosis becomes almost a matter of chance. It is dependent on the training, experience and personal philosophy of the particular psychiatrist who examines the offender and the circumstances under which the offender is examined. Speculations made as to the offender's emotional state at the time of the crime are even more unreliable. What too often happens is that the judge and jury are subjected to a variety of opinions, all of which may disagree and all of which may have a certain relevance.

The problem can be illustrated more clearly by a hypothetical case. While the example is fictional, all the disagreements recorded here have occurred more than once in the state of Wiscosin and certainly must have occurred in other states.

Mr. K. was arrested for the crime of forgery. While in the county jail he was noted to be behaving peculiarly and the sheriff requested a psychiatric examination. A psychiatrist examined the patient and stated that he was undergoing an acute schizophrenic reaction, that he was psychotic and that he needed immediate hospitalization. The judge then committed Mr. K. to Hospital X for thirty days. At that institution a thorough examination was done, and it was concluded that Mr. K. was suffering from a chronic schizophrenic reaction, undifferentiated type, and that he was not able to stand trial. The judge then committed Mr. K. to Hospital Y (a hospital for the criminally insane) until he was felt to be sufficiently recovered to stand trial. After he had spent two months at Hospital Y the staff felt that the patient was no longer psychotic and in their report expressed the view that he had never been schizophrenic but was more correctly labeled a passive aggressive personality, aggressive type. Mr. K. was then returned to court to stand trial for his offense. At the time of the trial the patient's attorneys raised the plea of not guilty by reason of insanity. Two psychiatrists testified that Mr. K. was sane at the time of his offense and two testified that he was not. During the course of a lengthy trial a great amount of psychiatric testimony was heard. In some ways there was considerable agreement among the psychiatric witnesses. They all agreed that Mr. K. was a seriously disturbed person. They agreed that at times his behavior was ineffective and peculiar. There was further agreement that Mr. K. needed treatment and that it would be of benefit to him. Yet when forced to "strait-jacket" their testimony into issues such as responsibility and mental illness, the psychiatrists disagreed. The judge found that Mr. K. was sane and sentenced him to the state prison. Within two weeks after his arrival at the prison the patient became extremely disturbed; he hallucinated and was unable to function. The prison psychiatrist found him to be psychotic and he was immediately transferred to State Hospital Y. Within a month he appeared to have recovered and hospital psychiatrists recommended his return to the prison.

There are two problems here. One is that disturbed offenders show rapid fluctuations in their emotional state. The patient's immediate environment plays a major role in whatever psychological picture predominates at a given moment. A second problem is that even though Wisconsin psychiatrists are no less homogeneous than those in other states they do differ widely in their concepts of psychosis and mental illness, particularly as applied to so-called "borderline states" of mental condition. As human beings who hold to a variety of ethical positions, they also differ as to the degrees to which they would hold a man responsible for his behavior. These differences characterize not only individual psychiatrists but are also true at an institutional level. Thus one hospital staff may regularly utilize criteria of psychosis which are quite different from those preferred by the staff of another institution which may be located just a few miles away.

It is hoped that the reader has noted that in the example given psychiatrists may have disagreed as to philosophical issues and problems of categorization but that there was general agreement as to what was wrong with the patient. The writer is not arguing that psychiatry is an inconsistent discipline or that psychiatrists must always disagree with one another. When the psychiatrist confines himself simply to trying to understand and treat the disturbed individual, he uncovers dynamic patterns and uses techniques which are relatively consistent. In the courtroom, however, it often appears that psychiatrists are a group of inconsistent, disagreeable and even ludicrous philosophers.

Before leaving our discussion of the ill effects of psychiatric participation in courtroom decisions of criminal responsibility, one final point will be made. The author feels that the most serious indictment against psychiatric participation in the insanity trial is that such activity exerts a pernicious influence upon the profession itself. Although most psychiatrists are unwilling to testify in criminal trials, the number who are willing to testify is far greater than the number of psychiatrists who are willing to work with the criminal in any other way. The efforts of psychiatrists to deal with unresolvable legal and philosophical issues must be viewed as a distressing waste of psychiatric energy and talent. If all the effort that has been funneled into legal activity were instead directed toward treatment of offenders, psychiatrists might have made far more useful contributions to criminology.

## The Urge to Testify

At a time when attacks on the specialty of psychiatry, and particularly forensic psychiatry, are coming from many directions, it is important to examine some of the possible motivations for psychiatric involvement in the problem of criminal responsibility. This writer is in staunch disagreement with those authorities, psychiatric or otherwise, who speak of a conspiracy of forensic psychiatrists to broaden their influence in the legal process and to gain financial rewards or status.[36, 37, 38] It is hard to believe that status or prestige seekers would be willing to risk the tremendous buffeting and criticism which are associated with courtroom testimony. The psychiatrist who enters the courtroom may receive a great deal of publicity, but he is rarely likely to survive the experience without having to fend off serious attacks upon his dignity, his honesty and his intelligence. It is also difficult to believe that the forensic psychiatrist is interested in money. As medical specialties go, forensic psychiatry does not pay very well. Courtroom work requires many hours of arduous preparation, and the fees are rarely comparable with what the average psychiatrist can earn in private practice.

We must search for other motivations. The most important reason for psychiatric participation in the criminal trial is a humanitarian zeal to temper the harshness of punishment. Psychiatrists, perhaps more than other individuals, are repelled by cruelty, even when it is imposed by society. They are familiar with the malignant effects of arbitrary punishment and are deeply aware of the limitations of punishment in controlling behavior. In a case where capital punishment is at stake, the forensic psychiatrist fights to preserve the life of the disturbed offender. The passion and the degree of involvement which characterize all psychiatric writing and participation in legal issues serve as an indicator as to how deeply committed most psychiatrists are to social change in accordance with their own ethical and political principles.

A second possible reason for the commitment which characterizes forensic psychiatry seems to be more of a defensive one. The reader of psychiatric forensic literature gains the distinct impression that the authors feel that criticism of psychiatric intervention in the legal processes is criticism of psychiatry as a whole. It is as though the writers are defending psychiatry by attempting to prove that its practitioners are capable of determining which offenders are mentally ill and nonresponsible. Of course, vigorous and sometimes vicious attacks upon forensic psychiatry have contributed to this defensive attitude. Such attacks help to crystallize an evangelistic attitude toward the law and the correctional system. When psychiatrists respond so defensively to criticisms of their role in the legal process, they forget that it is neither their profession nor their knowledge that is being attacked but rather a particular social function or philosophical position which a few of their members have assumed. Some psychiatrists react to the criminal trial as though it were a battleground upon which they must prove their mettle. They forget that it is only a social ritual which meets some of the practical needs of our society.

A final and perhaps least admirable reason for psychiatric participation in the insanity trial might be that it affords the practitioner an exciting distraction from the sometimes tedious medical work of diagnosis and treatment. While the psychiatrist certainly undertakes serious risks to his dignity and status when he enters the courtroom, he also becomes a participant in one of the most exciting rituals our society can create. There is no mistaking the fantastic intellectual and emotional appeal of the insanity trial. Such trials receive detailed attention from the mass communications media and have even inspired a number of best-selling novels. When the entire future of a man is at stake and when the deepest secrets of his intimate life are to be revealed in public, other men become involved; they take sides; they hold and express opinions.

The psychiatrist is not immune to these temptations. If he is a person who enjoys intellectual challenge, who is articulate and who is not too shy to participate in public debate, he can experience his involvement as excitingly meaningful. If the psychiatrist can at the same time convince himself that he is promoting social reform and helping his own profession, his urge to testify may overcome his intellectual doubts or his fears of public humiliation.

In spite of a high level of enthusiasm and commitment, the psychiatrist has been ineffective in his efforts to promote changes in social attitudes toward the criminal. The plea of not guilty by reason of insanity may now be invoked with more frequency and it is more likely to be found to be an excusing condition, but psychiatry cannot take credit for these reforms. What has happened is that society has become a little more humane and is now more willing to utilize psychiatric testimony to provide a rationale for its wish to excuse certain offenders.[39] In most sanity trials it is not too difficult to predict the outcome if information is available as to the type of crime committed, as to the status of the criminal in the community and, most important, as to the attitude of that community toward the offender. The psychiatrist is used to lend "scientific" authenticity to a social ritual. He is much more of a pawn than a knight.

## Are There Alternatives?

Much of what is decided in the courtroom is influenced by the manner in which our society treats convicted offenders. If our correctional system were more concerned with rehabilitation than with punishment, society would not be so preoccupied with finding the mentally ill nonresponsible. If we knew that the disturbed offender would be subjected to real treatment rather than neglect or cruelty, we would have little need to wrestle with unanswerable philosophical questions. One recourse for providing a rational role for psychiatry in the legal process would therefore require a radical alteration of many correctional practices. In a later chapter we will discuss in greater detail some suggestions for changes in the American system of administration of criminal justice.

It can be asserted here than an enlightened correctional system would employ psychiatrists for only two purposes: (1) to help to diagnose, treat and rehabilitate all classes of offenders; and (2) to help control dangerous offenders. If punishment were not the major issue, all offenders, including those believed to be emotionally disturbed, would be tried in court for the sole purpose of determining if they had actually committed an illegal act. Mental illness would not mitigate criminal intent. All persons found to have committed a crime (except where *mens rea* does not exist for reasons other than mental illness) would be considered fully responsible. Psychiatrists and other behavioral scientists would be able to confine their role to assisting in the determination of what is to be done with the individual offender.*

If it was assumed that the goal of society was to rehabilitate all offenders who could be helped and to control all those who remained dangerous to the society, the psychiatrist could be used as a resource whose advice would serve the judge or jury in the question of disposition. The offender whose behavior was felt to represent a public danger would also receive treatment, but his behavior would be subjected to greater control.

Many systems have been proposed which would not allow the psychiatrist to testify as to responsibility but would use him to aid in disposition and treatment. Even a brief list of psychiatrists who have advocated such changes includes men of such diverse orientation as Karl Menninger,[40] Phillip Roche,[41] William Haines[42] and Dale Cameron.[43] These systems could be unwieldy, would certainly pose many new problems and might require radical alterations in some of our laws and attitudes. Up to now, the legal profession has shown little enthusiasm for such changes.

Any radical change in our legal system would be subjected to vigorous scrutiny and, if adopted at all, would be done cautiously. It is unlikely that a complete abolishment of the insanity plea would be easily accepted by many segments of our society. Assuming that such changes are many years away, there are nevertheless less radical changes, which could be made immediately, which would allow the psychiatrist to assist the judicial process

* An enlightened system of justice would have to do away with the death penalty. As long as we continue to execute people, psychiatrists and others will be tempted to perjure themselves for humanitarian purposes.

without involving himself in the unresolvable question of man's responsibility. These changes would not tamper with the concept of *mens rea* as applied to the seriously emotionally disturbed.

The psychiatrist is the only expert witness who is asked to present opinions as to man's responsibility and man's punishability. The toxicologist may testify as to the amount of poison in a victim's body and give an opinion as to whether it was sufficient to cause death. The orthopedic surgeon testifies as to the degree of motor incapacitation and its possible causes. The fingerprint or ballistics experts give opinions which are strictly limited to their fields of competence. None of these experts is ever asked to give an opinion as to the guilt or responsibility of the offender. Only the psychiatrist is asked to testify and answer questions which go beyond his own training or competence.

There is no rational reason why the psychiatrist couldn't be allowed to testify like other expert witnesses, i.e., present all the information available as to why a man committed a certain crime and as to the extent of his psychological impairment, without having to ponder whether the offender knew right or wrong or if one of his behaviors was the product of another. Under such a directive the psychiatrist could describe in detail the emotional state of the offender at the time of the crime without answering the impossible questions posed by M'Naghton or Durham. The judge or jury could then make up their own minds as to whether the offender possessed evil intent and should be punished. In making such decisions, they would be assisted only by psychiatric fact and opinion and would not be influenced by the philosophical speculations of a single professional discipline. Ultimately, if the decision of responsibility is to be made at all, it must be entirely in the hands of the judge or jury.

It could, of course, be argued that jurists are not capable of deciding upon the responsibility of mentally ill offenders without receiving considerable direction from psychiatrists. Yet if the community wishes to punish some and excuse others, it could just as easily make such decisions itself without forcing the problem upon the psychiatrist. In many European countries psychiatrists are asked to testify as to fact and are not forced to take a direct stand on the offender's responsibility.[44] As things stand today, the psychiatrist is often exploited to provide a pseudo-scientific rationalization for actions which the community would take anyway. Changes in the current legal code which would make the psychiatrist more of an expert witness and the judge or jury more of a decision-making body would simply put each group into its proper and traditional role.

## The Problem of Pretrial Commitments

One practical issue with which our legal system must engage is what to do with the offender who does not appear to be well enough to stand trial. Irrespective of the stand it takes on the issue of criminal responsibility a humane society cannot afford to have confused or disorganized citizens tried in its courts. It is unlikely that such persons could adequately defend themselves or receive a fair trial. In most jurisdictions an alleged offender who is unable to understand the charges against him, who is unable to understand the proceedings which are to be invoked or who is unable to assist his counsel is judged incompetent. He is then committed to a unit for the criminally insane until he regains his competency. All such commitments are based upon psychiatric testimony.

On the face of it, this procedure appears to be straightforward and humane. Yet it may impose undue hardships upon the incompetent offender. Confinement to an institution for the criminally insane represents a loss of freedom and is experienced as a form of punishment. If the offender does not recover, he can spend the rest of his life behind bars. If he recovers slowly, he will still spend a great deal of time in confinement even though he has not been convicted of a crime. Many of our hospitals for the criminally insane are so deplorably understaffed that opportunities for recovery may be sorely limited. The offender is placed in even greater jeopardy when judges and district attorneys who may be reluctant to try a questionable case sometimes subtly encourage the offender's continued confinement in a hospital. Obviously, in such a situation the civil liberties of an emotionally disturbed offender are seriously threatened. He is deprived of constitutional guarantees for a speedy trial. He is also placed in a kind of double jeopardy since time spent in the hospital is not considered as a part of his future sentence. The disturbing kinds of injustice which have been perpetrated under this system have been exceptionally well described by J. H. Hess and H. E. Thomas,[45] Thomas Szasz[46] and Sol Rubin.[47]

Again we find that psychiatrists in a conscientious search for humanistic goals have unwittingly contributed to social injustices. Many of the psychiatrists who testify on the issue of competency to stand trial are unfamiliar with conditions in hospitals for the criminally insane. Their diagnoses of incompetency are intended to help sick people, but too often they result only in an arbitrary restriction of freedom. Part of the problem lies in the vagueness of terms such as "ability to understand charges," "ability to understand legal proceedings" or "ability to assist counsel." These terms can only be defined quantitatively. A given group of either normal or disturbed people will demonstrate all degrees of ability to comprehend charges and proceedings and all degrees of ability to cooperate. In the author's view psychiatrists, particularly those who are dynamically oriented, expect too much of a man before they call him competent. Many offenders who are now judged incompetent could probably do an adequate job of protecting their interest in the courtroom. It seems that because of the enormous potential threat to civil liberties psychiatrists would do better to define incompetency only in the most severe case of deficiency, confusion or disorganization. Such a policy might result in a number of disturbed persons reaching the mental hospital only after having been given criminal commitment. The possibility of some offenders having to find a circuitous route to the hospital would, however, be preferable to the frightening possibility that larger groups of offenders could be subjected to endless incarceration without trial.

Actually, if hospitals for the criminally insane were upgraded to levels possible in modern psychiatry, the great majority of incompetent offenders could be provided with enough help so that they would be well enough to return to court in a few months. The only major exceptions to this statement would be brain-damaged offenders or severely defective offenders. Unfortunately, no hospital for the criminally insane approaches the adequacy of private psychiatric hospitals or even public ones. There is also great variability of policy in hospitals for the criminally insane. Some of their superintendents work diligently to return their patients to court as soon as possible. Others do not. Some courts encourage the hospitals to return offenders as rapidly as possible. Others do not. In order to improve the plight of the incompetent offender, there would not only be a need for better hospitals but also a need to persuade psychiatrists, judges and attorneys to guard the right to speedy trial with greater diligence.

Even if psychiatrists were more careful in defining competency and even if psychiatrists and attorneys were more diligent in returning offenders to court, some offenders might still need lengthy hospitalization. A certain number of the severely disturbed and the severely retarded will not recover. What is to be done with this small but troubling group? One solution would be to release all chronically incompetent individuals from all criminal charges and give then an ordinary civil commitment. This would at least entitle them to the possibility of parole and release. A mentally defective person, for example, might never be legally competent, but he could become sufficiently well socialized so that he could be released. While the writer realizes that there are hazards and potential injustices associated with ordinary civil commitment (especially when proof of deviant behavior is not established), this does seem like a more humane approach. Ultimately, the disposition of these offenders must be determined by society's assessment of their dangerousness or social hazardousness. This problem will be explored more fully in the following chapter.

# Chapter 16

# CONTROL AND TREATMENT

MOVING away from questions of criminal responsibility, we can begin to examine the psychiatrist's even more complex role in the control and treatment of deviant behavior. The psychiatrist's role in the correctional process is usually limited to working with convicted offenders who are considered to be mentally ill or who are behaving in an obviously unreasonable manner. (There are some important exceptions. In hospitals for the criminally insane the psychiatrist works with suspected offenders who have never been convicted of a crime. In some clinics and institutions he may work with less unreasonable offenders.) Adult offenders may never see a psychiatrist if the unreasonable aspect of their crime is not immediately apparent. Restriction of psychiatric services to only one class of offenders can create social injustices. There is a possibility, just as there is in those cases where a few offenders are found nonresponsible for reasons of mental illness, that humane treatment for a few may encourage society to ignore the sorry plight of the majority. Nevertheless, referral to a psychiatrist once a man is convicted of a crime is usually based on more socially realistic criteria than referral to determine if a man is not guilty by reason of insanity. Those offenders whom the psychiatrist is asked to examine, control or treat are frequently those who are the most disturbed and the most disturbing to the community.

Whether we examine a purely psychiatric setting or a correctional setting, the issues of control and treatment are incredibly complicated. Unfortunately, both correctional administrators and psychiatrists are frequently guilty of discussing control and treatment without defining what they mean.

Serious problems in communication arise when the same words are used to describe different happenings. Our effort in this chapter will be to clarify the various meanings of "control" and "treatment" of deviant behavior. We will then consider the social and ethical justifications of the psychiatrist's role in criminology.

## Psychiatry and Social Control

Many emotionally disturbed individuals and most criminals do not actively seek the attention of their community. If their behavior is offensive, society must nevertheless do something to protect itself. The person who attempts to hurt himself or others, or the person who lashes out against society in a disorganized manner, is usually subjected to involuntary restrictions. Often it is the psychiatric physician who is entrusted with responsibility for imposing control. This is true whenever an emotionally disturbed person is involuntarily committed to a mental hospital or whenever an offender is committed to an institution (such as a hospital for the criminally insane) which is largely administered by psychiatric personnel.*

Psychiatric control of deviant behavior is motivated by wishes to protect the society and the patient. It differs from other forms of control which seek punishment or retribution. The physician believes that control will be in the patient's long-term interest. Unfortunately, however, the patient or offender rarely appreciates the benevolent motivations of psychiatric control. He is more likely to experience any kind of involuntary restraint as punishment. The restrained person might also disagree with the psychiatrist's contention that control will have long-term value. If the patient is restrained from committing suicide, he may later be grateful, but if he is restrained from carrying out less self-destructive social protests, he may remain bitter and resentful. This means that the physician's and the patient's perception of the doctor's role will differ. The psychiatrist experiences himself as a helping person, but his patient may see him as a jailer. Both views are partially correct.

To the extent that the patient feels better after a period of restraint, and is willing to acknowledge that it was "good for him," the physician need not be too uneasy as to the inconsistencies of his role. The psychiatrist, however, is not always successful in helping the socially deviant person. When treatment fails and the patient is still deprived of freedom, the psy-

* A mingling of helping and coercively restraining roles arises in any situation in which the patient does not consider himself in need of help and is characteristic of psychiatric practice in mental hospitals and correctional agencies. It is most removed from private-practice aspects of psychiatry, such as psychoanalysis.

chiatrist is little more than a humane jailer. When he lends his services to help control offenders in correctional institutions, he may become part of a controlling administration that is not even humane. The ethical problems created by such situations are frequently ignored, but they are complex and important enough to be examined in some detail.

To begin with, it seems almost inherently contradictory for the physician to lend his services to the control of his fellow human beings. The medical doctor comes from a tradition in which respect for individual liberties and service to individual needs are primary. Medical practice in our country has developed as a private contractual relationship in which it is expected that the physician will serve his patient. Concern for the manner in which the patient's behavior influences the rest of society is usually secondary. A few public health physicians do assume responsibility for controlling the behavior of their fellow citizens, but they do this only when communicable diseases or careless use of drugs threaten the public. In such functions the physician is clearly an employee of the community, and he makes little pretense of serving the individual patient. It is only in psychiatry, or more precisely in that psychiatry which deals with nonvoluntary patients, that we see a mingling of roles in which the physician attempts to serve the patient and to protect society at the same time.

In practice the individual and society do not always have compatible interests. What is good for the individual or what serves the needs of the individual may not be good for society. On the other hand, what is bad for the individual may be quite good for society. Unreasonable behavior viewed as an adaptational device may help the individual to sustain himself, but it is rarely welcomed by the society. At the same time, the society makes rules and regulations which may be indispensable to its continued existence but which are onerous to certain individuals. It is true, of course, that much of the time the interests of society and the individual are similar. The problem, however, with any role which is designed to serve the needs of both at the same time is that it encourages the assumption of compatible interests. This assumption is not always justified.

Another way of phrasing this problem is that the psychiatric physician has difficulty in being an agent for the state and for the patient at the same time. This is an especially ambiguous position for those raised in the medical tradition. The lay public usually assumes that whatever the physician does is in the interest of the patient. When the psychiatrist as a physician implies that confinement is a part of treatment which is imposed upon the patient for his own good, this belief is accepted literally by most people. The psychiatrist is thereby endowed with an exceptional degree of unquestioned power over those he designates as mentally ill.[1] Recently, a number of critics have commented upon the possible dangers of abuse of this power.

The critics of psychiatry point out that the physician represents an insidious threat to the civil liberties of the mental patient or criminal since he encourages society to cloak coercive practices under the mantle of medical treatment.[2, 3, 4, 5] They cite cases in which the psychiatrist, representing himself as an agent of the patient, has (in the guise of medical treatment) assisted the community in depriving the patient of liberties which probably could have been enjoyed without danger to anyone. Injustices are most often described in cases of involuntary civil commitment of the mentally ill, but they have also been reported with criminals. Some of the most flagrant abuses have occurred in the operation of sex-crimes programs. Many of these programs allow the psychiatrist to institutionalize sex offenders whose behavior may have been only irritating and not actually dangerous to the society. Under the assumption that such people are mentally ill they have frequently been subjected to lengthy, severe and unjustified restraint. I believe that most psychiatrists are much more concerned with the civil liberties of our patients than our critics realize, and, it might be added, less guilty of "atrocities" than other professional groups. In the author's experience in a correctional setting, social workers and sociologists have been far less aware of and far more exploitative of the "double agent" role. They are often guilty of telling inmates that their sole purpose is to help them, even when this obviously cannot be true. Perhaps critics are more indignant with psychiatric abuse of the patient's freedom because they expect more of the physician and are shaken when he errs. It must be admitted, however, that psychiatrists frequently fail to comprehend or clarify to their patients the dual roles which they so often play.

The question of whose agent the psychiatric physician is at any given moment is a crucial one, which will appear repeatedly in our future discussion of psychiatry's role in the correctional process. Before we can consider this question as it relates to specific psychiatric roles, we must first examine various definitions of correctional treatment.

## What Does Treatment Mean?

Up to now we have used terms such as "treatment" or "rehabilitation" loosely and have implied that there is general agreement as to their meaning. Real consensus, however, is rare. In criminology the use of the word "treatment" is especially imprecise, and may be applied to a variety of unrelated activities.

All definitions of treatment assume that something is done to a person to change his physiological state, his attitude or his psychological behavior in a manner which satisfies certain goals of the treated subject or the treating agency. Treatment can be examined either in terms of what is done to a person or in terms of the changes or goals which are sought. For the moment let us consider treatment of the criminal in terms of desired goals.

In its harshest sense, treatment could mean control of unacceptable behavior with total disregard for the psychological state of the offender. Some would argue that as long as the criminal is restrained from violating the laws of the community he is being treated. The goal in this definition is simply prevention, and the means are irrelevant. Treatment could include exile, incarceration, physical or chemical restraint. This is almost a purely "society-oriented" definition, which would rarely be acceptable to a democratic nation.

For most people, treatment of the criminal implies changing his personality, beliefs or motivations so that he will be able to refrain voluntarily from committing criminal acts. This meaning of treatment equates it with a quest for internalized control. (We are again using the term "control" mainly for convenience to describe a complicated shift away from tendencies to seek a criminal adaptation.) Although different groups would favor varying means of obtaining such control, the definition implies a consistent end result, namely, abstention from criminality without the need for external restraint or punishment. It would make little difference whether control was gained through the offender's becoming more withdrawn, more passive, more mentally ill or more nonproductive. As long as he did not violate the law, the level of his personal comfort or effectiveness would be irrelevant.

The use of statistics of criminal recidivism as a measure of treatment success are compatible with this kind of definition. Recidivism rates tell only whether or not a new crime is committed, and whether the offender is free or not free of a legal status. They reveal nothing about the psychological status of the criminal. This definition of treatment is partly "individual-oriented," since it considers the state of freedom of the treated subject, but it remains primarily "society-oriented" insofar as its first concern is with the prevention of crime and the economic advantages of having fewer criminals living in institutions.

For many people with intense humanistic inclinations, treatment means not only the acquisition of internal controls but an acquisition of controls which is accompanied by greater personal comfort and effectiveness. At the very least it means an acquisition of controls which is gained without sacrificing personal comfort or effectiveness. With this definition a criminal would not be looked upon as having been successsfully treated if he stopped committing crimes but continued to be unhappy and ineffectual. Those who hold to such a goal would recognize that the offender might experience more anxiety and discomfort once he abandoned criminal activities. It would be hoped, however, that this disadvantage would be outweighed by two factors: first, the newer potentialities of the noncriminal life and, second, the decrease in those stresses which previously resulted from society's continuing efforts to deprive the offender of freedom. This definition considers the psychological needs of the individual. It is compatible with the avowed policies and practices of the helping professions of psychiatry, psychology and social work.

In classical psychotherapeutic terms, the goals of treatment are comfort, effectiveness and self-awareness. As applied to the criminal, this definition implies that a man is successfully treated when he no longer feels driven to respond to unrealistic oppression and can respond appropriately to realistic oppression. The more psychotherapy is based on psychoanalysis, the greater is the emphasis on acquisition of self-knowledge. Classical psychoanalytic psychotherapy would not insist upon abstention from criminality as a necessary condition of effective treatment. The psychoanalyst would hold that the successfully treated person could make a rational choice as to whether he wished to continue to indulge in criminal activities or not. It would, of course, be assumed that an individual who is no longer inclined to respond to unrealistic oppression would be less likely to resort to crime and certainly less likely to indulge in unreasonable crime.

The preceding four definitions of treatment were arranged in an order of increasing concern with the needs of individuals and decreasing concern with the needs of society as a whole. Each implies a different value judgment as to what types of ethical precepts will guide the treating agency. The psychiatrist would be most comfortable with the latter two. Psychiatrists believe either that people should be freed of their neurotic conflicts and allowed to make their own decisions or that they should be directed into a more conforming but productive and happier way of life. It must also be admitted that at times psychiatrists operate on the basis of definitions No. 1 and No. 2. In dealing with extremely dangerous offenders whom they despair of ever helping, they sometimes argue that treatment is simply the imposition of external control which protects the public and prevents the criminal from doing anything that would make his situation worse. In other instances psychiatrists either unwittingly or through a sense of obligation to the state look upon treatment as internal control, irrespective of its psychological impact upon the individual.

Another way of looking upon treatment in criminology is in terms of potential directions of attack upon criminal behavior. In an earlier chapter we listed six means or directions: (1) elimination of objective oppression, (2) elimination of perceived unrealistic oppression, (3) elimination of access to the criminal role, (4) strengthening pressure for conformity, (5) strengthening abilities for activism, (6) allowing more access to mental illness.

It can be seen that goal definitions of treatment can be matched with specific directional or means definitions of treatment. Some goals would be compatible with any means. Others would be consistent with only limited directions or means. If the goal of treatment is merely external control, the treating agency need not be concerned with any means of treatment other than elimination of access to the criminal role. On the other hand, if the goal is greater internal control, any of the six directions of treatment we have listed would be helpful. Those who would see treatment as successful only when control was also accompanied by greater comfort and effectiveness would enthusiastically adhere to directions of treatment which aimed to reduce objective or unrealistic oppression. In some situations they would accept those directions that eliminated access to the criminal role or strengthened capacities for conformity and activism. Finally, those who hold to a classical psychoanalytic conception of treatment would be concerned primarily with the elimination of perceived unrealistic oppression and might, with some reservations, accept elimination of objective oppression or strengthening of abilities for activism as legitimate treatment modalities.

## An Ethical Basis for Psychiatric Criminology

We are now in a position to examine the ethical and social implications of specific psychiatric roles. Psychiatric participation in criminology leads to a certain amount of involuntary control over the patient. When the psychiatrist assumes controlling roles, he differs in motivation from other criminologists who are concerned with punishing the criminal. We have previously noted, however, that although he may not intend to punish, any degree of control which the psychiatrist assumes over another person's life can be experienced as punitive by that person. It then becomes especially important to clarify the extent to which a psychiatric role is coercive, or the extent to which the role calls for putting society's needs ahead of the offender's needs in a manner which may be painful to the offender.

Throughout the remainder of this book we will describe various activities which the psychiatrist undertakes to assist in the administration of correctional justice. All these roles overlap, and since we are interested here only in examining them in terms of the issue of control, they will not be discussed in the same order as in subsequent chapters.

The psychiatrist as evaluator. In this role the psychiatrist's impressions and reports may turn out to be quite valuable to the offender's long-term interest. They also, however, may be used to justify a number of unwelcome controlling actions such as confinement to a maximum-security institution, indeterminate sentencing and refusal of parole.

The psychiatrist as therapist. This is about as purely individually oriented a role as the psychiatrist can assume with the criminal. Psychotherapy is usually directed toward serving individual needs. We will note in a later chapter, however, that certain techniques that are related to psychotherapy can also be used to direct people toward behavior that is not in their own interests.

The psychiatrist as creator of a therapeutic milieu. In some children's institutions, hospitals for the criminally insane and other agencies the psychiatrist seeks to create a total environment which is conducive to personality change. The milieu can be structured so that it primarily serves the long-term interests of the offender, but it is sometimes structured in a manner that seeks a painful conformity that is mainly compatible with society's needs.

The psychiatrist as educator. Psychiatrists often attempt to share their knowledge and insights with judges, parole officers and custodians. Again, this knowledge can be used to benefit the offender or to hurt him.

The psychiatrist as administrator. When the psychiatrist administers a sex-deviate program, a hospital for the criminally insane or a children's institution, his primary obligation is to the society which employs him. Although he may seek to help the individual, he will frequently be in a position where he must sacrifice individual needs in favor of community needs.

It is apparent that any psychiatric role in a correctional setting can be both helpful and painfully controlling. Faced with a dilemma which has few parallels in other aspects of medical practice, psychiatrists have taken differing positions as to the extent of justifiable involvement. Some insist that any role other than a purely psychotherapeutic one is too complex and loaded with pitfalls to be helpful or ethical. Extreme protagonists of this view would insist that any form of coercive psychiatry is a corruption of the medical tradition. On the other hand, many more psychiatrists believe that since the physician's intentions are always nonpunitive, and because his patients are emotionally disturbed people, almost any type of control can be justified. This argument in its most naïve form implies that sick people do not know what is best for them and that psychiatric treatment will invariably result in "cure." In its most sophisticated form it is based upon the conviction that the psychiatrist has some responsibility to the society as a whole and that he is obligated to share his skills in efforts to find humane solutions to social problems.

What this controversy really centers about is the ethical and political convictions of both the psychiatrist and the community. The psychiatrist who insists that any coercive practice is unjustified if it takes place outside of a contractual or legalistic framework is really an archindividualist. The psychiatrist who is eager to assume obligations to the community and who is less concerned with unfavorable effects upon the individual is much more of a collectivist. Of course, neither position can be held unless the prevailing political climate allows for it. The community uses psychiatry according to its needs. Private practice of psychiatry (and especially psychotherapy) is possible only in a capitalistic nation which has great concern for individual liberties. The use of psychiatry to control deviant behavior is more characteristic of a welfare state or a totalitarian state.

The author's own political and ethical position is that the psychiatrist has some responsibility to assist in the humane care of the socially deviant (even when he must control them against their will), particularly when deviant behavior is maladaptive and where the psychiatrist's efforts promise to alleviate suffering. The author also believes, however, that individual liberties must be protected to the greatest extent possible without endangering the safety of others. This compromise position is not unique and is probably held by the majority of psychiatrists. It recognizes that the psychiatrist cannot assume responsibility for controlling large groups of people without hurting some of them, but assumes that the psychiatrist is ethically obligated to keep such painful side effects to a minimum.

As applied to the question of civil commitment, this ethic would condone involuntary hospitalization where the psychiatrist believes that there is a high probability that if the patient were free he would harm himself or others. When these criteria are utilized in a scrupulously honest and consistent manner, commitments are less likely to result in painful and unnecessary deprivations of liberty.

The role of the psychiatrist in a hospital for the criminally insane, a program for sex deviates or a prison is somewhat different. In such situations the psychiatrist is not directly responsible for the patient's institutionalization. He may feel that his patients are not dangerous and that they could be allowed to go free. Yet the peculiarities of our correctional system are such that the psychiatrist is often entrusted with the total responsibility for the control and treatment of people for whom he would not have recommended commitment under ordinary circumstances. Quite often the legal conditions of commitment make it impossible for him to work toward the release of such patients even when he is convinced that they are well enough to be free.

In the author's opinion, the psychiatrist's participation in the control of criminals for whose original commitment he is not responsible can be justified only if the following two conditions are met.

1. The psychiatrist must be motivated by a treatment definition which not only seeks the elimination of deviant behavior but seeks to do so without increasing the long-term discomfort and effectiveness of the individual.

2. The psychiatrist must rigidly and scrupulously inform his patients as to the limits of his ability to serve individual interests. The patient must never be deceived into believing that the actions of the psychiatric criminologist always have the same individually oriented direction as that of most other physicians.

The first condition implies that the treated offender must eventually reach a more favorable adaptation than his previous criminality had brought him. If the psychiatrist willingly participates in a treatment process which leaves the criminal more conforming but more miserable, he has moved so far away from traditional medical practice as to be unethical. The only exception to this statement would occur when the psychiatrist deals with a person who represents a serious danger to the community.* If the psychiatrist finds himself participating in treatment situations in which better adaptations are not possible and where the patient is not dangerous (a situation which not infrequently arises), he must either protest or get out.

It is not always possible, of course, for the physician to keep to his dual goals of control plus helpfulness. Often he continues to help restrain people in situations where real psychological help seems possible but elusive. It is then easy for the psychiatrist to deceive himself. He may encourage

* Dangerousness has to be defined carefully in this context, and we will attempt to do so in the next section.

control while forgetting about helpfulness, or he may invoke treatment modalities which force submission without psychological growth. Obviously, the psychiatrist or any other professional will be constantly tempted to control people in ways and for durations which are neither helpful nor necessary. To the extent that he succumbs to such temptations he violates the ethical codes of his profession.

Condition 2 is essential to preserve the deviant person's right to be treated as a responsible, mature individual who will not be deceived as though he were a child. Any psychiatrist who works with offenders is obligated to inform his patient as to his treatment goals and his commitments to the community. The offender must be clearly told that the administrative physician cannot always be on his side. He must be aware of the therapist's commitment to social agencies and must have some idea as to how much antisocial behavior the therapist will be allowed to tolerate. He must also be informed as to the potential restrictive uses which may be made of the psychiatric evaluator's report. Failure to supply this minimum degree of honesty implies a profound disrespect for individual rights and values.

There is an unfortunate tendency in psychiatry and correctional administration to refer to anything that is done to offenders, even obvious punitive acts, as treatment. For example, the author once heard a perfectly sincere correctional administrator refer to the pleasant pastel shades that had been painted on the walls of an isolation cell as an example of "color therapy." Since the offender is an unsophisticated person who usually believes that treatment implies something that is good for him, such misrepresentation is a serious form of dishonesty. To tell an offender that coercive actions are taken for his own good when it is obvious that they serve only the needs of an institutional system or society is to treat him like a subhuman creature to be stripped of all rights and dignity.

It is difficult to overestimate the mischief and damage that are created by professional dishonesty in the field of criminology. The "double-binded" offender cannot help but experience rage, distrust and despair, feelings that will perpetuate his criminal behavior. It is not only the criminal who is misled. The public assumes that when the correctional workers talk about treating the criminal, something is being done to make him a better and happier citizen. This allows the more humanistic element in society happily to deceive themselves and ignore whatever guilt or uncertainty they have as to what is actually being done to offenders. The experienced administrator knows that the more he talks about treatment, the better are his public relations and public image and the easier it is to "sweep problems under the rug." Granted that honesty toward the patient may not relieve the emotional suffering that goes with coercive control, it at least does not compound it. Dishonesty toward the criminal is shameful enough in any correctional worker, but when it comes from a professional such as the physician it is inexcusable.

### The Problems of Indeterminacy and Dangerousness

When a mentally ill person is involuntarily sent to a hospital, his commitment is for an indeterminate period. Many offenders are also subject to legal procedures which allow for indeterminate medical control.* In American criminology indeterminate commitment to facilities administered by psychiatrists is utilized with those who have been judged incompetent to stand trial, the criminally insane, many sex deviates, some sociopaths and some narcotic addicts.

Commitment for these groups is usually based on special legislation. The offender is not treated like an ordinary criminal, but neither is he treated like the ordinary mentally ill. Most mentally ill persons are civilly committed by a judge on the basis of a psychiatrist's diagnosis of illness. In civil commitments the psychiatrist theoretically assists in the commitment of only those who are believed to be both mentally ill and potentially dangerous to themselves and others. In practice, however, he often commits people simply on the basis of a diagnosis of mental illness. In all the specialized indeterminate commitments we are considering (for the criminally insane, sex deviate, etc.), however, there has been not only a diagnosis of mental illness but also a great deal of certainty on the part of the community that the individual has committed an illegal act. The psychiatrist's diagnosis is in this instance only a part of the reason for commitment, and the offender is certainly not treated just like any other mentally ill person. All the specialized programs for indeterminate commitment of offenders also have certain restrictive qualifications which make release of the offender to the community complicated and difficult. Release dates are usually determined by parole boards which are subject to judicial review and community pressure.

* It should be noted that the model of indeterminate sentencing is used in many situations which do not involve psychiatry. In effect, any correctional system which guarantees the possibility of parole is really a form of indeterminate sentencing. Such systems do, however, have a maximum possible sentence. When we talk about psychiatric involvement in indeterminate confinement, we are referring to a situation in which there is no maximum sentence and in which at least theoretically there may not be a minimum sentence. We are also assuming considerable psychiatric responsibility for supervision of such a program.

Specialized indeterminate commitment for offenders who are to be controlled and treated by the psychiatric profession is usually justified on the grounds that these offenders are sick people. Once this premise is accepted, the rest of the argument flows smoothly. No one would condone the sentencing of a patient with smallpox to a fixed length of time in a hospital. Rather, a rational society would argue that such a patient should be released as soon as he is well and should be hospitalized for as long as he remains ill. The same argument is applied to the mentally ill offender. Indeterminate control under psychiatric administration implies that the patient will be released as soon as he is rehabilitated or retained as long as he remains disturbed.

Unfortunately, serious inconstencies arise when we invoke this analogy to the medical model of illness. First of all, the designation of some offenders as mentally ill is an extremely arbitrary matter. Smallpox can be diagnosed with some precision and consistency, but determining who is a sex deviate, a psychopath or an insane criminal is a much more arbitrary matter. A second problem is that the illness model upon which such control is based assumes that the patient wishes to get well and assumes that he enters the hospital voluntarily. Even if we grant that certain criminals should be defined as mentally ill, we cannot assume that they would accept institutionalization as willingly as the physically ill. A third problem is that the diagnosis of mental illness does not automatically require institutional treatment. Some offenders who are held indeterminately in psychiatric units would probably never have been committted unless they had also been convicted or suspected of a criminal offense. If a patient with homosexual tendencies sought outpatient treatment, his private psychiatrist would be unlikely to consider hospitalization. If such a person were arrested for homosexual behavior, however, he might in some states be committed under an indeterminate sex-crimes law which required that his psychiatric treatment be undertaken in a closed institution. It is not just his illness which would lead to his indeterminate confinement, but a peculiar mixture of helping and punitive motivations.[6]

Another problem with indeterminate programs for control of special categories of criminals is that they are often more concerned with indeterminacy in terms of a maximum sentence than with indeterminacy in terms of a minimum sentence. The ordinary mental hospital has in recent years sought to release its inmates at the earliest possible date. Specialized indeterminate programs for offenders, however, are much more concerned with control and with protection of the public. It is a rare sex offender who is released as improved after a month or two of treatment. On the other hand, many sex offenders have been restrained for years and even for life. In such a situation unjustified deprivations of liberty are possible. Many offenders who are diagnosed as mentally ill are not dangerous people. If they are involuntarily restrained for longer periods than offenders who commit similar offenses but are not diagnosed as mentally ill, they are being discriminated against and deprived of equal justice.

In spite of all these considerations, the idea of detaining criminals for an indeterminate period is appealing. This approach has an inherent quality of nonpunitiveness and rationality. Such a system could be justified if the following conditions were met.

Pressures from judicial and community agencies must not be allowed to exert an extraordinary degree of influence in interfering with early release. If there is to be no maximum sentence, there should also be no minimum sentence, and release of some offenders in one to two months should be a realistic possibility.

Institutions for control and treatment of offenders must be capable of providing treatment facilities which are comparable to those available in our better mental hospitals.

Legal safeguards must be available which would prevent indefinite and inordinately prolonged commitment of nondangerous offenders.

Our current system of indeterminate commitment of only *selected offenders* could be more easily justified if, in addition to these conditions, psychiatrists would use more precise criteria for commitment than those implied in the vague designation of mental illness. These criteria can be sought either in the treatment needs of the individual or in society's need to protect itself from dangerous offenders.

When psychiatric treatment is capable of favorably influencing unreasonable behaviors, a fixed period of confinement serves only a punitive purpose since the offender could conceivably be rehabilitated in a much shorter period of time. The problem with current criteria for indeterminacy which are based on the presence of mental illness is that some offenders whom we call mentally ill are relatively inaccessible to treatment and some offenders whom we do not call mentally ill respond quite well to psychiatric techniques. It would make more sense to utilize indeterminate sentencing for those individuals who would have a high probability of improving, irrespective of their diagnostic category. This would eliminate some of the possible injustice of prolonged institutionalization for those adjudicated mentally ill but who are neither treatable nor dangerous.

Of course, neither a treatability nor a mental-illness criterion of indeterminacy could be justified in the absence of a truly indeterminate minimum sentence, legal safeguards and adequate facilities for treatment. The latter condition is especially important. To sentence offenders into an indeterminate program on the basis of a promise of help and then not supply that help is deceptive. The offender surrenders the certainties of a fixed sentence for an elusive promise of nonavailable assistance. When indeterminacy means only prolonged custody without help, the offender perceives himself as the victim of a sadistic hoax. This unfortunate situation arises with some frequency in our present-day correctional system.

Even in the absence of a probability that treatment will be effective and even when facilities may not be adequate, there is still one other situation in which indeterminate control of selected groups of emotionally disturbed offenders is necessary and justifiable. This is when the offender has committed acts which are dangerous to others and when he is believed to be likely to commit similar acts. Dangerous acts are here defined as crimes against persons which result or threaten to result in the infliction of serious bodily harm or serious and direct psychological harm. This definition is concerned only with crimes of violence and would not include crimes against property unless such crimes (arson, for example) led to bodily harm. Serious psychological harm refers mainly to sex offenses such as rape or molestation of minors.

With the exception of crimes committed by syndicate racketeers or revolutionaries most violent crimes could also be viewed as unreasonable crimes. Dangerousness has been defined in terms of the offender's capacities to repeat a violent act. Repeated violence is likely to be characterized by a high degree of unreasonableness. Such behavior is, therefore, quite familiar to the psychiatric physician. There are many precedents for medical participation in efforts to control those who endanger the community. Traditionally, individuals who carry diseases which threaten community health are involuntarily and indeterminately hospitalized or quarantined even where it is against their wishes. There would appear to be similar justification for psychiatric diagnosis of dangerousness and for psychiatric participation in the indeterminate control of unreasonable offenders who are capable of hurting their fellow man.

Let us briefly summarize these complicated issues. We have argued that indeterminate sentencing could be a sound and humane practice. As parole systems become more liberal, sentencing for criminals will become more indeterminate and hence more like civil commitment for the mentally ill. While this trend is praiseworthy insofar as it will allow many offenders to leave prisons at an earlier and more realistic date, it could also have certain social dangers. There is a disturbing possibility that some nondangerous and nontreatable mentally ill offenders could be institutionalized for life. The pressures against releasing men who are known to have committed crimes will always be greater than those which operate in ordinary civil commitments. Legal safeguards, respect for the use of an indeterminate minimum sentence and adequate treatment facilities are prerequisites for any type of indeterminate program. If indeterminacy is used primarily for certain categories of emotionally disturbed offenders, however, the more precise selection criteria of treatability and dangerousness would be preferable to the more arbitrary criterion of mental illness.

## Chapter 17

# NONPENOLOGICAL ROLES

THE institutional role of psychiatric criminology is many-faceted, complex and often controversial. Involved are many techniques, situations and values, and, as we shall see, the professional who works in this area faces a spectrum of special problems.

We should first clarify a matter of terminology. As we discuss institutional settings and roles through the next five chapters, we will, for the sake of convenience, refer to the activities of psychiatrists. It should be noted, however, that many of these functions are often performed by other professionals. Psychologists and social workers do not, of course, prescribe drugs, nor do they assume total responsibility for hospital care, but in the correctional setting they do take on many important functions, including administration of treatment programs, working to maintain a therapeutic milieu, evaluation, psychotherapy and counseling. Insofar as psychologists and social workers follow a model in which treatment is considered in terms of individual needs, their philosophies and practices are quite similar to those of the psychiatrist. Most correctional administrators have discovered that assignment of responsibilities on any basis other than ability is uneconomical and absurd.

Not all professionals would wish to identify themselves with the "individual-oriented" aspects of the medical model. Most of the real cleavages in the field of corrections are between those who feel that control must not be obtained at the expense of individual comfort or effectiveness and those who feel that it does not make any difference. Unfortunately, a good many social workers (and less frequently psychologists and psychiatrists) have become identified with the latter position. They have forsaken any sense of commitment to individual values and function entirely as agents of the state. Such professionals would be unlikely to identify themselves with the roles or activities we are about to discuss.

### The Court Clinic

The psychiatric court clinic has held a responsible place in the diagnosis and treatment of offenders since 1909 when William Healy founded the first juvenile court clinic in Chicago. During the second and third decades of this century adult and juvenile court clinics multiplied rapidly and were welcomed as a useful innovation by attorneys, judges, correctional workers and psychiatrists.[1] In spite of widespread recognition of their value, they have unfortunately never become a consistent part of the American correctional system. Court clinics have appeared only in metropolitan centers concentrated mainly in the Eastern and Midwestern states. As of 1960 there were eleven juvenile court clinics in the United States and ten adult criminal court clinics located in large cities outside of the state of Massachusetts. In the last few years Massachusetts has expanded its program to include fifteen court clinics but is the only state which offers this extent of service.

The court clinic psychiatrist directs himself to one of three major tasks. He may assist the court in obtaining impartial psychiatric data as to the emotional status of the accused offender. When a convicted offender is involved, the psychiatrist may advise as to disposition of the offender or participate in efforts to treat and rehabilitate him. In addition to these major functions, some courts assign a number of minor medical and psychiatric duties to the clinic, such as examining witnesses to judge competency, determining the physical status of offenders before trial or during probation or supervising laboratory studies such as blood typing or blood serology when these are of legal concern.[2]

The relative amount of time spent on each activity varies with the clinic. Some clinics devote most of their attention to preparing reports as to the sanity of the offender. Others spend more time advising as to the disposition of convicted offenders. Still others are primarily concerned with treatment. The juvenile court clinics place heavy emphasis upon assistance in disposition and treatment. Adult courts are more likely to use psychiatric clinics for assistance in determining legal competence and sanity.

When court clinics report as to the offender's pretrial emotional status, they are usually requested to respond to the issue of the defendant's sanity and responsibility. This function requires that the psychiatrist become a participant in courtroom procedures which determine guilt or innocence. We have previously discussed and criticized this role. Our previous insistence as to the psychiatrist's lack of capacity to judge the issue of a man's responsibility is also applicable in this situation. In fairness, however, it must be noted that the participation of court clinic psychiatrists in the sanity trial has some advantages over the usual proceedings. Since the court clinic psychiatrist is available at the court's discretion, the judge and opposing attorneys are willing to consider the possibility of insanity as a defense in a large number of cases. The issues of insanity and nonresponsibility are likely to be raised in a more judicious manner than if they were left entirely to defense attorneys and their clients. Court clinics, therefore, help to modify inequalities in justice that are related to social class or race. Another advantage is that the court clinic serves as an impartial agency which shares its material with both the defense and prosecution. It therefore helps to eliminate the courtroom battle of psychiatric experts, which has clouded psychiatry's public image. If our society is determined to find some of its offenders not guilty by reason of insanity, the use of impartial court clinic psychiatrists seems to be a more prudent manner of dealing with the problem than the laissez-faire system which is employed in most jurisdictions.

Of much more value to the community is the use of the court clinic psychiatrist to help the judge determine the disposition of offenders. The usefulness of psychiatric evaluation to the sentencing agency is contingent upon the psychiatrist's ability to predict subsequent behavior. This is a skill which is regularly acknowledged and utilized in treatment of the mentally ill. If psychiatrists do indeed have such skills, their use would seem to be as applicable to those who are labeled criminal.

In many clinics the psychiatrist prepares a lengthy report which offers suggestions as to disposition. These suggestions are based upon a study of the offender's needs and personality. The psychiatrist may recommend probation for certain offenders, and he may outline the conditions under which probation would be most likely to succeed. He may also help to determine the length and the place of penal confinement. In the model proposed by the most outstanding court clinic psychiatrist, Dr. Manfred Guttmacher, an effort is made to base all recommendations primarily upon psychiatric and social data.[3] The psychiatrist does not comment upon such issues as community attitudes or the deterrent effect of punishment. In this sense his report represents only one piece of data, which does not bind the judge to a final decision.

One possible criticism of this psychiatric role might be that it places too much power in the hands of the psychiatrist. Dr. Guttmacher reports that over 90 percent of the recommendations of his clinic are accepted.[4] This is a rather high figure, and some would be concerned as to whether the clinic could actually usurp the duties of the judge. Of course, the manner in which psychiatric data are utilized depends upon the relationship of the judge and the psychiatrist. Their personalities, their skills and their sensitivity as to the prerogatives of their professions can assume extraordinary significance. In discussing the ethical problems of court clinics, Milton Miller and I have noted:

> This situation cannot be evaluated only on the basis of the apparent success of the involved pair, the psychiatrist and judge. The ground rules for the relationship must be clearly spelled out lest an over-enthusiastic successor to either profession use the established precedent in a less constructive manner. With an ineffective judge or imprudent psychiatrist operating outside of an adversary system there is always the danger that profound legal decisions will be made without providing the patient with full opportunity for due process. At its very worst, such a system could result in the medical evaluation becoming a decision-making document, even a kind of sentence.[5]

It appears that while court clinics may at present operate safely and effectively on an intimate unstructured basis, more rigorous procedures and greater safeguards might be necessary should dispositional functions ever expand. The author believes that reports to the court should not include specific recommendations but should rather focus upon a more detailed description of the dynamics of the criminal's behavior. Ultimately, it is the judge (who represents all of society) who must decide what is to be done with the offender. A comprehensive psychiatric report which explains why the criminal behaved as he did and speculates as to the criminal's future behavior should be enough material for any conscientious judge. The psychiatric report should be used in a manner quite similar to that of presentence investigations which are prepared by parole agents. It should be an information-providing document which is not binding but which helps to clarify the value of alternative dispositions.

A third task which some court clinics have assumed is that of providing psychiatric treatment for the offender. This function has been developed most effectively in the state of Massachusetts.[6] Court clinics in Massachusetts provide therapy for probationers, for parolees and even for past offenders who may at that moment be free of legal restraint. Psychotherapy may be required as a condition of parole or probation. It is also available on an entirely voluntary basis. This service seems to be as worthwhile a contribution to criminology as the psychiatrist is capable of making. It is based on a philosophy of helping the criminal. Although a certain amount of coercion may be associated with involuntary treatment, the offender is deprived of few basic liberties. The only negative thing that can be said about this function is that, compared to the need, the extent of services currently offered is negligible.

There is still one other service which only a few clinics have recently begun to provide, but which may be quite useful to correctional workers and their clients. This service can be described as an effort to consult with and educate parole officers and others who work with the offender in the field. Some states with enlightened correctional programs encourage parole officers to conduct group and individual therapy with their parolees and probationers. Since the average parole officer has not had sufficient opportunity to acquire the knowledge and skill necessary to perform effective psychotherapy, he desperately needs the educative and supervisory skills of the psychiatric consultant. Many correctional administrators had anticipated that such consultative services would be provided by community mental health clinics. Unfortunately, these clinics have been unable to offer much help. Overwhelmed with other community demands, they have been relatively uninterested in working with the offender or in assisting correctional agencies. It appears that correctional agencies will have to find their own community facilities. The court clinic may well be that agency which is in the best position to provide consultation to those who must work directly with parolees and probationers.

## The Unit for the Criminally Insane

In discussing facilities for the treatment of the so-called insane criminal, it is necessary to talk about units rather than hospitals. Many states have built separate facilities for the treatment of severely disturbed offenders which can be appropriately called hospitals, but other states have not. Some states house all psychotically disturbed offenders in a separate unit of the prison. Others place them in a separate ward or unit in one of the state hospitals for the mentally ill.[7] In all but a few states units for the criminally insane are deplorably understaffed and neglected.[8] Conditions in some of these units are often worse than conditions in the same state's prisons.[9] The offender who is believed to need special care and humane treatment is sometimes subjected to greater neglect and cruelty than if he had been judged normal. This is unfortunate and unnecessary, because if properly staffed and managed, units for the criminally insane are capable of providing useful services to the disturbed offender.

The major group of offenders treated in a unit for the criminally insane includes those who have been found incompetent to stand trial, those who have been found insane and therefore not guilty and convicted offenders who have experienced psychological decompensation while serving a prison sentence. Some units also care for convicted sex offenders or narcotics addicts. All units occasionally receive patients who have been civilly committed as mentally ill but who have become too assaultive to be managed in the usual mental hospital setting. A large number of those confined to units for the criminally insane are individuals who are mentally defective, who have been accused of committing a crime and then committed as incompetent to stand trial.

Units for the criminally insane are usually administered by psychiatrists who are given full responsibility for the control of the offender. In these units an alert and sensitive psychiatric staff can be especially helpful to offenders who have been judged incompetent. The great majority of such offenders will improve quickly in institutions which offer psychotherapy and milieu therapy.* If their cases can be adjudicated before they have spent months or years in an oppressive institution, both individual and community interests are served. For those offenders who have been found to be incompetent and who do not recover (including many of the mentally defective), there is still much that can be done. The majority of these individuals can reach a state of psychological improvement which allows them to manage their lives in a relatively open setting. This group would include those offenders who might be unable to master the intellectual rigors and emotional stress of the courtroom situation (and would therefore continually be judged incompetent) but who could nevertheless manage to function in a protective setting within the community. These individuals can eventually be paroled to a status of free, tax-paying citizens.

The rehabilitation of offenders sent to units for the criminally insane following a decision of not guilty by reason of insanity is often hindered by community pressures. Commitment of those adjudicated nonresponsible is likely to be invoked primarily to reassure the public that one who has offended but who is found not guilty will, nevertheless, be controlled. Too often the civil commitment becomes a symbolic vehicle for society's frus-

* The term "milieu therapy" is here used to describe the same kind of therapeutic activity as would be available in any psychiatric hospital. It would include efforts to maintain a therapeutic attitude on the part of all personnel, individual-attitude therapy for specific offenders, group and ward involvement in hospital decisions (therapeutic community), ready availability of physicians and counselors, occupational therapy, recreational therapy, pastoral therapy and regular planned contacts with the community. There is no reason why these kinds of therapeutic activities cannot be offered to the disturbed criminal in a hospital setting. The relatively free and open therapeutic community has been demonstrated by Maxwell Jones and others to be effective in treating serious character disorders.[10, 11]

trated vengeance. A person exonerated of a charge involving serious bodily harm is sometimes civilly committed, with the court stipulating that he not be released until he is totally "cured." Sometimes the superintendent of the unit for the criminally insane is required to assure the court that the offender will not commit a similar crime. Such legal restrictions which are supported by punitive community attitudes are not designed to encourage superintendents to release this type of patient quickly. In practice some units retain offenders who have been found not guilty by reason of insanity as long as or longer than offenders who have committed similar crimes and have been confined in prison under a criminal commitment.[12]

Determination of release by vindictive community attitudes rather than by criteria of psychological fitness to live in a free world subverts the humane intention of the law. If society wishes to continue to designate some offenders as nonresponsible and therefore not guilty of their crimes, it at least ought to be consistent and treat such individuals as sick people. The so-called nonresponsible offender often responds quickly to treatment and is ready to leave an institution after a short period of hospitalization. The most advanced units for the criminally insane attempt to work intensively with such offenders. The institutional staff prepares him for discharge or parole as soon as he no longer poses a danger to the community. Unfortunately, only a few institutions are courageous enough to follow such a procedure.

Many of the inmates confined to units for the criminally insane are sentenced offenders who have been unable to adjust to a prison environment.[13] When transferred to a unit which has even minimum psychiatric facilities, people in this group usually recover quickly. Serious problems arise, however, when it becomes necessary to return the patient to the prison. It is frustrating for both the patient and his physician when the patient improves and is immediately returned to the same environment which helped to produce his disturbance in the first place. Yet the physician has little choice. In most states time spent in a hospital for the criminally insane interferes with parole possibilities. The hospitalized offender cannot even earn time off for good behavior. A common problem with this group of offenders is that they reluctantly return to the prison, whereupon they soon experience another episode of psychotic disorganization. Their wasteful travel between the state hospital and the prison interferes with any realistic treatment goal. This situation could be remedied if correctional systems either improved their facilities or allowed offenders who could not adjust to the stresses of prison to serve out their sentences in institutions that were more similar to hospitals.

## Sex-Crimes Programs

More than 50 percent of states in this country have some type of law which provides for specialized treatment of sex offenders. Most of these laws were developed in the late 1940's or early 1950's at a time when little was known about the sex offender. Much of the hurried legislation has been directed against the so-called sexual psychopath and was encouraged by exceptional public alarm and indignation over highly publicized and brutal sex crimes.[14, 15] Some legislatures were so frightened of the sexual psychopath that they passed laws which provided for commitment on the basis of a diagnosis of sexual deviation alone without regard to the dangerousness of the offender and even in the absence of conviction for criminal behavior.[16] Fortunately, these early laws were found to be so unworkable and so dangerous to constitutional liberties that they were rarely used. More recent laws have stipulated that the offender must be convicted of a crime and that there must be some evidence of treatability or dangerousness before any type of specialized commitment is invoked.

No two states have developed exactly the same kind of legislation for dealing with sex offenders. Programs spawned by sex-crimes laws vary greatly. Almost every law provides for special diagnostic procedures to identify the compulsive, the deviated or the dangerous sex offender. Most laws also provide for indeterminate commitment of this special group to a state hospital, to a unit for the criminally insane or to a prison. In some states only a diagnostic phase of the law is operative. Specialized sentencing or treatment is not available. In other states laws which provide for indeterminate sentencing result in commitment of sex offenders to institutions which are incapable of providing adequate treatment. These are the state programs which have caused many attorneys to fear that indeterminacy will lead to injustices. As might be expected, judges in these states frequently refuse to invoke a specialized commitment. Only a few states combine a program of indeterminate sentencing with provisions for realistic treatment facilities.

Unfortunately, the motivations which have produced most sex-crimes programs are more punitive than rehabilitative and more controlling than kindly. Sex-crimes laws are aimed primarily at the dangerous offender. They are sometimes written by legislators who make the erroneous assumption that all sexually disturbed people are dangerous. The laws seem to ignore the fact that the major portion of sexally disturbed individuals do not commit crimes of violence.[17, 18] Many of the problems of implementing or sustaining a program for sex offenders arise out of this misconception. In emphasizing control rather than treatment, sex-crimes programs reflect a greatly magnified fear of the sex offender and an unjustified pessimism as to his treatability.

Perhaps the easiest way to clarify the relationship of psychiatry to the administration of sex-crimes laws is to examine in detail the program of one state. The author is most familiar with the Wisconsin program, with which he has been associated for the past seven years. He is convinced that this program, while by no means faultless, is the most successful means of dealing with large groups of disturbed sex offenders which has been developed to date.

Wisconsin's Sex Crimes Law was enacted on July 27, 1951. Before that time a sex-crimes law had been passed (1947) which provided for diagnosis but which did not establish adequate facilities for treatment. Under the 1947 law no commitments were ever made, and prior to 1951 sex offenders in Wisconsin were committed under the usual criminal codes. Provisions were not available to detain dangerous offenders who had served out their original commitment. The 1951 law sought to establish legal and administrative procedures which would allow for identification and special treatment and insure that the dangerous sex offender could be detained for an indeterminate period.[19]

The current law provides that any person convicted of the crimes of rape, attempted rape or indecent sexual behavior with a child must be committed to the State Department of Public Welfare for a presentence examination. The Department must complete this examination within sixty days and submit a report of its findings and recommendations to the court. If, as a result of its findings, the Department determines that the individual is not in need of specialized treatment for mental or physical aberrations, the court must impose sentence, as provided by the criminal code. If, however, the individual is found in need of specialized treatment, the court must either place him on probation on the condition that he receive outpatient psychiatric treatment or the court must institutionalize him for an indefinite period.

Once committed under this law, the sex offender may be administratively handled in several different ways. Parole may be granted at any time, or the offender may be discharged at the expiration of the maximum term prescribed by the criminal law for the offense for which he is committed. When discharge of an offender is considered dangerous to the public, continuance of control beyond the maximum term may be recommended. These various dispositions allow for a sentence that is almost completely indeterminate. The offender can be put on probation, can be released within a few months after his commitment, or he can be institutionalized for life.

Decisions as to parole are made by a special review board. This board, appointed by the Department of Public Welfare, is entrusted with the task of evaluating the offender's capabilities of adjusting to a free society. The composition of the board includes representatives of the disciplines of law, psychiatry and social work. Once an individual is paroled, the technical conditions of his parole are regulated by the Department in the same manner as for individuals committed under criminal statutes. The Department may grant discharge from parole when there is a reasonable probability that the offender can be released from supervision without endangering the public.

Prolonged institutionalization (beyond the length of time the individual would have served under the criminal code) is invoked only when the Department believes that the dicharge of a person from the institution could be dangerous to the public. At the expiration of the maximum term prescribed by law for the particular offense, application is made to the committing court for a continuance of control. The offender can protest this petition, and although he is not entitled to trial by jury, he does have a right to counsel and to an examination and use of the testimony of a psychiatrist of his own choosing. If the court finds that the offender's discharge would be dangerous to the public, it may extend the Department's control for a period of five years. Subsequent five-year commitments can be continued indefinitely (by the court) as long as the individual is felt to be dangerous. During the eleven years from June, 1951, to June, 1962, sixty-two offenders had their commitments extended once, and two offenders had their commitments extended twice.

The major concern of those entrusted with operating the diagnostic phase of the law is determining who is to be committed for specialized treatment and who is to be handled under the usual criminal statutes. The wording of the statutes is vague. The psychiatrist is asked only to determine whether the sex offender is in need of specialized treatment for mental or physical aberrations. The presence of such aberrations, however, does not require the psychiatrist to recommend a specialized commitment. This means that the psychiatrist is given considerable leeway in formulating his own criteria as to who is to be given an indeterminate commitment. On the other hand, although the psychiatrist can determine the type of commitment, he is given absolutely no power to decide who is to be put on probation and who is to be institutionalized. In this sense his role differs greatly from that which is taken in ordinary civil commitments.

From the inception of the program, the working philosophy of the psychiatric staff has been to recommend specialized treatment for those believed to be "sexually deviated." This criterion still leaves considerable ambiguity as the term "deviated" can be defined in a number of different ways. Since 1960 an effort has been made to diagnose sexual deviation on the basis of two formal criteria: first, an immaturity in the development of sexual functions; second, a deviation in the offender's sexual aim or object which he feels driven to satisfy and which he feels he cannot control. These criteria imply that an individual who adapts to stress by acting upon sexually immature motivations is likely to commit further crimes unless he is provided with some kind of treatment. Although this interpretation of sexual deviation provides the psychiatrist with a more precise guideline for recommending specialized treatment, it still suffers from serious shortcomings, which we will consider in a later part of this chapter.

The court determines what is to be done with the individual who is found to be "deviated." Probation with mandatory psychiatric outpatient treatment is sometimes ordered. The great majority of those called deviates, however, receive treatment in the highly restrictive setting of the Wisconsin State Prison. Here the sex offender is handled in almost the same way as any other prisoner. The one major exception to this statement is that the sex deviate is almost always required to participate in a program of individual or group psychotherapy.

One of the convictions of those entrusted with the operation of this program is that decisions as to diagnosis or treatment include so many variables and have such an important meaning to the offender and society that they should not be made by a single professional person. Wherever possible, consensus as to dispositional decisions is arrived at by several persons working in a staff setting. A formal "staffing" is always utilized to determine who is to be committed indeterminately and to determine if sentence is to be extended on the basis of potential dangerousness.

Although the Wisconsin State Sex Crimes Program operates far more smoothly than most similar programs in other states, there are many aspects of the program which can be criticized. It was developed at a time when there was great public alarm, but very little available knowledge, as to the dangerousness of sex offenders. As such, the law, like other sex-crimes laws, leans heavily toward control. Most disturbingly, it does not discriminate between control of offenders who are dangerous and control of those who are not. The criteria for determining what we would call "sexual deviancy" are based entirely upon concepts of mental illness. Immature behavior in the sense we have used it here implies unreasonable behavior, and a compulsive need to act upon deviant impulses suggests that the individual cannot control himself. Unfortunately, use of criteria derived wholly from concepts of mental illness leads to the commitment of some offenders who are neither dangerous nor treatable.

It might be assumed that offenders who are required to have a mandatory examination would be mainly dangerous individuals since they have all committed crimes of rape, attempted rape or indecent liberties with a child. This is not always the case. A certain number of offenders convicted of such crimes may have been influenced by unusual circumstances which would not be likely to recur. For many, the shame and public humiliation of arrest and trial are sufficient future deterrents. It might also be assumed that all sex deviates are amenable to psychiatric treatment. This again is not true. While sex offenders as a group respond well to psychotherapy, some seem to lack even the minimum amount of motivation that is necessary for change. Some of those we call deviated are neither dangerous nor treatable and yet can be committed for longer periods than if they had been sentenced under the criminal code. This undesirable situation could be remedied if the factors of dangerousness and treatability were added to our criteria for specialized treatment. At the present time efforts are being made to integrate these criteria into the diagnostic process, but there has been considerable resistance and it is unlikely that they will be accepted in the immediate future.

We have previously expressed the opinion that confinement for an indeterminate period of time to an institution which does not provide adequate treatment is a cruel punishment for the offender. It is especially cruel if that confinement is to a prison. Although Wisconsin State Prison is probably one of the best institutions of its kind, it still remains an oppressive fortress which fosters practices and attitudes which are sometimes detrimental and even opposed to rehabilitative goals. The prison is an especially unfortunate placement for the sex offender. He is restricted to an environment which is more likely to push him in the direction of developing further aberrant sexual tendencies. He is deprived of contacts with women, put into situations which encourage primitive sexual fantasies and exposed to the constant temptation of homosexuality. In such a setting the odds are stacked against resolving sexual conflicts. The prison environment also makes gradual release into the community almost impossible. Contact with the outside world, in the form of weekend passes or temporary leaves, is unfortunately never allowed. The use of the prison as a "treatment" institution represents one of the more serious shortcomings of Wisconsin's program. Fortunately, this situation may soon be remedied. The state of Wisconsin is now allocating funds for a new institution which will house sex offenders. This institution will be less restrictive than a maximum-security prison and will contain modern treatment facilities.

While psychotherapy or counseling is more readily available to the offender committed under Wisconsin's Sex Crimes Law than to offenders in most other programs, the quantity of service offered still does not fulfill what many psychiatrists would consider to be minimum standards. The current staff of psychiatric consultants, psychologists and social workers is sufficiently numerous so that it is possible to give far more psychotherapeutic time to each individual than is offered in the average state hospital. There are still, however, a small percentage of offenders who are seen as infrequently as every other week and some who are seen monthly. This group is largely made up of offenders who have had a trial of therapy, have not responded and are still felt to be too dangerous to leave the institution. Their situation is analogous to that of the chronically psychotic in the mental hospital who do not seem to be capable of being rehabilitated and yet may be too dangerous to be released.

As long as the author has been involved as one of the administrators of this program, minimum standards of treatment have been defined as the availability of at least one hour a week of group (or individual) psychotherapy for each offender who is felt to be capable of benefiting from it. The program administrators have agreed that if a time came when such a standard could no longer be maintained, a sincere effort would be made to change the law so that indeterminacy would be recommended only for those who could be provided with adequate treatment.

Still another criticism of the Wisconsin Sex Crimes Program is that there has never been sufficient staff to allow for independent evaluation as to when an offender will be allowed an early appearance before the special review board. At present the offender's own therapist makes this decision, although every offender is seen routinely on an annual basis. We have previously noted the conflicts generated when a psychiatrist attempts to be both the patient's agent and society's agent at the same time. A mingling of evaluative and psychotherapeutic functions is especially difficult. A therapist has great difficulty in encouraging honest rapport if the patient knows that his doctor will have considerable influence in deciding what is going to happen to him. The offender in such a situation is tempted to look as "healthy as possible," and his therapy is hindered by the fear that his confidential communications of "weaknesses" (supposedly confidential) will be used to hurt him. In practice the offender is told that the content of his communications during therapy will always be confidential unless they refer to intended physical harm to other inmates, the institution or to the patient himself. He is clearly informed, however, that he is constantly being evaluated and that reports as to his progress will be presented to those who must make decisions as to the length of his confinement.

A final criticism which could be made of the Wisconsin State Sex Crimes Program is that it encourages a disproportionate emphasis on the problems of one class of offenders. Since state law requires that the sex deviate be treated, this class of offenders very quickly uses up the time of prison psychiatrists and other psychotherapists. The ordinary offender in Wisconsin institutions is hard pressed to find adequate psychiatric care.[20] There also may be individuals in our prisons who are as dangerous as or more dangerous to their fellow men than most sex offenders. It makes little sense to direct extremely scarce psychiatric personnel to spend all their time caring for a group of offenders who may not be the most treatable or the most dangerous.

The author is hesitant to quote some of the statistical results of the program because these are expressed mainly in terms of recidivism rates. Recidivism rates are notoriously misleading. They give only a superficial picture of the offender's behavior and say nothing about his community adjustment or his psychological status. They do not tell us whether the offender is in a mental hospital or is a reasonably well-adjusted taxpaying citizen. Recidivism rates are used mainly for rhetorical purposes. If they are low, it can be argued that treatment has been successful. If they are high, it can be argued that parole officers are doing an exceptionally fine job of supervising their clients or that greater facilities are very much needed.

In the absence of control groups and thorough follow-ups of the psychological and social status of the released offender, there is no scientific validation of the usefulness of our program. The following data cover only the first nine years of the program's operation. They are suggestive and hopeful, but certainly not conclusive.[21]

During the period July, 1951, through May, 1960, a total of 1,605 male sex offenders were examined for diagnostic purposes. Of this total 783 (49 percent) were found to be deviated, 66 (4 percent) were found to be psychotic, mentally deficient or epileptic and were committed to the state hospital for the criminally insane and 75 (47 percent) were nondeviated. Of the 783 individuals who were found to be deviated and handled under the sex-crimes act, 146 were given probation with outpatient psychiatric treatment and 632 were committed to the Wisconsin State Prison. Of these 632 individuals, 475 had been granted parole through May 31, 1960. Only 81 violated that parole. This is a violation rate of 17 percent. Of this group only 43, or 9 percent, violated their parole by committing a new sex crime. Of those 414 individuals who were totally discharged from departmental control so that they were no longer on parole, 29, or 7 percent, committed a new offense.

In spite of its may obvious limitations, a sex-crimes program, such as that which is currently operating in Wisconsin, is a useful model and represents a small step in the right direction. The law upon which it is founded provides for a more scientific control of dangerous offenders and, more importantly, it offers the possibility of treatment and early release for others. Although many mistakes have been made in developing an extensive program centered around only one type of offender, the model has much to recommend it. The principles which guide the operation of the Wisconsin Sex Crimes Program could also be applied to other kinds of unreasonable and dangerous behaviors.

## The Diagnostic Reception Center

In a few states convicted felons are sent to a closed hospital-type institution for psychiatric examination either before being sentenced or before they begin serving a prison term. In the state of New Jersey selected offenders are examined before sentencing at the New Jersey Diagnostic Center. This reception center functions very much like a court clinic except that the offender spends a period of several weeks under observation in a closed institution. The Federal Prison system currently uses the Springfield Medical Center for Federal Prisoners for the same purpose. Under Public Law 752 the sentencing judge may request that the offender be given a psychiatric examination at a federal institution prior to imposition of sentence. The state of Kansas utilizes separate facilites for diagnostic study of offenders who have already been sentenced. In California all convicted offenders are examined (either before or after sentencing) at the state medical facility in Vacaville or at other reception centers located within the state prisons. Michigan, Illinois and Minnesota have similar programs.

The psychiatrist in such a setting is primarily a diagnostician. It is true that the short period the offender spends in the reception center may lead to a number of therapeutic interactions which may "soften" the experience of subsequent incarceration. Little in the way of formal therapy can, however, be carried out during a short evaluation. The main values of the reception center are that it guides the offender to the proper institution (or in some cases probation), that it instructs those who are to work with the offender about specific problems which might arise and that it recommends therapeutic attitudes which might be useful.

The ultimate value of the psychiatrist's diagnostic report is dependent upon what is done with it. In some states, once the offender leaves the benign atmosphere of the reception center to enter the restrictive environment of the prison, all the arduously prepared formulations of the psychiatrist are either ignored or are found to be too impractical to implement. Diagnostic reception centers seem to be most effective in states, such as California, which are capable of implementing specific treatment recommendations. The great variety of institutions in California, some of which have impressive rehabilitative programs, offers the possibility of utilizing psychiatric data to make individualized placements which have a greater likelihood of being therapeutically useful.

### The Prison Hospital

Some state prisons have set aside small units for the treatment of emotionally disturbed inmates. Most of these provide only minimum care designed to carry the inmate through a rough period. Large-scale treatment of convicted offenders in a prison hospital setting is currently available only in California and in the Federal Prison system. Both the California Medical Facility (Vacaville) and the Medical Center for Federal Prisoners (Springfield) carry out diagnostic work designed to aid in the disposition process. Their major function, however, is to provide psychiatric treatment for disturbed offenders who are felt to be more likely to respond to a hospital than to a traditional prison setting. Both institutions greatly resemble prisons insofar as they are custody-minded, but they differ from traditional prisons insofar as they offer individualized attention and a great variety of psychiatric and medical treatments. Both institutions are also similar to hospitals for the criminally insane insofar as they are administered by physicians. They differ here in that they treat only convicted men who actually serve their sentences at that institution.

In California, state law provides that any male under correctional custody who is so physically and mentally disabled as to require medical care may be admitted to the California Medical Facility.[22] A considerable number of emotionally disturbed offenders are admitted to Vacaville directly from reception centers. The remainder of the population is made up of offenders who are transferred from other institutions. The Medical Center for Federal Prisoners (which also contains a large medical and surgical service) receives almost all of their psychiatric patients from other prisons, and puts greater emphasis upon treating offenders who have decompensated under the stress of incarceration.

The potential value of prison hospitals can be illustrated by a brief description of the Vacaville program.[23] The hospital unit treats approximately one thousand patients and houses an additional three hundred inmate workers. Staff organization is not patterned along classic prison lines. The institution is divided into five units where inmates undergo treatment under the same staff members on a daily basis. An effort is made to involve every patient in treatment and every employee (including those defined as custodial) as active participants in the treatment process. Therapy sessions, which average two hours weekly, are combined with milieu activites, including academic education, vocational training, religious programs, occupational therapy, handicrafts, social clubs, library and music. The three hundred inmate workers who do not receive formal psychotherapy are required to participate in group counseling conducted by custodial staff members. Although acknowledging that it is still a prison, the Vacaville facility attempts to utilize every aspect of institutional living to facilitate therapeutic change. The staff is committed to a working philosophy which seeks to prevent institutional needs or security requirements from interfering with the treatment program.

One of the most important functions of the prison hospital is to serve as a model for the rest of the correctional system. It is no coincidence that the two programs which have the most effective prison hospitals also have developed two of the nation's better correctional programs. Prisons in California and the federal system seem to have borrowed some philosophies of treatment from their hospital institutions. This is not only because the prison hospital trains personnel who will later work in other institutions, but also because it demonstrates to the entire prison system that criminals can change if somebody is willing to work with them.

## THE PATUXENT INSTITUTION

A unique experiment in medical treatment and control of dangerous criminal behavior was made possible by the Maryland "defective delinquent" law, a law which led to the establishment of the Patuxent Institution in January of 1955. The law provides for indeterminate commitment and specialized treatment for the "defective delinquent," who defined as "an individual who by the demonstration of persistent, aggravated, antisocial or criminal behavior evidences a propensity toward criminal activity and is found to have either some intellectual deficiency or emotional imbalance or both as to clearly demonstrate an actual danger to society."[24] This definition is vague. It seems to call for the utilization of criteria of both emotional disturbance and dangerousness to recommend an indeterminate commitment. (The term "defective delinquent" is unfortunate since it implies mental retardation. Most of the offenders who are sentenced under this program have intellectual capacities which are similar to those of any other group of offenders. It seems that the founders of the law had something more similar to "psychopathy" in mind.) In practice the law does not restrict commitment to offenders who have committed crimes against persons. It therefore can lead to the commitment of almost any type of repeated offender, including some whose dangerousness is questionable.

The Patuxent Institution tries to maintain a therapeutic orientation similar to that of a mental hospital. Concepts of milieu therapy are accepted and group or individual psychotherapy is available. Some inmates are given the privilege of leaving the institution for short passes on holidays or weekends. Arrangements are possible which permit a few selected inmates to leave the institution to work at normal occupations during the day and to return at night.[25] Because the Patuxent Institution cares for many dangerous offenders, it has exerted great restraint in paroling its inmates. The recidivism rate of those released has up to now been no worse than that of less troublesome prisoners released from other institutions.

For the past ten years the Patuxent Institution has with remarkably little fanfare conducted a truly indeterminate program of control and treatment of socially hazardous offenders. The program is probably less well known to psychiatrists and correctional workers than it is to attorneys. Some attorneys, sensing potential threats to the "defective delinquent's" civil liberties, have seriously scrutinized and questioned the constitutionality of the law.[26] Up to this point, however, the program has been allowed to continue with little change. This writer feels that the Patuxent program could serve as a model for the treatment of dangerous offenders if two major conditions were met.* First, there has to be some guarantee that treatment facilities and levels of staff competence are kept high enough so that constant efforts are made to rehabilitate indeterminately sentenced offenders. Second, it would seem useful to spell out criteria for dangerousness in such a way that they would limit the program to treatment of the offender who commits crimes against persons.

## The Narcotics Hospital

There is probably no other form of social deviation that produces such a variety of conflicting attitudes and recommendations for social change as that of narcotic addiction. Some say that the narcotic addict is a sick

* The reader will note that the basic model of the Patuxent program is similar to the Wisconsin Sex Crimes Program. Although there are technical differences in implementation, the Maryland law applies the same principles of treatment and control to a broader class of offenders.

person who uses drugs for the same reason an individual might use a tranquilizer. They would argue that the addict should be treated by the physician.[27] Others believe that the individual who uses or sells drugs is a criminal.[28] The latter group insists that the addict must be punished and deterred. They argue that only harsh measures will stop the flow of drugs to this country. At the moment the philosophy of punitiveness is dominant. In the United States the narcotic addict is a criminal. Physicians are allowed only minimal contact with the addict and risk being defined as criminals themselves when they attempt to prescribe drugs or to treat addicts on an outpatient basis. Some legislators have recommended increased use of civil commitment for the narcotic user, but their motivations seems to be engendered more by a wish to establish greater external control than by a desire to rehabilitate. At the present time most narcotic addicts are subjected to involuntary institutional commitment, which usually means imprisonment. Another sizable group either voluntarily commit themselves or are involuntarily committed by the courts to the federal narcotics hospitals at Lexington or Fort Worth.

In the federal narcotics hospitals psychiatrists attempt to rehabilitate the user through a milieu and psychotherapy approach. The most effective aspect of the program involves a carefully supervised withdrawal from the drug. Gradually decreasing dosages of narcotic and other tranquilizing drugs are given until the addict is able to be reasonably comfortable in a drug-free condition. The narcotics hospital is effective in withdrawing offenders from addicting drugs and in keeping them in a fairly comfortable stage as long as they are institutionalized. Once the offender returns to the community, however, he is likely to experience new difficulties.

It has been estimated that less than 15 percent of those who have been treated ultimately abstain from further drug usage.[29] This high rate of failure should not be unexpected. In addition to the fact that drug addicts are socially immature individuals and the fact that the drugs (particularly heroin) offer such a marvelously effective source of relief from feelings of oppression, the confused attitude of society seems to make things even worse. Exposing the drug addict to a medical model of treatment and then returning him to the streets, where no help is offered and where any further usage will define him as a criminal, is not calculated to relieve oppressive stress. Not a single community in this country makes a reasonable effort to treat its narcotic users. Humane service in the narcotics hospital is not enough. As long as a rehabilitative approach is rigorously excluded from the community setting there can be little realistic hope of treating the drug addict.[30]

### The Psychiatrist and the Police

The police officer is probably the most important person in maintaining law and order and preventing crime.[31] It is unfortunate, therefore, that behavioral scientists have paid so little attention to his needs and problems. Psychiatrists have been particularly negligent. Periodically, psychiatrists have been employed as consultants to large-city police forces, but few sustained or intensive relationships have ever developed. Often the skills of the police psychiatrist are used only for crime detection (e.g., running a polygraph) or determining the competency of plaintiffs. A more effective current use of psychiatric consultants is to screen police applicants and examine police officers who are believed to be emotionally disturbed. Even here the use of psychiatry has been quite spotty. In many municipalities the extent of "screening" service provided is limited to group psychological testing.

When the psychiatrist does agree to examine potential police recruits, he is more of an agent for the state than for the patient. He therefore has an obligation to clarify to those he examines that he is not operating within the usual doctor-patient relationship and that confidentially will not be honored. When examining police officers whose emotional disturbances are believed to be interfering with their work, the physician's responsibilities are much broader. In such cases the physician not only is interested in reporting to the organization but also has the opportunity to be helpful to the officer. While still fulfilling his responsibilities to the police organization he may be able to help the individual officer work out some of his problems. If the physician feels that the nature of his "double agent" relationship cannot be conducive to effective therapy, he has a moral obligation to make certain that the officer receives the help he needs from a more neutral therapist.

There has been little emphasis on the educating of police officers to a better understanding of human behavior and even less emphasis upon helping the police officer to understand himself. Both educative functions could be extremely valuable. The police officer who is aware of the motivations and conflicts of criminals is in a better position to deal with criminals. If he is aware of his own blind spots, his own motivations and his own strengths, he will be even more effective in his work. Although a few municipalities offer orientation courses in human behavior, there remains an enormous need for psychiatric participation in the ongoing training and counseling of police officers.

*Chapter 18*

# PSYCHIATRY AND THE JUVENILE DELINQUENT

THE medical model of treatment has had a broad influence in shaping the entire system of correctional justice for juveniles. For the most part, this influence has been beneficial. Before we can describe the usefulness of the psychiatric approach, however, we must also examine some possible adverse effects of utilizing a medical model to determine the disposition of youthful offenders. In an earlier chapter we discussed inconsistencies in the adult American culture which posed serious conflicts for the adolescent. At this point we will examine some of the practices of juvenile courts and professional youth workers, which, although based on a medical model of helpfulness, seem to encourage new and incapacitating maladaptive responses.

The first juvenile court in America was established in Cook County, Illinois, in 1899. Its aim was to offer adolescent offenders individualized justice and treatment rather than impartial justice and punishment. Provisions were made for civil rather than criminal commitment. By 1945 juvenile courts had been established in every state in the country. Today, with few exceptions, a child under the age of seventeen or eighteen who violates a penal law is not designated a criminal but is called a juvenile delinquent. He retains a civil status, and his disposition is determined in much the same way as a person who is legally defined as mentally ill.[1, 2]

Juvenile courts were initially developed to protect the child from exposure to the harsh punishments found in traditional correctional institutions. They were oriented toward individual needs. Society was to be served only insofar as it was hoped that rehabilitated delinquents would not become adult criminals. The origins of this philosophy in the medical model of treatment are apparent. One judge has expressed the juvenile court philosophy as follows: "The court is more like a hospital or clinic than like anything else. If a person's bodily functions deviate so far from normal that he cannot be properly treated in his home, he is ordered to a hospital. If a child's conduct deviates so far from normal that he cannot be successfully corrected in the home, he is ordered to a juvenile court."[3]

Adhering to a belief in treatment rather than punishment, the juvenile court seeks to avoid conventional legal processes. Courtroom proceedings are often conducted in secrecy, with the hope that the child will be protected from publicity. Proof of guilt for the commission of a crime is not a requirement for court action since the concern is for the needs of the child rather than for social justice. In practice a child can be sent to an institution because his parents, his teachers or the court feel that it will be for his own welfare. Commitment is almost as indeterminate as for the mentally ill. The child is routinely committed until the age of twenty-one, when he legally becomes an adult.

The apparent advantages of such a system are obvious. First of all, its philosophy is humane and nonpunitive. The delinquent is seen as an individual who needs the services of the community, and the court is given much leeway in providing help. Protection from a lengthy fixed commitment (which in earlier days usually meant sentencing to an institution where he associated with older felons) is guaranteed, and the child can be released as soon as he is rehabilitated. He is spared publicity and is offered a kind of paternalistic protection which may well be needed during a troubled phase in his life.

In practice, unfortunately, the juvenile court is capable of perpetrating a wide variety of injustices.[4] An obvious problem is that the suspected delinquent is not afforded due process. He can be arrested and institutionalized without any proof of a crime having been committed. He does not have an opportunity to defend himself in court. Many delinquents are committed to institutions for activities which would not have been defined as crimes if they had been carried out by adults. This is especially true in the case of girls, who, as we have noted, are most often committed for promiscuity and running away from home. Even with boys, "offenses" such as smoking, truancy, unconventional dress, promiscuity or disrespectfulness not infrequently result in threatened or actual commitment. The adolescent is subjected to a peculiarly stern kind of oppressive justice (under the guise of treatment) which is rarely imposed upon people who may be just a few years older. He is practically helpless in fighting back. Since he is being "treated" rather than punished, he has no protection from an insensitive judge, unloving parents or an unconcerned community.[5, 6]

In practice juvenile courts commit many youths who can hardly be considered criminals but who rather have created a minor social problem for which the parents and the community are unwilling to take responsibility. The list of "atrocity stories" in this area is endless. The author has personally observed cases of children committed for such "crimes" as dating a boy of a different race, consenting to sexual intercourse, talking back to one's parents, truancy or "incorrigibility." It is, of course, always argued that such commitments are made not on the basis of an offense but rather on the basis of the child's needs. Yet in the majority of instances the child's record did not convince the author that institutionalization was necessary.

The juvenile court system is especially discriminatory against members of the lower socioeconomic classes. If parents are negligent or unwilling or unable to care for their children, commitment for juvenile delinquency is much more likely. The author knows of a number of cases in which parents simply wanted to rid themselves of the burdensome responsibility of raising a child and the court clinic obliged by declaring that child delinquent. Sometimes the court responds to pressures from schools, churches and other agencies by removing the child from the community and placing him in a training school.

All this might be justifiable if every institution for juvenile delinquents was dedicated to providing high levels of social and medical care. This, unfortunately, is not the case. Some institutions for juvenile delinquents do make sincere attempts to offer the best kind of individualized treatment, but many children's institutions are no less cruel and barbaric than our adult prisons. Under the older system of criminal commitment the adolescent at least had the opportunity to be released from an institution after a reasonably short fixed sentence. Under an indeterminate code a child of thirteen who is committed for truancy could spend eight years in confinement. Indeterminate commitment to an oppressive institution is not only harmful to the child but ultimately hurts the community, since the training school is too often nothing more than a breeding place for more crime.

An especially frightening aspect of the juvenile court system is that a child confined to a juvenile institution can be transferred to an adult institution even if he has never committed a criminal act.[6] Some children who are committed for treatment purposes become serious disciplinary problems within juvenile institutions. If they are felt to be unmanageable, they are likely to be transferred to state prisons and reformatories. As our juvenile institutions become overcrowded, the number of "unmanageable" delinquents transferred to reformatories or prisons is rapidly increasing. In a small state such as Wisconsin, for example, there are almost two hundred juveniles at the reformatory. Under the current system it is possible for a boy to be committed for truancy, spend many years in adult institutions, come out a confirmed criminal and perhaps spend the major part of his life behind bars.

If we weigh advantages against disadvantages, it is extremely difficult to justify our current juvenile court system except in those few states that provide exceptionally fine facilities for treatment. It is discouraging to consider the potential impact of our current system upon disturbed adolescents. The system can have adverse effects both upon those who have never committed a crime and upon those who have. Regulations which are backed up by the threat of imprisonment and which are applicable only to people of a certain age group are easily experienced as an arbitrary source of oppression. Many adolescents come to feel that they are being overly controlled by a society which punishes them for behaviors in which adults indulge with impunity. One observer, David Matza, has suggested that this special imposition of stress may in itself be a cause of delinquency.[7] He argues that the juvenile court system defines delinquency as a greater problem than it actually is and that the court's paternalism is often despotic. Faced with unusual oppression, the adolescent comes to react to the adult world with an increased sense of injustice and a decreased sense of social responsibility. Matza believes that the imposition of a separate system of correctional justice upon juveniles may contribute to the rebelliousness that characterizes our adolescent population. Whether this system actually does produce more delinquency is debatable. Its impact upon the adolescent who has been defined as delinquent, or is about to be defined as delinquent, is more observable.

There is reason to ask ourselves whether the delinquent child can come away from the juvenile court experience without feeling that he has been treated in a dishonest manner. It would seem likely that the child who is sent to a punitive institution because he created a minor disturbance and who is then told that he is being given treatment for his own good might experience bitterness and resentment. In an earlier publication, the author has attempted to examine this problem from a different vantage point, namely, in terms of the impact of similar dishonest conmmunications coming from professional workers (teachers, social workers, psychologists and psychiatrists). An adolescent who is in trouble and who is subjected to the control of various agencies (some of which are attached to the juvenile court and some of which are not) may be seriously damaged by professional workers who do not present their intentions in a straightforward manner. The end results may be distrust and rebelliousness toward all helping agencies. While the following material is concerned with the impact of dishonesty in a clinical setting, most of the observations would be as relevant or perhaps even more relevant in the courtroom.

There are seven major areas in which adolescent clients are deceived by professional workers. While the professional may not be aware of his own deceptions and may see himself as an entirely benevolent person, the adolescent is more likely to perceive these communications as lies.

## The Lie of Adult Morality*

In confronting the chaotic sexuality and poorly controlled aggressiveness of the adolescent, most professional workers communicate the possibility of a world in which such impulses are resolved easily. They imply that adults control their impulses and that success in the world is dependent upon such restraint. To a limited extent this is certainly true. Too often, however, they present a picture of the world that is far removed from reality and does not take cognizance of the social usefulness of certain kinds of aggressive and sexual behavior. The adolescent boy knows that aggressiveness, and sometimes unscrupulous aggressiveness, may be a prerequisite for success. He knows that the interviewer sitting behind the desk has probably struggled aggressively to gain the status of a professional position. The sexually promiscuous adolescent girl knows (even if she has not read the Kinsey report) that on a statistical basis the professional person with whom she interacts has probably at some time in his life been guilty of the same behavior for which she is being punished.

It may be unrealistic to communicate readily the worker's own deficiencies and therefore provide the adolescent rationalizations for disturbed behavior. There is a frequent tendency, however, to err in the other direction. Professionals communicate a picture of themselves and their world as one in which only the highest type of values and moral standards prevail. The adolescent cannot understand this. His personal experiences, his observational powers and his intuitiveness tell him that something is wrong. He wants to like and to identify with adults, but he is painfully aware of an inconsistency or basic dishonesty in their approach. He may then come to believe that adults are incapable of being anything but "phony" and react by rebellious behavior or isolation from the adult world.

This type of dishonesty is seen with considerably less frequency in private psychotherapeutic interactions, especially with adults. Here the worker tries to produce a climate in which the universality of antisocial impulses

* The following material, up to and including the first paragraph on p. 275, is quoted with permission from *Social Work,* 8:2 (April, 1963), 48–53.[8]

is recognized and usually discussed freely. An unwillingness to extend this same honesty to a large portion of adolescent patients is a serious error. The adolescent is struggling to understand the adult world. He will learn the truth about it whether he is told or not.

### The Lie of Professional Helpfulness

The professional worker who confronts adolescents in the courtroom, the community clinic or the state institution serves a dual role, as an agent of the community and as a helping person. The community wants him to control, attenuate or in some way modify the behavior of an individual who is causing it some distress. The worker is also interested in his client; he feels some wish to make the disturbed adolescent a more comfortable and effective person. It is important to understand, however, that in the majority of these situations the worker does not function as an agent of the adolescent patient. His salary is paid by the community. When the community's needs conflict with the adolescent's needs, it is often the community that must be obeyed and decisions are not always made entirely in the patient's interest. It is still possible within the limitations of this role for the worker to maintain an honest identification as someone who wants to help the adolescent. If he does not communicate, however, that one of his most basic roles is other than help-oriented, he is being dishonest.

Most adolescents do not seek help; they are sent for it. For example, take the case of an adolescent boy who has been a behavior problem in school and has been referred to the school psychologist. The boy is told that he must see a professional person and that the psychologist will try to help him. He knows, however, that the school is somewhat provoked with him and that its officials are going to act to prevent him from being an annoyance. He does not know what will be done. He does know that the school psychologist, functioning as the agent of the community, may exert a tremendous amount of power over him. As a result of his interaction with this professional worker he may be removed from school, forced to attend special classes or even removed from his home and sent to an institution. No matter how benign a person the school psychologist then turns out to be, it is very difficult for the adolescent to perceive him as a helping person.

As long as the worker and the adolescent are aware of the fact that the professional may be participating in mutually antagonistic roles, effective communication is possible. The situation is complicated, however, when the worker pretends that his only motivation in seeing the adolescent is to help him. The adolescent realizes that this is obviously untrue. He then perceives the adult worker as dishonest, which only makes him want to be dishonest in return. Experienced workers have learned that the word "help" rarely evinces a positive response from the adolescent. He experiences it as a kind of "Kafka"-like double-talk. In many settings, then, the word "help" is perceived by the adolescent as an unreliable and perhaps dangerous word.

### The Lie of Confidentiality

The issue of confidentiality is closely related to the problem of helpfulness. Most case workers, psychologists and psychiatrists have been taught that the model for a professional helping relationship is derived from the psychotherapeutic situation. In traditional forms of psychotherapy the communications of the patient or client to the worker are considered private material to be shared with no one outside the treatment situation. Many of the techniques professional workers use in interviewing, evaluating, diagnosing or counseling the adolescent are derived from what they were taught about psychotherapy. Often the worker behaves as though the adolescent were entitled to expect confidentiality and as though it were going to be provided. It is extremely rare for the adolescent to be told directly who is going to see the report the worker writes and with whom the case is going to be discussed.

The issue here, as with helpfulness, is that the worker cannot always guarantee confidentiality to the patient since he is not the agent of the patient. The worker has obligations to the child's family, his clinic, his agency or his institution. Even if after submitting an initial diagnostic report he begins to see the adolescent in a more traditional psychotherapeutic relationship, complete confidentiality can rarely be promised. While it is true that useful communication can take place between the worker and the adolescent without the guarantee of confidentiality, it is also true that to imply that this guarantee is extended, or to extend it with the full knowledge that it is not meant to be kept, can result in development of situations that inhibit communication. It does not take a very clever adolescent to understand that the worker has primary responsibilities to his agency and to the community. He may fully understand that whatever information he gives will be shared with others and can be used in making important decisions about him. If professionals do not let him know this, he will perceive their behavior as dishonest, and his communications to the adult world will be effectively diminished.

## The Lie of Rewards for Conformity

The necessity of conforming to adult standards is most often communicated to adolescents whose behavior deviates from the norms of the community. To this sizable proportion of disturbed adolescents, professional workers seem to be saying, "Your behavior is unacceptable. It produces more difficulty and leads you to experience more pain. It is to your own infinite advantage to be passive, to conform, to obey." There is ample evidence, however, that in attacking the behavioral defenses of the adolescent, workers remove character armor, leaving him more susceptible to anxiety. There is really little in the way of pleasure that can be promised to the adolescent if he risks giving up characterological defenses. This has been discussed previously in terms of the problems imposed on the criminal when he is viewed as a "patient."

> Society and the psychiatrist in particular may be imposing an almost intolerable burden on the delinquent in asking him to exchange the "bad" role for the sick role. It is not surprising that the criminal looks upon the usual rehabilitation program with cynicism and distrust. Only when those in charge of treatment searchingly ask themselves what they are trying to do to the delinquent when they try to make him into a conforming citizen and are able to appreciate what he is giving up in accepting the sick role can therapy be successful.[9]

It is always a moving, sometimes an overwhelming, experience to see an adolescent abandon behavioral expressions of conflict for a more introspective way of life. This is never accomplished without considerable pain and sometimes despair. If the adolescent is told that the simple expedient of conforming to adult standards produces pleasure, he is told a lie. Conformity on the part of the adolescent certainly meets the immediate needs of the community; whether it meets his needs is questionable. When workers pretend to him that it does, they encounter only confusion and anger, especially when he experiences the inevitable anxieties that come when he attempts to control his behavior.

## Denial of Limitations

The majority of adolescents who come to the attention of community agencies are from troubled homes and lower socioeconomic groups. Many of them have been subjected to severe psychological and economic deprivations. Their educational experiences have been limited. Psychiatric studies have produced data which indicate that the effects of early emotional deprivation are to a certain extent unmodifiable.[10, 11, 12] Deficiencies in early educational experiences may also seriously limit potentialities for achievement in the world.

The average professional worker comes from a middle-class background, which in our culture implies a far greater potentiality than that seen in most adolescent clients. (Here we must, of course, exclude selected disturbed adolescents of superior intelligence, of middle-class background or from reasonably, well-integrated homes.) Many workers fail to see that, with a few exceptions, they are dealing with people of limited potential who will never be like them. Failing to realize this fact, the worker may then encourage identifications, ambitions and achievements that are not possible for his client and which leave the adolescent with a feeling of frustration.

Few workers are guilty of consciously pushing their clients to achieve beyond their limits. Many of them, however, repeatedly deny the impressive limitations of some of their patients and assure them that the development of certain identifications and goals is entirely possible. This is a type of unconscious dishonesty that may produce considerable harm. The adolescent may righteously say to himself, "Who is this guy kidding? Is he trying to reassure me or reassure himself? Maybe he's trying to humiliate me by throwing my inadequacies in my face. He'll never understand me."

## "Open Up, Trust Me, All Will Go Well"

A close relationship is a foundation of any successful therapeutic interaction. Experiencing closeness to another person leads to the possibility of examining one's behavior in such a way that unfavorable personality defenses can be modified or exchanged for more useful ones. Most professional workers leave school with the feeling that they will be successful with clients if they can persuade them to be open and close. The adolescent, however, especially the disturbed adolescent, frequently is struggling with some of the negative aspects of closeness that he experiences as stultifying or smothering. He has begun to find certain types of relationships among his peers that provide him with a feeling of considerably more safety. To abandon movement in this direction and again attempt to develop a close relationship with an adult involves grave risk-taking for him. He is well aware that the little freedom he has gained may have to be surrendered if too much closeness develops.

If the worker realizes this, he can gently, tactfully and with some humility gradually allow a meaningful, nonsymbiotic relationship to develop between him and the child. In a healthy close relationship between adolescent and adult, the adolescent is allowed certain kinds of independence, dignity and, of course, distance when he wants it. The social structure in which most professional workers function makes it extremely difficult to provide this kind of relationship. They usually begin in settings in which they have tremendous power over the adolescent, who is thrown into a forced dependency. The adolescent is often forced into a relationship that he, at least on a conscious level, has not sought. The possibility of prolonged relationships is often limited by the fact that both professionals and their clients are extremely mobile, frequently changing responsibilities, jobs and geographical locations. A sustained, intensive relationship is not a common occurrence in most situations developed in community agencies.

Professional workers are guilty, nevertheless, of continuously exhorting the adolescent to "Open up, trust me, if you rely on me and share things with me, all will go well." But the disturbed adolescent knows that this is not true! He knows that the person who is pleading with him to expose himself may be a person with whom he will have only limited future contacts and whom he can see few reasons for trusting. He is further aware of the possibility that he can lose much in such a relationship and that the worker may not really be offering a true intimacy between equals. To the adolescent it seems like a poor bargain. He feels that the worker is dishonest in offering this type of bargain, and he reacts with fear, distrust and cynicism.

## "We Like You But Not Your Behavior"

Anyone who has spent much time with adolescents knows that their behavior can be provocative, frustrating and at times infuriating. It is distressing to see how few professional workers are willing to admit honestly how angry they get with their adolescent clients. This anger frequently is rationalized with statements to the effect that "I like you but not your behavior." Sometimes the worker's anger is totally denied but comes out only through his behavior toward the adolescent. In these types of situations workers sometimes tell the adolescent that they are not really angry with him but they feel that he must be disciplined for his own good, and that by depriving him of privileges or changing his situation they are really trying to help him. Frequently this anger is displaced onto the parents or onto other professional workers. Anyone who works with adolescents in a community or institutional setting is painfully aware of the extreme rivalry and sometimes open animosity between individual professionals and their groups. The fact is that it is almost impossible to work with adolescents for any period of time without becoming periodically angered.

It is dishonest and unfair both to the worker and to the adolescent to deny, rationalize or displace this anger. It belongs in the therapeutic situation and should be communicated with as much restraint, tact and honesty as the worker is capable of providing. To do less than this establishes a basically dishonest pattern of interaction and precludes the possibility of the adolescent experiencing positive emotional growth. He knows that adults at times find him intolerable, and he cannot be expected to cooperate or communicate with people who are unwilling to admit this fact.

In an earlier chapter we intimated that a certain amount of dishonest communication is necessary if we are to rear children in an atmosphere which offers a reasonable degree of security. The truth to children could be unbearable. If a relatively nonchaotic way of life is to be maintained, it is essential that children at times be deceived or at the very least kept in the dark as to issues they are not yet ready to master. We have also noted, however, that the adolescent is in a position to correct dishonest or paradoxical communication and that he is likely to respond to such communication in a rebellious manner. The child who is sent to the juvenile court has probably had considerable experience in deciphering the dishonest communications of his parents and relatives. As he becomes involved with professional youth workers, he encounters many more unnecessary dishonesties. By the time a delinquent reaches an institution his rebelliousness cannot all be explained away in terms of unresolved authority problems or neurosis. Much of it is better understood as a realistic response to a "double-binding" and sometimes dishonest system which regularly confuses its wishes to help the adolescent with its wishes to control him arbitrarily.

## A Suggested Therapeutic Approach to the Adolescent Delinquent

Faced with a client who is peculiarly sensitized to the potential "phoniness" of helping relationships, any person who works with the delinquent finds himself in a delicate position. In addition to his problems of dual allegiance to his patient and to his agency, he also must confront subjects whose rebelliousness may have been nurtured by the dishonesty of fellow professionals. The juvenile court judge is, of course, responsible to the whole community and is guided by an ethic that allows him to subordinate the delinquent's interest to community stability. Other professional workers (psychiatrists, psychologists, social workers, educators), however, cannot dismiss this problem so easily. They need to find an ethical code which will assist them in approaching their clients. The following guidelines are suggested. (This code is equally applicable to adult prisoners. The author is assuming, however [perhaps incorrectly], that professionals are more likely to be honest with adults.)

The professional worker (psychiatrist, psychologist or social worker) should be wary of expressing a moralistic attitude toward the adolescent's antisocial behavior. It is more helpful to consider such behavior as something the community (rightly or wrongly) will not tolerate if done openly and as something that has not served the social or personal needs of the adolescent. The wise professional openly acknowledges the social usefulness of certain kinds of aggressive behavior.

The professional might at times wish to communicate his own moral standards, which could be more or less stringent than those of his patient. He then has the obligation to label these as his personal beliefs and to make clear that they may not be appropriate for the patient.

The professional who is in a position of evaluating a patient must always explain his obligations as precisely as possible during the initial interview. The child should be told who is employing the examiner, what the examiner's responsibilities to his employer are, what kind of report will be written and exactly who will see and discuss it.

The professional must avoid any moral exhortations that adjustment or conformity to adult standards breeds comfort and contentment. To do this, of course, he must have a deep and thorough understanding of the role of antisocial behavior in maintaining the adolescent's equilibrium. Adjustment to the adult world should never be presented as something that automatically brings pleasure but rather as a necessary and sometimes unpleasant requisite to survival.

The professional must carefully avoid any communication that adolescent clients have the same potential as himself unless this is actually the case. Barriers to advancement which minority-group adolescents profess are more correctly accepted as realities than interpreted as projections. A useful general attitude is that this can be a "tough world" in which only a determined few manage to overcome earlier deprivations.

All efforts should be made to let the adolescent develop a relationship with the professional at his own pace and without extravagant promise of its value. The patient should be told exactly when and for how long the worker will be available. The adolescent has some right to be warned of the risks he takes in developing a relationship.

Exhortations to trust the professional should be rigorously avoided. It is much more useful to inform the adolescent that he can come to a decision as to his worker's trustworthiness on the basis of his own experience.

The professional has some obligation to communicate angry feelings which invariably develop toward adolescent patients. The rebellious adolescent has some right to know clearly and unequivocally when his behavior has stimulated feelings of disapproval or dislike.

This code of therapeutic conduct does not afford a magical system for gaining rapport with the adolescent patient. It does, however, suggest an attitudinal set which allows one to approach an extremely distrustful client. It avoids any aspect of saccharine or insincere helpfulness, which the adolescent is particularly adept at exploiting. Whether involved in psychotherapy, counseling, community therapy or efforts to create a therapeutic milieu, the professional who adheres to the above code will at least have a chance of reaching and helping his patients.

Considerable space has been devoted to reviewing some of the inconsistencies and dishonesties which seem to arise in a system of justice that is founded upon a treatment model. We have also pointed out that much of the difficulty stems from the carelessness and sloppy thinking of professional persons and that a more rigid adherence to individually oriented ethical principles could be extremely helpful. There is a limit, however, to the extent of helpfulness of even the most ethical professional conduct in a system which sends children who have not committed crimes to a correctional institution. Our society must eventually reconsider its entire system of correctional justice for adolescents and would probably do better to invoke involuntary institutional treatment only for those who could be proven to have committed crimes.

## Psychiatric Roles in the Training School

Training schools for delinquents are often small institutions, and their philosophies of treatment are usually dominated by one or two individuals. They are therefore likely to offer a great variety of programs. While all training schools tend to be more permissive than adult institutions, some simply do not welcome psychiatric techniques. Others are interested in using the psychiatrist only for diagnosis and treatment of selected delinquents. Still other programs involve the psychiatrist (or at least psychiatric techniques) in the entire milieu program.[13]*

* We as still using the generic term "psychiatrist" to include all helping professionals. In many institutions techniques derived from psychiatry are utilized by psychologists and particularly by psychiatric social workers. Many of the counseling and guided interaction techniques which sociologists have begun to employ, although perhaps based on a different theoretical rationale, bear marked similarities to conventional psychiatric techniques.

A few institutions have adopted programs based almost entirely upon psychiatric principles. The Boys' Industrial School in Topeka, Kansas, is an outstanding example of such an institution.[14] Its clinical director is a child psychiatrist, and although the school usually cares for less than two hundred boys, the staff includes two full-time psychiatrists, three psychologists and five social workers. The school is also a part of the largest psychiatric training program in the country (the Menninger School of Psychiatry), which brings additional skilled professionals in contact with the institutional program.

Every boy who enters the institution is given a thorough social, educational and psychiatric evaluation. A formal staff conference is then held to set up a program based upon his individual needs. Institutional or community pressures are not allowed to take precedent over treatment needs. If the staff feels that it would be advantageous for a particular boy to work with the kind of man or learn the kind of skills available in the print shop, he is assigned to that facility. If educational needs are felt to be more important, he spends the entire day in school. Efforts are made to place the child in work and school assignments with individuals who may be specifically trained or skilled in working with the kinds of problems that he presents.

With a relatively high availability of therapists in the Topeka area, it is possible to offer the great majority of boys some type of analytically oriented group or individual psychotherapy. This, however, is not seen as the main treatment modality. The focus is rather upon making the day-to-day living experience a therapeutic one. To this effect every staff person from houseparent to cook is looked upon as an integral part of the program. Everyone participates in some type of conference or training situation designed to improve his therapeutic skills.

A unique feature of the Boys' Industrial School is the cottage-committee system. The students live in cottages or units which can accommodate ten to thirty boys. There is no fence on the school grounds, and the boys are allowed considerable freedom. Houseparents, some of whom live in the cottage, are directly responsible for the boys' welfare. A social worker and a psychiatrist or psychologist are also assigned to each cottage. The houseparent, social worker and the psychiatrist (and sometimes teachers and recreational therapists) meet each day as a cottage committee to review the progress of individual boys and to investigate any staff problems. During these meetings boys may be interviewed either individually or in groups. Sometimes the committee simply talks about the boys or attempts to iron out its own problems. The psychiatrist is assigned one of two major roles.

During the early stages of the development of the Boys' Industrial School program he functioned entirely as a resource person whose job was to interpret the behavior of the boys and at times the behavior of the staff. In recent years he has been asked to take more direct administrative responsibility for decisions as to programming and release.

The cottage-committee system has been uniquely successful in creating a dynamic millieu characterized by enthusiasm and optimism. One has to spend only a few minutes on the Boys' Industrial School campus to feel the kind of mutual respect and even trust which radiates between staff and boys. The recidivism rates are extraordinarily low (9 percent). Like all such rates, however, they are probably quite deceptive. What is important is that the boys do leave the school more comfortable, more mature and far better equipped to deal with the oppressive environments which have contributed to their delinquency.

The Boys' Industrial School model has much to recommend it. This is one institution in which psychiatry has demonstrated what can be done with a nonpunitive, rational approach. Few institutions are in such a fortunate position to obtain psychiatric resources as the Kansas school. The author believes, however, that the basic model and philosophy of the program could be modified and profitably borrowed by most juvenile institutions.

## Homosexuality in the Training School

Whenever children are isolated in a closed institution some sexual activity between members of the same sex will inevitably take place. Since the staff may be deeply troubled by homosexual behavior, it comes to rely on the psychiatrist for help in understanding this phenomenon. Often the psychiatrist's usefulness is gauged by his response to the following questions: Are the boys or girls who participate in homosexual activities emotionally disturbed or is such behavior normal in a sexually segregated institution? What are the inherent factors in training schools that foster and perpetuate homosexual practices? What needs other than sexual are being met by these practices? Will the adolescent continue to engage in homosexual behavior following his release? Should the staff adopt a permissive or a punitive attitude?

No matter how antisocially oriented or how "tough" the delinquent child may be, his initial confrontation with the training school environment is likely to be frightening. Isolated from family, acquaintances and familiar surroundings, he will seek friendships and closeness in whatever form he can find them. In the absence of heterosexual outlets a number of these relationships eventually are characterized by some homosexual behavior. Of course, the emotionally disturbed child or the child who has doubts about his sexual identity will be more likely to seek deviant sexual activities. It is difficult, however, to predict who will indulge. In any closed institutional system some sexually "normal" people will find a temporary deviant outlet.

In addition to gratifying immediate needs for erotic stimulation, warmth and closeness, homosexual behavior can be an effective means for combating boredom or attacking the structure of the institution. Participation in homosexually tinged activities leads to extremely exciting games, which are not only gratifying in themselves but which also express contemptuousness toward adult and particularly staff values. For these reasons homosexual behavior is more prevalent in those training schools which do not have adequate treatment programs. An increase in such behavior in any institution usually indicates some breakdown in the program and greater distrust between the adolescents and the staff.

The question as to whether homosexual behavior in the training school environment will later result in fixed deviant patterns is a reasonable one but unfortunately very difficult to study quantitatively. The best clinical evidence suggests that deviant sexual experiences take on greatest meaning when they come at a time in life when the child is in exceptional need of nurturance and comfort.[15] Certainly, a child newly arrived at a training school is in a vulnerable position. Yet the great majority of adolescents who indulge in some kind of homosexual activity during their training school stay seem to be no more harmed by this experience than if it had occurred at a more favorable time in their lives. In one study of homosexual behavior in a training school for girls, Marvin Hersko and I noted that the percentage of girls who vowed some intention or need to continue in homosexual activities after leaving the institution was exactly equal to the percentage of girls who had participated in homosexual acts before they entered the institution.[16]

Although some training schools are characterized by a great deal of permissiveness, they are required to take a strong stand against homosexual conduct. Homosexuality is first of all an unacceptable form of social behavior which generally is not tolerated in the community. It is also a regressive phenomenon, a rule-breaking behavior which tends to encourage an impulse-ridden, uncommitted existence. Furthermore, it is a vehicle by which adolescents with authority problems avoid encounter with the staff and thereby diminish the possibility of learning about potentially healthy relationships with adults.

Part of the function of any psychiatrist in a training school is to disseminate information as to sexual deviation. He can also repeatedly point out that if homosexual behavior is ultimately a vote of "no confidence" in the adult staff, then the surest preventative must be an effective program and milieu which allow for meaningful communication between staff and child. It is extremely important that the mystical and frightening aura surrounding homosexual activity be kept to a minimum. There is always some danger that the staff will increase the problem by becoming obsessed with it. The psychiatrist can help staff members to understand that close friendships between adolescents are necessary and desirable and that occasional incidents of deviant sexual behavior are only disruptive and not disastrous. The institution which takes a firm but casual attitude toward homosexuality and attends to the more urgent problems of establishing its treatment program will reap the rewards of stability and therapeutic success.

## Chapter 19

# PSYCHIATRIC SERVICE IN PRISON

THE major contact between the psychiatrist and the criminal takes place in the forbidding atmosphere of the prison. The psychiatrist's position in the prison setting has rarely been an esteemed one. He has usually found himself relegated to the role of agitator, ineffective do-gooder, barely tolerable eccentric or an accomplice to the goals of custody and punishment. Since the latter part of the nineteenth century a small but earnest group of psychiatrists have, nevertheless, devoted a major part of their careers to working with the imprisoned offender.

Before discussing the psychiatrist's activities in the prison setting it is necessary to review some of the very serious shortcomings of the American penological system. I believe that adult prisons are with rare exceptions so dominated by punitive philosophies that they must be considered archaic if not barbaric institutional systems. This is not to quarrel with the assumption that criminals must be punished. I am dismayed by the excessive degree of punishment in most American prisons. A decrease in the use of corporal punishment during the past century does not negate this observation. Mental oppression can be crueler than physical oppression, and it is difficult to conceive of a structure that could produce more dehumanization, more despair or more helplessness than the modern American prison. Although the public seems continually to demand harsher punishment, it is unlikely that the American people would tolerate our current system if they really could understand what happens to human beings inside prison walls. Unfortunately, few law-abiding Americans ever see the inside of a prison (except on carefully guided tours).[1] Most of them do not want to see it. Prisons in America, much like the concentration camps of Nazi Germany, are kept out of the public's immediate vision, allowing most of us to be comfortably ignorant of what is happening. If the day ever comes when the public conscience and public awareness lead to humanitarian reforms (as it has in our mental hospitals), there will no doubt be many who, like the German people of the Nazi era, will shamefully utter the half-truth, "I didn't know what was going on."

Observers and scientists of all orientations have been critical of the American prison.[2, 3, 4, 5, 6] For that matter, there is hardly a person who has ever worked in a prison setting, be he physician or guard, who has not come away with the feeling that something is drastically wrong. Most critiques center around the proposition that society's apathy and inconsistent feelings toward the criminal allow for the creation of a prison system primarily concerned with punishment and control. This system is characterized by a total authority which smothers any concern for individual values. It creates a social milieu in which favorable attitudinal or behavioral change is extremely unlikely.

Unlike mental hospitals or even units for the criminally insane, prisons are concerned with far more than control or treatment. They have been established to accomplish one or more of four major goals:

1. Punishment of the offender for punishment's sake. Imprisonment in this sense represents society's vengeance, a form of retribution imposed upon the offender.

2. Deterring the criminal from committing any more crimes (both while he is in prison and, hopefully, after release) and setting an example of punishment which will deter others from committing crimes.

3. Reformation of the criminal. This usually means treatment with one of two goals in mind: (a) an increase in internal controls with increased psychological improvement or (b) an increase in internal controls without regard to the offender's psychological state. Punishment itself can be viewed as a means of achieving the latter kind of reformation since it may condition the offender to avoid criminal action.

4. Protection of the public.

The effectiveness of the prison system can be examined in terms of each of these four goals.

There is no question that the prison succeeds in punishing. We shall later attempt to document the peculiarly dehumanizing nature of prison practices, but even a cursory inspection reveals that there is more emphasis on punishment in the American correctional system than on anything else. Prison terms are ludicrously long. In the belief that prolonged deprivation of liberty is not sufficient punishment, the inmate is systematically degraded and denied the ordinary comforts of life. A total deprivation is imposed upon a majority of offenders, who are neither dangerous nor likely to make escape attempts. The social system of the prison also sets into motion attitudes and practices which are calculated to inflict great psychological pain.[7] In practice punishment inflicted for the sake of punishment alone seems to reign as the dominant correctional goal.

The effectiveness of our prison system as a deterrent to crime is much more difficult to evaluate. Certainly, while the offender is in prison he cannot commit crimes. It is also possible that his recollection of prison experiences may serve as a deterring influence once he is free. A high percentage of criminals do, however, commit new crimes upon release, which must mean that they were neither sufficiently reformed nor deterred by their prison experience. The value of imprisonment as a deterrent to other potential criminals is also questionable. This concept of deterrence implies that criminals will behave in a reasonable or rational manner and will weigh the potential gains of their criminality against the possible miseries of punishment. We have argued that a significant number of criminals cannot be expected to behave in a reasonable manner. Certainly, the high crime rate in our country suggests that imprisonment has not been an effective deterrent to potential new offenders.

Some authorities continue to claim that the primary goal of imprisonment is reformation of the criminal. This may be one of the goals, but it is usually placed in a secondary position. Reformation goals are more often talked about than put into practice. Even the best prisons place custody or maintenance needs ahead of treatment needs, and the extent of control which is inflicted upon the majority of prisoners is often gauged by the escape potential of a few aggressive men.[8] Even prison industries which could present an outlet for active expression of energy or alloplastic resolution of conflict are geared to a rigid institutional system. Prison industries are rarely competitive, practically never teach skills that have marketplace value and are not calculated to offer the inmate a sense of pride in his work. Ordinarily, prison industries are only allowed to undertake manufacture of products which are not already made by private industries in the same state. The commonest articles made by prison industries are license plates and cheap furniture. Obviously, this kind of work is not designed to teach a man to survive in a competitive society and particularly in a society that will soon be dominated by automation. The inmate knows that his job rarely represents a useful piece of work that the society needs to have done but is more likely a task that has been arbitrarily assigned to keep him busy. Work itself then becomes a kind of punishment rather than a rehabilitative experience, in effect a more sophisticated version of the old-fashioned rock pile.

Classification programs are designed to individualize disposition, but they are always most mindful of the need to control the offender. Although psychotherapy and counseling are proudly advertised as illustrations of the prison's intention to rehabilitate, they are rarely allowed to interfere with punitive or custodial requirements.

It is quite unlikely that prisons succeed in reforming many people. There is greater probability that those criminals who do not become recidivists find a new adaptation because of events which are unrelated to their prison experience. Circumstances such as a fortunate marriage, a good job, an interested parole officer, the death of an oppressive parent or an intervening mental illness keep many men from returning to prison. The aging process in itself probably has more to do with reformation than all our correctional endeavors combined.[9]

Reform within the prison is more likely to be accidental than planned. An occasional inmate does find a new sense of peace in conformity, a new and sustaining belief system or an interest in new kinds of work. Sometimes he even learns that it is possible safely to experience closeness to another person such as an inmate, a guard, a social worker or psychiatrist, and this new closeness may be accompanied by a diminished need to seek antisocial adaptations. Such reformations are, however, exceptional. They are more than counterbalanced by the number of men who learn new criminal techniques or who are driven toward further criminality through an increase of oppressive stress emanating from the prison environment itself.

It might be argued that some criminals do respond to severe punishment and may even have a psychological need for it. The man who has murdered his wife during an argument, for example, might become severely depressed if the society did not find some way of punishing him. This type of criminal, however, is quite rare. *Most offenders do not see themselves as aggressors against society but rather as victims of society.* They look upon their crimes as necessary means of survival in a cruel and oppressive world. Whether they are correct in this appraisal is debatable, but it is nevertheless hard to find an inmate in prison who does not feel that he has been wronged by some external source. Even the man who says, "I have no one to blame but myself," is more likely to make such a statement to influence others than to reflect his true feelings. If such a person is interviewed for more than a few minutes, he usually voices feelings of having been victimized by his wife, his family, the police, alcohol or illness. In effect, most offenders see themselves as being punished for having been victimized. The harshness of American penological practices is of such a degree that it is seen as a new oppression which convinces the offender of his persecuted status and justifies his continued hatred of society's norms.

The value of imprisonment in achieving the fourth possible goal, protection of the public, is again difficult to determine. Certainly, while a dangerous man is locked behind bars the public is safe. The great majority of offenders do, however, eventually reach the streets, and it is questionable whether imprisonment succeeds in making them less dangerous. The simplest way for prisons to protect the public would be to keep all dangerous individuals locked up for life. In the absence of such highly restrictive measures, protection is dependent upon the effectiveness of reformation. It is quite likely that many offenders will come out of prison no less dangerous than they were when they went in. Others may be even more dangerous.

The obvious problem with prisons is that the four goals of punishment, deterrence, reformation and protection cannot always be pursued at the same time. A limited amount of punishment may satisfy the needs of the society and may even be useful to the reformation process. It is not inconsistent to assume that we can treat and rehabilitate a man who is at the same time being punished by deprivation of liberty. Once punishment becomes arbitrary, cruel and excessive, however, reformation is no longer possible. Beyond a certain point a person cannot be helped by making him suffer. It is possible to reduce him to a state of slavish conformity, but it is unlikely that the excessively punished person will ever take his place as a free and productive citizen in a democratic society.

## Imprisonment and Mental Illness

Inconsistencies in prison practices are, of course, apparent to almost anyone who has worked with the criminal. The psychiatrist who ventures to offer his services to a prison must, however, resolve even greater conflicts. Since he is a person dedicated to helping others, he is dismayed to find himself part of a system that is dedicated to the infliction of psychological pain. In fact, the prison environment is almost diabolically conceived to force the offender to experience the pangs of what many psychiatrists would describe as mental illness.[10] A brief look at the prison environment will indicate that it contains the most pernicious factors that are listed as causes of mental illness in our psychiatric textbooks. Let us list just a few of these stresses.

Absence of close interpersonal relationships. Prisoners are isolated from their loved ones. They are discouraged from forming close relationships with other inmates or custodial officers. Sexual or nonsexual love of any type is vigorously restricted.

Socially acceptable sexual outlets are denied. The only outlets for sexual gratification are autoeroticism or homosexuality. Neither of these practices is likely to increase self-esteem. Homosexual involvement can lead to serious psychological disturbance.

Prisoners are more isolated and more idle than is generally felt to be conducive to emotional health. Loneliness and inactivity lead to narcissistic withdrawal and overreliance on autistic fantasy.

Many prisoners are subjected to solitary confinement. This is a form of sensory deprivation. We know that if volunteers are subjected to sensory deprivation for more than several hours, hallucinations and other symptoms of psychosis begin to occur.[11] It is quite likely that inmates in solitary confinement for more than a day or two have occasional hallucinatory and psychotic experiences. Some men seem to recover, but many are permanently scarred.

Prisoners are deprived of the opportunity of doing socially useful work. Activist tendencies such as reform or political activities are vigorously discouraged.

Prisoners are deliberately and steadily deprived of a sense of autonomy. Those areas in which they are allowed to make decisions are highly restricted. What happens to the prisoner is rarely a matter of what he chooses to do except in the negative sense that if he breaks rules he will be punished. Prisoners are encouraged to be dependent. The prisoner relies on his keepers for food, clothing, cigarettes and even exercise. In such a setting he is unlikely to develop a meaningful sense of social responsibility.

Repetitive attempts are made to break down the inmate's self-esteem and identity. In many institutions custodial officers do not afford him the amenities or courtesies which symbolize recognition as a man in our society. The prisoner is called by his first name (or last name without the "Mr."), he is required to remain standing when visitors appear, and he is subjected to a thousand similar indignities. Efforts are made to force the inmate to feel like a lesser being, humanoid rather than human. The relationship of many prison workers to inmates is reminiscent of that of the bigoted white Southerner to the Negro. The inmate can be tolerated, joked with, even on occasion treated kindly "as long as he knows his place."

The prison squashes all manifestations of useful aggression. Adequate mental health is dependent upon honest recognition of feelings of resentment and anger. The prisoner who shows evidence of anger or even verbalizes his feelings is in danger of being label a rebel, a troublemaker or a paranoid. He also faces the threat of additional punishment.

In addition to all the above stressful experiences, the prisoner is subjected to an insidious series of paradoxical messages. Every message he receives which states, "You are being treated for your own good and we are here to help you," is deceptive. Even the most punitive institution has some need to pretend that it is treating and reforming criminals. A jargon of helpfulness (which is often based on medical clichés) is sometimes inflicted upon even the most abused prisoner. Since the prisoner is dependent upon his captors and is hopeful that they will be good to him, he may accept such statements and ignore the reality of what is being done to him. To the extent that he is incapable of deciphering the dishonesty implied in paradoxical communication he will suffer the pangs of being oppressed, without even being able to ascertain who is hurting him.

### Pyschiatric Activities in Prison

The reader may by this time be wondering why any psychiatrist would be asked to work or would be willing to work in a prison. If the prison environment is designed to create emotional suffering, then why hire a person whose task is to prevent or alleviate emotional suffering? Perhaps the most paradoxical viewpoint which is sometimes expressed by correctional administrators is that the prison psychiatrist is needed to maintain a climate of proper mental hygiene. This ridiculous statement represents only one of the many frustrating and inconsistent philosophies which arise when medical models are insensitively used to rationalize a punitive system.

The psychiatrist has difficulty in completely rejecting his responsibility to these fallen and downtrodden men. In spite of all the therapeutic limitations of the oppressive custodial environment, the author believes that the psychiatrist can still play an honorable and useful role in the prison. We must begin a discussion of this role, however, with a detailed examination of its most agonizing aspects.

One of the inescapable functions of the psychiatrist in the prison is the undoing of the bad effects of the prison itself. Some would question the wisdom or honor of such a role. They would ask, "Does the psychiatrist not actually condone prison practices by attempting to repair the damage done by the prison? Would he not do better to disassociate himself from any involvement at all?" This argument has considerable idealistic appeal, but it ignores some practical issues. The prison psychiatrist can be compared to the military surgeon who treats the casualities of war. His presence on the battlefield could encourage a continuation of combat but does not necessarily mean that he approves of war. The military surgeon or the prison psychiatrist might think, "I am repelled by what is happening, but I cannot stop it. To refuse to comfort those who are being wounded would be inhumane."

In effect, the prison authorities tell the psychiatrist, "We are going to make these prisoners suffer, but we don't want them to suffer too much. If they become so disturbed that they cannot go along with our program or if they behave in an unreasonable and disruptive way, your job is to make them adjust to this environment or transfer them to a hospital." Such a frame of reference makes the question, "Whose agent is the psychiatric physician?," excruciating. The psychiatrist may be able to serve the institution and the inmate at the same time, but there are too many instances in which he cannot do both. If he believes the institution is advocating destructive practices, his decision to serve as the institution's agent must be accompanied by considerable anguish.

Another painful problem arises when the prison environment forces the psychiatrist to choose whether he should identify himself with the long-term or the short-term interests of his patient. Many of the patient's reactions to an oppressive prison regime, for example, anger, would be quite justifiable in terms of ordinary societal values, but they are condemned in the prison. The psychiatrist often finds himself in the position of sympathizing with the inmate's rebellious behavior but wondering if he should support it. He recognizes that in the long run it may be to the inmate's advantage to be at least superficially conforming while in prison. If the prisoner is unwilling to agree with him, the psychiatrist may assume that "he knows what is best" and decide to work against the patient's immediate interests (rebellion, vengeance, pride) in favor of his ultimate interests (freedom). This assumption is always dangerous. It temporarily aligns the psychiatrist with the forces of oppression. It puts him in a position where he may feel justified in becoming overcontrolling or insidiously paternalistic. He may come to deny the ultimate autonomy of his patient by forgetting that the temporary loss of autonomy which he sees is largely fostered by an unnatural situation.

Nevertheless, there are times when the psychiatrist must assume that the combination of his patient's immaturity and the regression-favoring qualities of the prison environment requires him to take over. He may feel obligated to work against the patient's immediate interest in order to protect the patient's long-term interests. Such situations represent a supreme test of the psychiatrist's skill and humanity. To control a man (who might not need control in a more reasonable environment) without completely destroying that man's sense of autonomy, and without forgetting that his ultimate purpose is to help the individual, requires an unusual effort. This can be illustrated by an example of a type of situation which frequently confronts the prison psychiatrist.

A psychiatrist is requested to examine a man who has been in solitary confinement for four days. During that time the patient has become increasingly profane, cries frequently and has on one occasion obtained a sharp instrument with which he has made several small incisions on his arms. The custodial staff look upon his behavior as "attention-seeking" but are concerned enough (and perhaps guilty enough) to be worried about the possibiilty of violence or suicide. The psychiatrist is asked to see the inmate and answer one of three questions. (1.) "Is the inmate faking and isn't his behavior really an effort to seek attention?" (in which case he will be kept in solitary confinement longer). (2.) "Can you get him to quiet down?" (so that he can finish his confinement without incident and be returned to ordinary prison routine). (3.) "Is he dangerous or mentally ill?" (in which case we would like you to take over and put him in a hospital unit).

Let us assume that the psychiatrist knows that the inmate is in solitary confinement because he swore at a guard who reminded him of a rejecting father, and that the guard had actually provoked the inmate in a manner which would have justified some type of retaliation in the free world. The psychiatrist may, understandably, approach his assignment with the weary feeling that he is being asked to determine whether his patient is healthy enough to endure more torture. Nevertheless, if he flippantly dismisses or ignores such a request, he will only increase the probability that the inmate will be subjected to further punishment.

The psychiatrist joureys into the somber catacombs of the isolation unit and enters the cell of his unshaven, foul-smelling patient. After an initial greeting of abuse, followed by several minutes of silence, the patient begins to talk. He reveals that he is so tortured by feelings of injustice and retaliation that he is fearful of hurting someone. He discusses self-destructive fantasies while pausing to reassure himself that he does not actually wish to commit suicide. He insists that he does not want to be hospitalized, but at the same time doubts his ability to tolerate another hour of solitary confinement, and pleads with the psychiatrist to help get him out. He expresses skepticism as to the value of medication, but seems to be willing to take it.

The psychiatrist contemplates what he must do. If his actions are dictated by what the patient seems to be saying and if he decides not to intervene, the physician might be relegating his patient to more punishment and eventual violence or suicide. If he decides that he cannot allow the patient to determine what happens, the psychiatrist must search for values which will guide him in his precarious attempt to serve both the patient and the institution. He can then take a limited number of alternative actions, some of which are clearly more humane than others and yet none of which is in the patient's immediate interest. Once he elects to intervene, it is extremely difficult to determine what is best for the patient's long-term welfare. A "tough" action which would superficially seem to be nothing but a total acceptance of punishment and custody might ultimately be more helpful to a particular inmate than a "soft" one.

The easiest solution for the psychiatrist is to tell the custodians that the patient is faking, or is just seeking attention, thus allowing the punishment to continue. This implies that the psychiatrist believes that punishment is justified and is "for the patient's own good." He might order tranquilizing or sedative medication (as a form of chemical restraint) or physical restraint in order to assure against self-mutilation and to give the guards some peace. Although this action might endear the psychiatrist to the custodians, it is hardly in the tradition of Hippocrates.

There may be instances in which the psychiatrist might feel that punishment is totally unjustified, but that allowing the inmate to "tough it out" would not lead to irreparable damage, and would be a better alternative than transfer to a hospital. The skilled psychiatrist might then offer a variety of services to his embattled client. First of all he could provide medication in a helpful manner, asking the inmate how much tranquillity he thinks he needs to survive and then prescribing it to alleviate suffering rather than to restrain. He could also give emotional support, encouraging the inmate as to his capacity to "make it," clarifying what has happened to him and empathizing with the feelings that led to his revolt. Another form of support might be to encourage the inmate to continue taking his punishment but assure him that when he could no longer tolerate solitary confinement he would be sent to the hospital. In some instances even a small amount of insight therapy could take place. The therapist might point out the unresolved authority problems which led to the patient's unacceptable behavior.

A final alternative is to send the man to the prison hospital or a unit for the criminally insane. This is always a difficult decison. The inmate rarely approves since he is reluctant to be labeled insane. The custodial staff questions the implied tender-mindedness of the psychiatrist. Even the hospital may resent having to deal with an aggressive and questionably psychotic inmate. Finally, the psychiatrist may feel dishonest in the knowledge that he is hospitalizing a man whom few of his colleagues would call mentally ill. Yet there is often little choice. Sometimes transfer is the only way to break up a sadomasochistic relationship between guard and prisoner which is dangerous and harmful to both.

The author has described this gruesome aspect of prison pyschiatry for two reasons: first, to call attention to the complexities of finding a value system by which treatment can be carried out in an environment which is at base vicious; second, to point out that even in the most desperate circumstances there are some things that the psychiatrist can do that are helpful. These kinds of requests for service from the prison psychiatrist are not uncommon. The manner in which the psychiatrist resolves each case and in which he finally arrives at an ethical position will determine his value to the society and his value to the criminal. If he becomes nothing but an "institutional tranquilizer" whose main function is to keep the punishment process moving smoothly, he, in effect, prostitutes his medical skills. On the other hand, if he seeks refuge in ineffective and childish dissent, he not only denies reality but also fails to serve either his patient or the society. Somewhere and somehow the psychiatrist must find a middle ground, a philosophy which allows him to survive and be useful in an environment that is peculiarly designed to defeat his purposes.

Fortunately, the greater part of the prison psychiatrist's work is less complicated than the tasks we have described.[12, 13] Most of the time his patients are not in solitary confinement, and most of them come to him voluntarily. He can then say, "Look, I know that this is a difficult environment for you, and I understand the feelings of helplessness and rage which it produces. I am here for two purposes: to help you survive this ordeal with as little damage as possible and to help you understand yourself, to help you understand why you get into trouble and how you can stay out of it. You can either accept my services or reject them. They may help you get out of here sooner. On the other hand, they may not. In any case, I will try not to interfere with your existence unless I believe it is helpful to you." The value system reflected in this statement comes as close to a traditional medical model of treatment as is possible in the correctional setting.

The psychiatrist who accepts this orientation is free to use a number of conventional treatment modalities. He can prescribe drugs for his patient when it appears that continued experiencing of anxiety or depression will result only in greater damage to the personality. He can provide emotional support in times of crisis. A particularly useful function is the constant clarification of reality. Since the prisoner so often distrusts himself and others, he is greatly in need of contact with an objective observer who clarifies both his unrealistic self-abnegation and his defensive flirtings with grandiosity. In addition to counseling-type functions, the psychiatrist can provide more formal group or individual psychotherapy, which aims to free the inmate of maladaptive responses to internalized oppression and to strengthen his capacity to deal with external oppression.

The psychiatrist can also exert considerable influence to soften, or at least add a degree of rationality to, the prison milieu. In spite of the punitive roles which are thrust upon them, most correctional workers do have feelings about their charges and would like to help prisoners if they knew how. The author hopes that his criticism of the correctional environment is not construed as an attack upon the motivations of custodial officers. In many ways they are as victimized by the prison environment as their charges. Sometimes they show extraordinary concern for prisoners, far beyond that which is required by their position.

The psychiatrist is in an excellent position to educate the custodial staff as to the meanings of certain types of behavior. Sometimes he can enlist the aid of custodial officers to provide specific types of attitude therapy. In a few enlightened institutions it is possible to train guards to do group counseling. Other institutions make reasonable efforts to provide outlets for work and recreation that are appropriately therapeutic for a given inmate. The extent to which any of these efforts can be developed is ultimately dependent upon the flexibility of custodial personnel and the skill of the psychiatrist. Those institutions which have made some progress are characterized by an unusual degree of understanding between treatment and custodial staff.

The author firmly believes that, aside from the mandatory duties which are part of his daily work, the prison psychiatrist should also see himself as a reformer, as a person who constantly strives to diminish the extent of unnecessary and unreasonable punishment. Of course, this does not mean that the psychiatrist must be disruptive to the institution. The effective critic tries to obtain practical and constructive social change. Up to now the major shortcoming of psychiatric reformers is that they have simply made emotional pleas for change without knowledge, without alternatives and without the trust of prison officials. If a psychatrist approaches the problem with humility, develops trusting relationships with custodial personnel and demonstrates the rational basis of rehabilitative methods, he can often have a useful impact on an institution. Ideally, the prison administrator who hires a psychiatrist must recognize that he will have a friendly critic on his hands. The psychiatrist who pretends to abdicate the role of reformer may be a pleasant person to have around, but he is ultimately useful to no one.

## The Psychiatric Aspects of Prison Adaptation

Under the stress of incarceration the prisoner must find some means of adapting to a tremendous increase in the subjective experience of helplessness. In his insightful study of the prison environment, Gresham Sykes noted that the two most common responses to imprisonment involved either a search for gratification and meaning within the inmate's subculture or a rebellious attack upon the entire environment, including other inmates and custodians.[14] Both of these responses as well as several other possible adaptations present unique problems for psychiatric treatment and will be briefly discussed. The reader will, of course, recognize that the following adaptational devices are loosely defined patterns of behavior, several of which may be characteristic of the same inmate over a brief span of time.

After an initial frustrating confrontation with the unshakable power of the prison structure many inmates simply despair of any meaningful communication between themselves and the "free" world. They turn to other inmates and seem to say, "I do have friends here and if I find meaning in their values I can survive and I will not be powerless." The inmate subculture is a marvelous outlet for the prisoner's aggressive impulses as it is constantly at war with the custodial staff. It also provides outlets for a variety of meaningful games, friendships and even sexual activities. For many prisoners, relationships with fellow inmates become the only important aspects of their lives. The rest of the world is seen as untrustworthy and dishonest, as a target to be ridiculed and deceived whenever possible.

Some correctional administrators are content to live at peace with such a subculture since it drains off energies and enforces some stability within the institution. Others, however, recognize that its existence is an impediment to rehabilitation. The act of joining the inmate subculture is, in effect, a denial of the rules of the culture as a whole and imposes a slavish conformity to a new society which is ultimately opposed to law-abiding behavior. The psychiatrist, unfortunately, comes to be seen by prisoners as an unusually potent threat to the maintenance of the inmate subculture. If he is a reasonably likable, helping and trustworthy person, he challenges the belief system upon which the inmate's withdrawal from conventional norms is based.

The offender who seeks his values in the prison subculture is likely to be extremely distrustful of the psychiatrist. He often sees the psychiatrist as a smooth-talking representative of conformity to society as a whole who will take away the only suitable means for survival that the inmate can perceive.[15] This kind of inmate is likely to ignore the psychiatrist unless contact serves his immediate needs. When he ultimately decides to ask for help, his interactions with the therapist are inclined to be manipulative and dishonest. He is always burdened by a need to save face with his fellow inmates. He must pretend that he is "conning the bug doctor" even when he is desperately in need of help.

Some inmates, either because of pre-existing personality traits or because of the inordinate stress of prison, simply despair of trusting anyone. They are "loners" who constantly rebel against the restrictiveness of the institution and the demands of the inmate subculture. These individuals are likely to be a distressing problem for custodians insofar as they constantly test rules and have to be punished. As their battle with authority progresses, they begin to demonstrate great anxiety and unreasonable behavior. Eventually they come to the attention of the prison psychiatrist. Although these men seem to be behaving in an extremely desperate and inappropriate manner, they often are surprisingly easy to reach and gratifying to work with. They are, at least, still fighting and desperately trying to hold onto their dignity. One of the major problems of the psychiatrist who works with this kind of inmate is persuading the inmate to avoid actions which lead him into power struggles which can never be won. Another way of putting this is that the psychiatrist tries to help the patient avoid the masochistic aspect of his efforts to control or alter an all-powerful and unyielding environment.

A small group of inmates seem to repent their criminal actions and to find a more conforming existence from the moment they enter the prison. It is as if they said to themselves, "I have been bad. I have seen the wrongness of my way. I deserve to be punished, and I will take my punishment manfully." Most often, of course, this kind of statement is made by individuals who are still deeply rebellious and identified with the inmate subculture. In these instances it represents a deceptive and manipulative maneuver.

On the other hand, a few inmates do seem to convince at least themselves that they have done wrong and that they intend to reform. Both religion and organizations such as Alcoholics Anonymous tend to support this adaptation. The main advantage of this premature conformity is that it offers the prisoner a certain self-righteous satisfaction and sometimes considerable praise and privileges from the administrators. The major problem with the conformity adaptation is that it rarely holds up when the external restraints of the prison are terminated. More discouraging, as long as the inmate holds on to such a belief system he is refractory to any therapeutic intervention. The statement, "I have seen the errors of my ways and I have reformed," can also be viewed as a defensive maneuver designed to close off self-examination or personality change. The psychiatrist cannot hope to reach such an inmate unless he challenges this defense.

Another kind of autoplastic adaptation in the prison environment is excessive withdrawal and reliance on gratification through fantasy. A number of prisoners come to rely on their own thoughts, memories and hopes as the primary reason for survival. One problem with this defense mechanism is that withdrawal from others often leads to distortions of reality and preoccupation with grandiose and autistic ideas. During routine interviews the psychiatrist not uncommonly finds prisoners who have been regarded as well-adjusted "cons" who turn out to be harboring bizarre delusional systems. The psychiatrist is then in a difficult position. He may be tempted to challenge the delusional system, but he knows that it is this same system that enables the man to survive. Sometimes the psychiatrist must abandon his therapeutic zeal and conclude that the most humane thing he can do is leave that inmate alone and hope that he will receive help once he leaves the prison.

A large number of prisoners respond to the stress of imprisonment by developing chronic symptoms of anxiety, depression, psychosomatic illness or other physical illness. Hypochondriasis is a common symptom in prison, probably more comman than it is in a free environment. A high degree of illness behavior in prison should not be surprising to anyone who is aware of the oppressive nature of penal institutions. One of the more serious problems which confronts the prison psychiatrist, however, is the extent to which he should make illness available to the prisoner as an adaptation to such unusual stress. The suffering of the prisoner is great enough so that the presence of psychiatrists or other physicians encourages the communication of an increased number of symptoms. By redefining the meaning of suffering the physician allows his patients to adopt a role which offers some promise of help and kindness. Prisons could probably absorb and keep busy any number of psychiatrists. The problem is that once the illness role is accepted it is very difficult to abandon. In view of the limited psychiatric resources in most institutions, the prison psychiatrist must sometimes encourage many prisoners (whom he would elect to treat in the free world) to "tough it out."

Some inmates who were extraordinarily dependent before imprisonment readily accept the passive conformity which is imposed upon them in the correctional environment. These men find that gratification of dependency needs plus a total absence of responsibility are sufficient conditions for existence. In a sense they have accepted their status as subhuman or "humanoid" beings and have abandoned any hope of a better way of life. These are the men who have been institutionalized to the point where survival in the free world is unlikely. The psychiatrist is able to do very little for this group, and the most hopeful resolution of their cases usually requires placement in a protective but less restrictive environment.

A few inmates, particularly those who do not have inordinately long sentences, are able to sustain themselves through hope. They avoid either maladaptive attacks on the environment or entanglement in the inmate subculture. They may experience a considerable amount of anxiety and depression, but they keep it to themselves. Their behavioral pattern is dominated by a need to remain as unobtrusive and outwardly conforming as possible, and is sustained by the belief that they will find more favorable adaptational alternatives once they are free. Such offenders are ordinarily more stable than the average and are not likely to seek the psychiatrist's assistance. When they do occasionally consult him, they often turn out to be quite gratifying patients who are able to use the insights of psychotherapy to make meaningful personality changes.

A very small number of prisoners do seem to discover more meaningful adaptations in the prison environment. This is an extremely difficult phenomenon to understand. Somehow or other a few men do come to terms with thesmelves and either find a meaningful ideology or discover a vocation or activity that is worthwhile and sustaining. Robert Stroud (the "Bird Man of Alcatraz"), Nathan Leopold and Caryl Chessman would be outstanding examples. Most often these are individuals who come into the prison situation with considerable untapped creative and intellectual ability. They manage to use their time to develop skills which they never knew they had. These men seem to be saying, "In spite of the oppressive environment in which I must live I can find a means of sustaining myself and through my works or beliefs I can be a real person even though I am in prison." Their prison adaptation is characterized by a clinging to a sense of dignity which is refractory to the most oppressive attacks of the environment. Some inmates in this group are able to achieve this adaptation because of the help they receive from psychiatrists. More often a prison guard, a prison teacher or a prison chaplain has a similar influence. Most of the time, however, these men simply pull themselves up by their own bootstraps and are reluctant to allow anyone to tamper with their own private formulas for survival.

## Some Further Problems of the Psychiatrist in the Correctional Setting

Before concluding this chapter it may be useful to comment further upon the peculiar personal anguish which the psychiatrist experiences in the correctional setting. We might have appropriately entitled this section "The Emotional Problems of the Prison Psychiatrist." While many of the comments we are about to make also apply to social workers and psychologists, the prison psychiatrist is in an unusually vulnerable position.

We have repeatedly emphasized the restrictive setting of the prison, but up to now have commented upon its impact upon the prisoner rather than the correctional worker. It would be naïve to assume that the prison milieu did not have certain unfavorable influences upon the jailer as well as the jailed. The propensities of many criminals to act upon their impulses engenders adverse reactions in those who must work with them. Prisoners can be both frightening and charming. The prison worker (be he psychiatrist or guard) must sooner or later identify himself with the problems of his charges. He hears many tales of aggressivity and sexuality which may not be part of his ordinary life and which are bound to stimulate both fear and curiosity. At the same time counterforces are operative which inhibit expression of impulses. In the repressive fortress of a prison "the wages of sin" are all too apparent. Viewed in terms of a simplified psychoanalytic model, the prison brings to consciousness ordinarily repressed id impulses while at the same time it reinforces the fears of superego retaliation. This is a conflict situation, which must always produce anxiety or defensiveness.

Most correctional workers are more frightened of their own impulses than they need to be. Most commonly they defend themselves by trying to lead as conforming and conventional lives as possible. This adaptation, however, cuts them off from access to unconscious fantasy and is antagonistic to the kind of free and creative state of being which is most conducive to psychological growth. The correctional environment not only atttracts conservative people, but it also tends to make them more rigid. Not enough creative people work for very long in a prison. "Off-beat" people or eccentrics are not welcomed, nor do they desire to stay.

The psychiatrist's training encourages him to be open to his own feelings. He also carries with him an aura of mysticism and apparent freedom to delve into those aspects of life which most people are rarely willing to inspect. In many instances he comes to represent a threat to the emotional stability of other correctional workers. It is as though he stood for a lifting of all repression and an encouragement of abandoned aggressivity and sexuality. Unfortunately, too many prison psychiatrists nurture this image by careless use of jargon and irresponsible efforts to impress others with their openness. The result is often unfortunate. The psychiatrist, unless he is exceptionally competent or ingratiating, tends to find himself alienated from his fellow workers.

Another problem for the psychiatrist (although in some ways a happy problem) is that his salary is often three or four times larger than that of the average prison worker. This is particularly trying in his relationship with psychologists and social workers, who are often paid much less while doing almost exactly the same kind of work. In addition to all the hostility that is directed toward him by fellow employees as a result of irrational fear, there is also the more realistic resentment of the fact that co-workers who work just as hard and who may be just as effective receive relatively paltry remuneration.

Other stresses for the prison psychiatrist include lack of status in his own profession, constant frustration and guilt as to his inability to alter the oppressive prison regime and, of course, the kinds of fears and temptations that anyone experiences in working with criminals. All these stresses suggest that the prison psychiatrist is himself in danger of becoming an emotionally disturbed person. Three common and quite pernicious means of defending against anxiety in this situation are: (1) a tendency to withdraw from active involvement and work as little as possible; (2) an effort to become a messianic zealot (usually an ineffective one) who overidentifies with the inmate's needs; and (3) a tendency to overidentify with custody and to lose sight of one's obligations as a physician.[16]

The first type of defensive manouver is relatively common. The prison psychiatrist readily falls into the role of bureaucrat who does his job "according to the books" and does no more. Frankly, many prison psychiatrists turn out a shamefully small amount of work. Much like the inmates (and many other correctional workers), they despair of finding anything constructive in the prison environment and learn to spend their eight hours a day in long lunch hours, coffee breaks, paper work and ritual. The psychiatrist who overidentifies with inmates may be effective up to a point but sooner or later comes into conflict with the demands of custody, and at this point it is the inmate who usually suffers. The third defensive operation, identification with the goals of custody, has already been commented upon as a role hardly compatible with medical ethics.

In spite of the high degree of stressfulness of prison work, it is interesting to note that most of those physicians who are involuntarily assigned to work in a prison (through career-plan obligations or military obligations) usually retain at least some part-time commitment to psychiatric criminology for the remainder of their careers. Apparently, the work is so interesting and the needs so compelling that it is difficult to divorce oneself completely from the correctional environment. It must be stressed, however, that few of these men will continue in full-time positions. The psychiatric criminologist is most likely to remain psychologically healthy and useful if he acquires additional interests. It would seem especially important that full-time prison staff (including psychologists and social workers) have access to other part-time jobs, continued educational experiences and teaching opportunities.*

The correctional administrator who demands that clinical employees be on the institution grounds for a rigid forty-hour work week will ultimately defeat his own purposes by developing an uninspired, somber and "institution-wise" staff.

* Personal psychotherapy for psychiatrists, psychologists and social workers who work in a prison is valuable, perhaps more valuable and necessary than in other settings. For many reasons, and perhaps foremost because of the repressive and confirming milieu in which they work, correctional therapists seem more reluctant than most to seek help for themselves.

# Chapter 20

# EVALUATING THE OFFENDER

THE psychiatrist who evaluates offenders is in the position of being an agent of society as well as of the patient. His recommendations may lead to a variety of dispositions, all of which may be called treatment but not all of which are for the patient's welfare. The type, the place and even the duration of commitment are heavily influenced by his report. At the risk of being repetitious, we must again emphasize the psychiatrist's obligation to inform his patient clearly as to the nature of their relationship. No evaluation in the correctional setting should begin without the patient knowing how much confidentiality can be provided, the purpose of the psychiatrist's report, who will see it and how much influence it will have. It is the author's conviction that an honest and straightforward approach will always facilitate rather than hinder good rapport and useful communication.

## The Problem of Dishonesty—Some Comments on the Psychology of Lying

A certain degree of dishonesty is inevitable in a social situation in which the criminal has some wish to protect himself and in which society intends to hurt him. Correctional workers, and particularly those who are responsible for evaluating the offender, often become deeply preoccupied with the truthfulness of their client's communications. As some manifestations of dishonesty in the correctional setting are reviewed, however, it will become apparent that too much concern is unrewarding and unnecessary.

By the time the offender reaches the psychiatrist many of his unreasonable anxieties are under control and his major apprehension centers around what will be done with him. Unlike the patient seen in private practice, the offender may not sustain the slightest conviction that the physician is capable of helping him. He may, in fact, be unwilling to believe that the physician even wants to help. It is not surprising, therefore, that he often approaches an interview with an unwillingness to offer the kind of honest communication the evaluator seeks.

The behavior of a person subjected to an unsolicited interview is likely to be characterized by deceptiveness or lying. There are three common types of dishonest communication encountered in work with offenders. The offender may be evasive and deliberately leave out information which has been requested, in order to mislead the interviewer. He may refuse to acknowledge having said or done certain things when he knows that his denial is untrue. Or he may create false information, which is presented to the interviewer as the truth. The writer will take the liberty of referring to these three forms of deception as lies. If the psychiatrist does not anticipate and graciously accept some dishonesty on the part of the offender, he is liable to be disappointed or angered when he discovers that he has been deceived. Actually, there is little cause for him to become exercised. There are a number of reasons why an offender might wish to lie, and in his own phenomenological world deception may seem completely justified. The offender's dishonesty need not be an insurmountable obstacle to the goals of evaluation, and in fact it may reveal a great deal about him.

In the correctional setting dishonest communication often has a protective purpose. The offender may correctly or incorrectly feel that if he is completely honest he will have to say things that will be used against him. Sometimes the offender is not only distrustful of the evaluator but also fearful of his fellow inmates. He may be unwilling to report material that would implicate others or establish him as a friend of the authorities. While fear or self-protectiveness commonly leads to some dishonesty, it is usually only one of several motivations.

Dishonesty may, of course, have characterized the offender long before he was apprehended. Many criminal behaviors, such as swindling, check forging or impersonation, can in themselves be looked upon as examples of untruths in action. Aside from potential material gains such behaviors also provide a certain amount of power.[1] The person who poses as someone else, who forges or swindles, obtains a great deal of control over others. When the offender lies during a psychiatric interview, he may have similar motivations. Some offenders are eager to control the psychiatrist and deceive him into writing a favorable report. Others simply enjoy the power of knowing that only they are in a position to discern the truth. An involuntary patient, forced to submit to an examination by a professional person who is believed to possess exceptional abilities to judge human behavior, will experience many feelings of helplessness. One means of combating this effect is to be deceptive. As long as one is deceiving others one is not completely at their mercy.

Dishonesty equalizes differences in status. It offers an attractive means for making the offender-psychiatrist relationship more symmetrical. When the psychiatrist's intentions are frustrated, his position of being solidly "one up" is threatened.* The offender is likely to have had considerable opportunity to learn such maneuvers in his earlier experiences as a member of a lower socioeconomic group, for a traditional way in which downtrodden groups save face, and gain a modicum of control over their "betters," is to be deceptive.

Closely aligned to the power motivation is the pleasure associated with lying as a kind of game. Some criminals enjoy the challenge of deception and see it as a battle of intellects. After a period of time, the game becomes so satisfying that it is a sufficient motivation in itself.

Some offenders (and many other people) will lie simply to gain recognition. Often, the offender's self-esteem and self-concept have been so severely battered that he is willing to accept recognition wherever he finds it. The psychatrist is an important person whom the offender may be interested in impressing even when a favorable presentation will not lead to immediate advantages. Many offenders exaggerate, "spin tales" or give indications of previous accomplishments or skills which have no basis in reality. This kind of lying is more pathetic than aggressive, and is best looked upon as an indication of insecurity and unhappiness.

Closely related to lying for purposes of recognition is lying in order to be loved. Some offenders cannot tolerate having other people think badly of them and will do everything possible to deny factual material that puts them in a bad light. They leave out unfavorable details and exaggerate the more lovable aspects of their dispositions. The offender's primary motivation may be nothing more malicious than a wish to have the psychiatrist like him.

Lying for the single purpose of sadistically inflicting pain upon others is rarely seen in work with offenders. This form of aggression is perhaps more common among children or among those who are vindictively determined

* See Jay Haley for an intriguing description of power struggles in psychiatric and other interpersonal relationships.[2]

to gain revenge for real or imagined hurts. Even false gossip is relatively rare in the correctional setting since the possibilities of retaliation are far too great to allow for indulgence in aggressive whims. Lying for altruistic purposes is probably even more uncommon. Some offenders may believe that they are lying in order to protect their families or colleagues, but it is more likely that other motivations (particularly self-protection) are more powerful.

## Malingering and Hysteria

An interesting form of dishonest behavior which has received considerable attention in psychiatric literature is the feigning of mental illness. Malingering is most frequently encountered in pretrial examinations, particularly where the offender's life is at stake.[3] It is extremely difficult to feign mental illness for more than a few days unless one is equipped with grim determination and an excellent knowledge of psychiatry. For these reasons malingering of mental illness is quite easily detected.

When the malingerer is examined by psychiatrists, he is often found to be an emotionally disturbed person whose behavior is a response to greater needs than those that can be immediately gratified by deception.[4] An offender who senses imminent ego disruption may try to reassure himself by consciously playing the role of the mental patient. It is as though he were saying, "If I can pretend I am sick, what is happening will then be under my control. By controlling what appears to be a feigned illness, I can use the illness role to avoid facing the real despairs and fears which plague me." In this sense malingering is not different from traditional mental-illness behaviors insofar as it is a means of controlling feelings of helplessness by acting as if one were actually helpless. Sometimes offenders who are believed to be feigning insanity continue their behavior long after the realistic advantages of deception have disappeared. In such instances the maladaptive basis of malingering is more apparent.

Efforts to feign mental illness after sentencing or in the correctional institution are less frequent than is commonly supposed. In twelve years of prison work the writer has seen only a few individuals who might have been called malingerers. In each case the offender was motivated by a wish to be transferred to a unit for disturbed inmates in order to be close to a friend or a homosexual partner. Even here the need for the other person seemed to be so overwhelming and immutable that it was questionable how much choice these individuals felt they had.

Malingering is often contrasted with hysteria. Hysterical reactions can be looked upon as efforts to solve an adaptational problem by mimicking the symptoms of a mental or physical illness without an accompanying awareness of intention. Malingering implies a conscious choice to deceive. Hysteria is usually considered an unconscious form of deception which the individual cannot control. Although much attention has been paid to the differential diagnosis of malingering vs. hysteria, it is extremely difficult to categorize rigidly either behavior as a separate phenomenon. The degree of consciousness or choice in any indirect effort to influence the environment is almost impossible to discern. A man who cannot tolerate the restrictive environment of the prison may become depressed. He may realize that if his depression progresses to suicidal proportions he will be transferred out of the prison environment and into a unit for the criminally insane. Let us suppose that he actively desires such a transfer. How can we then determine if his "choice" to become more depressed is conscious or unconscious? The best we can do is talk about relative degrees of self-awareness. An unfortunate by-product of preoccupation with the question of malingering as opposed to hysteria is that the psychiatrist tends to lose sight of what is causing the patient's behavior and he may fail to act in a therapeutic manner. Seeking answers to the questions, "Why does this patient behave as he does?" and "What can I do for him that would be most helpful?," is far more meaningful than preoccupation with the question, "Is he a malingerer or an hysteric?"

One form of hysterical reaction by offenders which has received considerable attention in psychiatric literature is the "Ganser syndrome."[5,6] This condition is sometimes seen in offenders awaiting trial and is characterized by a rather unconvincing and ineffectual effort to portray an insane person. The literature suggests that such offenders are not consciously attempting to feign insanity but rather, in their wish to avoid some type of punishment, deceive themselves and unconsciously malinger insanity. Although they may give grossly inaccurate answers to routine questions, their responses suggest adequate contact with reality and a knowledge of what the examiner expects. The behavior of the person with the Ganser syndrome is said to include responses such as 2 and 2 equals 5, there are eight days in a week, thirteen months in a year, etc. These responses suggest that the person is capable of evaluating reality but does not wish to do so. In many cases the patient markedly improves once the disposition of his case is decided and he realizes that mental-illness behavior is no longer capable of influencing the environment.

The author is deeply opposed to the idea that the Ganser syndrome is a distinct and mysterious illness. First of all, this reaction is extremely uncommon. In twelve years of correctional work I have not seen a single case. When it does occur, it would seem to be not too dissimilar to any other mental illness behavior that is designed to alter the environment. There are certainly more troubling and interesting adaptations which merit the concern of the psychiatrist who works with offenders. Unfortunately, the issues of malingering and hysteria or of malingering and the Ganser syndrome are usually linked to questions of punishment. Too often the diagnosis of malingering means that the patient will be neglected or punished, and the diagnosis of hysteria or Ganser syndrome means that he will be treated a little more kindly. Malingering is looked upon as nastiness, and hysteria is reified as mental illness. Paying homage to behavioral patterns as if they were concrete entities caused by external events drives the psychiatrist to a preoccupation with questions of punishment and responsibility, a concern which interferes with rational evaluation of the patient's needs, his suffering or his treatability.

## Massive Denial

A more interesting and complicated form of self-deception is seen in some offenders who completely deny having committed a criminal act, even in the face of overwhelming evidence. Such denial is especially common when the criminal act is universally looked upon as reprehensible (for example, sex crimes or crimes of violence).[7] It is, of course, possible that some men who deny a crime are telling the truth, but in the cases the author is referring to there had usually been a massive amount of data pointing toward guilt. Others may be quite aware that they are deliberately lying. Frequently, however, the offender sticks to his denial so convincingly that one begins to suspect that he believes what he is saying. The likelihood that this is a form of self-deception is bolstered by the observation that such behavior has no apparent adaptive value. Most of the offenders who use massive-denial mechanisms do not make an effort to obtain release through legal assistance. Continued denial of the criminal act usually diminishes opportunities to obtain freedom since parole boards are reluctant to release a man who is unwilling to acknowledge or repent his guilt.

One possible explanation of such a maladaptive behavior is that the offender simply cannot acknowledge his criminal act to himself without experiencing enormous shame and self-contempt. The initial denial is likely to come after the shock effect of arrest, guilt and confessions has passed and when the offender is again feeling a desperate need to save face. Once having taken a dishonest stance, he is likely to be subjected to an onslaught of doubt, derision and questioning which threatens his self-esteem even further and which may encourage him to hold onto this defense with greater tenacity. Imprisonment is likely to accelerate this process. The prison environment takes such a derogatory attitude toward some crimes that heroic defenses are required to maintain an acceptable self-concept. The offender feels himself pushed further and further into a corner until an admission of guilt would be experienced as devastating. At this point becoming convinced of one's innocence takes on considerable adaptive value.

The most unfortunate aspect of this reaction is that it is difficult to maintain without resorting to unrealistic rationalizations and projections. A man who has been convicted of incest may come to the point of insisting that his nine-year-old daughter was promiscuous and that she and her mother fabricated a plot to cover up her behavior by implicating the subject. He may then go on to express a belief that his whole town was against him, the sheriff was vindictive or that the judge held old grudges. In the correctional milieu such statements are usually greeted with doubt or ridicule. As others begin aggressively to question his veracity, the patient feels even more alienated and his paranoid belief system becomes more divorced from reality.

The tenacity with which an offender can stick to such a defense is amazing. Sometimes a sex offender who is sentenced for an indeterminate period is in danger of spending many years in prison if he does not admit his crime (since those in charge of release are unlikely to believe that a man has been successfully treated if he is unwilling even to acknowledge his disturbance). The author has at times attempted to test the degree of defensiveness by suggesting that if he were in a similar situation and believed in his innocence he would still admit to having committed the crime so he could participate in therapy, please the parole board and be granted freedom. In each case the writer has been met with a response of extreme indignation. Usually the offender has insisted that rather than verbalize a false guilt he would spend the rest of his life in prison. Some have accused the author of attempting to persuade them to lie, and others have suspected him of being one more agent in a conspiracy to mistreat them.

Before leaving the subject of dishonesty it is important to re-emphasize one of its most adverse side effects in the correctional milieu. Correctional workers can become so preoccupied with the dishonesty of their clients that they are capable of forgetting about almost everything else. They begin to fear that they will be deceived into taking actions which assist the criminal's antisocial behavior and will thus become objects of universal ridicule. A key word heard in correctional agencies is "manipulation." Particularly in children's institutions the staff is often morbidly obsessed with the possibility that adolescents will manipulate them into behaving in an unprofessional manner. Status is often ascribed to the psychiatrist who is capable of detecting manipulators, and the inmate who is labeled a manipulator becomes a pariah.

I am convined that offenders are hardly more manipulative than any other group of people. Actually, the most successful manipulators, those who are successful in seducing others to do their bidding, are not likely to be found in a correctional setting (except perhaps among the staff). The psychiatrist who must make a major issue out of detecting manipulation reflects an insecurity in dealing with a behavior that should be quite familiar to him. Manipulation or, for that matter, all varieties of dishonesty are regularly encountered in daily work with any kind of patient.[8] Perhaps the combination of the inmate's personality and the correctional environment does lead to more efforts at manipulation than are seen in a free environment. These efforts are generally, however, singularly unsuccessful. Compared to many of the really skillful manipulators the psychiatrist sees in private practice, criminals are amateurs.

Similar comments may be made with regard to the phrase, "attention-getting." Correctional workers are frequently prone to write off extremely maladaptive and even self-destructive behavior as "nothing but attention-getting." This not only demeans the patient but is intellectually absurd. Almost all mental illness behavior is "attention-getting." No person would behave in a desperate or suicidal manner unless he wanted others to notice him.

## Evaluation of Reluctant Subjects—The Defense Interview

Psychiatric evaluation of offenders may have several purposes. The evaluator may be requested to assist the judge in making decisions as to sentencing, he may be seeking to determine if the offender qualifies for an indeterminate commitment, he may be trying to help the parole board decide as to release, or he may simply be attempting to determine for himself whether he can be useful to the offender in a psychotherapeutic relationship. Although there is always some effort to make every interview a therapeutic one, this is not the primary goal. The evaluator is mainly interested in gathering information which will help to answer one of three kinds of question. (1) What can be said as to why this man behaves as he does? What is the historical basis of his criminality? (2) How does this man behave at the present time? Can I describe his behavior in a way which will help myself or others to predict how he might react in a given situation? (3) How likely is this man to commit a dangerous act?

Psychodynamic explanations of criminality are dependent upon relating past history to current behavior. The availability of historical data in the correctional setting is, however, quite variable. Rarely is the psychiatrist provided with the amount of objective information available in a clinic or community agency. Evaluation must often begin with the patient. The offender, as we have noted, is not always inclined to be cooperative. Sometimes his evasions and distortions frustrate all efforts to obtain an accurate history.

Before the psychiatrist despairs of producing a useful report he must recall that psychodynamic explanation is only one goal of evaluation. Responses to questions concerned with the "how" rather than the "why" of behavior are important enough in themselves. It is also much easier to derive answers to the "how" type of question with uncooperative subjects. Even without a great deal of objective data the psychiatrist can judge how well the offender assesses reality, how coherent his thought processes are, how intelligent he is, how he relates to people, how well he rationalizes, how much denial he needs to utilize, how much projection, how much guilt he feels, how troubled he is by his criminal behavior, how depressed he is, how much anxiety he shows, how much psychological strength is available to sustain him through a lengthy institutionalization, how he feels about religion, work and education.

Of course, all these judgments are more easily made if there are objective historical data or if the psychiatrist, on the basis of his experience, can at least make inferences as to the past. There is still, however, much that can be learned by skillful observation.[9] No person, even a man who wishes to conceal his past life, is ever totally unwilling to interact with an interested observer. While the psychiatrist may have to observe his patient in a strained and unnatural setting, the offender's manner of relating and his repertoire of interpersonal maneuvers will still reveal a great deal.

The psychiatrist as an evaluator must learn to rely more on observation of defense mechanisms than on the patient's history. He must trust the interview itself as his primary source of data. "Defense interviewing," which is the effort to obtain information as to the psychological status of the reluctant subject, is a difficult skill. It requires that the interviewer be fully aware of his own immediate feelings and motivations so that he can judge how he is influencing the offender's behavior. It requires a considerable background of experience with other patients against which the individual offender's responses can be measured. Most important, it requires activity on the part of the interviewer. He cannot be a passive scribe but must repeatedly seek ways of finding meaningful interactions with his subject. All this must be done in a manner which, if not actually helpful to the patient, does not leave him feeling worse.

It would be impossible to describe how any given psychiatrist conducts a defense interview. Each uses his own personality and observational powers and depends upon those techniques which have become most comfortable for him. In the following section I shall briefly describe some of the observations and technical maneuvers that I have found useful in evaluating uncooperative offenders. This material is not comprehensive nor is it offered with the intention of advising how others should interview. It is included primarily to offer examples of the kinds of attitudinal sets and activities that are associated with the interview of the reluctant subject.

Not all offenders who communicate dishonestly are successful in their deception. If even a small amount of objective history is available, dishonesties quickly become apparent. Inconsistencies may also be noted within the patient's own story. At this point, the examiner is in a position to evaluate the effectiveness of the offender's dishonesty. Effective lying is an art which requires considerable skill. He who wishes to deceive gracefully must have some intelligence, some capacity to integrate ideas and a clear sensorium. He also needs calmness and confidence. When the psychiatrist suspects that he is receiving a dishonest communication, he may wish to express very gently his dubiousness and observe the offender's capacity to maintain his story convincingly and consistently. The offender's responses may reveal a great deal as to the state of his emotional and intellectual processes.

At some stage in the evaluative procedure, even in the first interview, the psychiatrist should make an effort to confront the reluctant subject with an inconsistency or an inappropriate attitude or feeling tone. This confrontation may consist of a simple questioning of discrepancies. It may be an effort to point out an attitude of hostility or uncooperativeness which is emanating from the subject. Or it may simply be an acknowledgement that the psychiatrist feels uneasy about the patient. Open confrontation is not common in conventional social intercourse and either encourages others to reveal themselves more openly or to become more defensive. The former response is always welcome, and the latter response may afford the psychiatrist some insight into the kinds of defenses the offender will utilize under stress.

Sometimes the interviewer may find it useful to attack the basis of a projective or rationalizing defense more vigorously. The psychiatrist might say, "Look, none of the things you have told me so far really make sense, and I have the feeling that the trouble may lie somewhere inside of you rather than in terms of what others have done to you. Perhaps you blame others in order to avoid looking at something in yourself." Such an interpretation must lead to reactions which communicate something about the offender's behavior under stress. A defense can also be attacked in a more indirect manner. Suggesting to an inmate who is using massive denial that he admit to something he insists he did not do is also likely to elicit interesting responses which we have previously discussed. Sometimes rigid defenses manifested by statements such as "I know I did wrong, but I'll never do it again" are best reacted to with questions such as "What was wrong with what you did?" or "What would your life be like if you stopped doing it?" In responding to such questions the offender often reveals attitudes toward the rightness or wrongness of his behavior, or toward his concept of personal responsibility, that were not suggested by his initial statements.

Sometimes the criminal's attitudes toward his behavior can be evaluated only in an indirect manner. It is useful at times to ask questions such as "I wonder how your victim felt?," "What do you think should be done with a man who committed a crime such as the one of which you are accused?," "What would be your feeling if you were exposed to a situation exactly similar to the one which preceded your crime?" The response to these questions may reveal a great deal about the extent of the offender's guilt feelings and remorse. Posing hypothetical questions is, of course, of limited value when the inmate responds with bland or stereotyped answers. This is a more valuable technique when the offender becomes intrigued with such questions and is willing to relax his defenses.

In many interviews the psychiatrist is likely to feel strongly toward his subject and will experience a great deal of concern and empathy. He may even find himself strongly agreeing with the patient's attitudes and behaviors. It is sometimes useful to communicate such feelings, and it is always important to observe how the patient responds to interest and warmth. Sometimes he is more frightened than comforted, and closeness leads only to greater defensiveness. On the other hand, the patient may respond by relating more intimately and developing better rapport. In either case a great deal has been learned as to the offender's willingness to accept warmth or intimacy.

On the other hand, if the subject is frustrating the interviewer, a direct communication of the examiner's annoyance sometimes leads to interesting reactions. Most offenders are pleased at such an unexpected and human response and will relate more easily. Others become more defensive. At times the interviewer might realize that he has had deviant thoughts or experiences quite similar to the subject's, and might communicate these to gain rapport and to observe how the offender reacts to evidence that his own behavior has not been so strange or unique.

Sometimes the offender's incompetence as a criminal is immediately apparent. The examiner might wish to chide the offender as to his ineptness, the ease with which he was apprehended or his consistent lack of success as a criminal. This can be a therapeutic maneuver since it confronts the offender with the maladaptiveness of his criminal behavior. It is also useful to note how the offender reacts to mild derision. Is he troubled by the evidence of his ineptness? Does he deny it? Does he agree with the interviewer's evaluation too quickly or does he become angry?

Some offenders will refuse to answer questions about their personal lives but will discuss less emotionally charged subjects such as politics, philosophy or religion. It is especially useful for the examiner periodically to interject his own opinions and attitudes on these subjects. This may lead to a relaxed discussion of feelings about authority, the meaning of life, and belief systems which reveals more about the offender's motivations and defenses than would unyielding attempts to force him to contemplate his criminality.

The alert interviewer also listens for metaphorical communications. Offenders who are too defensive to communicate directly will often reveal their own attitudes and feelings through verbal symbolism. In referring to the behavior of other objects, both animate and inanimate, patients are frequently trying to tell others something about themselves.[10] The animal who has been mistreated, the friend who has committed terrible acts and the car that is worn out and ready to be junked may all be indirect references to the patient's own feelings or behavior. Understanding metaphorical communication allows the evaluator to encourage the patient to reveal himself by entering into the metaphor, for example, by asking questions such as "Why does the car have to be junked?" or "Why does your friend do such things?" These techniques are learned only with experience, but they do enable the psychiatrist to make many valuable inferences.

The author always tries to present at least one dynamic explanation of the offender's criminal behavior during an evaluative interview. It is, of course, hoped that a small bit of insight will be therapeutic. What is perhaps more important, however, is observing how the inmate reacts to such unsolicited communications. Does he accept them grudgingly? Does he agree prematurely while failing to give any indication that he believes or understands what has been said? Does he become anxious, relieved, angry or curious? Any response says something about the kind of man who is being evaluated. This technique is especially useful in providing clues as to the offender's capacity to utilize psychiatric techniques for personality change.

Every inference which the psychiatrist makes must be evaluated in the light of the offender's apparent psychological sophistication. Some offenders easily pick up cues from a psychiatrist and are prone to offer whatever kind of response is inferentially requested. With such men it is easy to overestimate the status of mental health and treatability. The psychiatrist must take into consideration the possibility that he is dealing with a person who has learned psychiatric dogma and is repeating it for manipulative purposes. Other offenders have a great deal of difficulty in understanding what the examiner is looking for, and their inappropriate responses may reflect intellectual limitations or socioeconomic class differences. The psychiatrist who is not aware of the troubles some offenders have in trying to ascertain what is expected of them will often diagnose more illness than actually exists.

Since the psychiatrist possesses knowledge and skills which are not available to his subject, there is always the danger that an evaluation interview will take on too much of an exploitative quality. This can be minimized if the psychiatrist constantly reminds himself that he has some need to serve his patient as well as his society. Insulting the offender or bludgeoning him into revealing material that could be used against him is never justified. Aggressive interviewing is easier to condone when it leads to discovery of better means of helping the patient. The evaluator always hopes that information obtained in a skillful "defense" interview will be favorable to the subject's interest. It must be admitted, however, that when the psychiatrist detects tendencies toward dangerous behavior, he has used his skills to obtain information that might lead to greater deprivations of his patient's liberties. In such case the only comfort the psychiatrist has is the hope that continued control and treatment may be compatible with the patient's ultimate interests.

## The Evaluation of Dangerous Behavior

The psychiatrist has few more important functions in criminology than evaluating the probability that a given offender is likely to do violence to his fellow man. It must be reluctantly admitted that there is little science to be brought to this most sensitive task. Research in the area of dangerous behavior (other than generalizations from case material) is practically nonexistent. Predictive studies which have examined the probability of recidivism have not focused on the issue of dangerousness. If the psychiatrist or any other behavioral scientist were asked to show proof of his predictive skills, objective data could not be offered. The most a psychiatrist can say is that he has had considerable experience in dealing with disturbed people who commit dangerous acts, that he has been designated by society to diagnose and treat such individuals, and that his skill in treating dangerous behavior in those diagnosed as mentally ill has generally been appreciated.

Psychiatric evaluation of dangerous behavior therefore remains a matter of clinical judgment. This means the examiner must rely upon past experience, anecdotal material, a good many theoretical models and often plain intuition. His over-all impressions of a given person may at times lead him to suspect dangerousness when he is incapable of communicating the basis of his impressions to others. Often he simply must say, "My experience and intuition tell me that this man is potentially capable of repeating a violent act, but I cannot spell out exactly why I feel this way." While such clinical judgments must be respected, they are hardly a scientific basis for indeterminate commitment. The author acknowledges this deficiency with considerable humility. Yet upon psychiatric examination it is often surprisingly clear that some offenders are quite likely to commit a dangerous act. Too often, when medical advice is ignored, the offender's subsequent violence provides gruesome evidence of the psychiatrist's skills. One is reminded of Lee Harvey Oswald, who was examined by a psychiatrist during adolescence and was described as a person who without treatment would be capable of seriously injuring others.

All that has been thus far said as to the adaptive value of crime is relevant to the dangerous offender. There are, however, some factors which are more distinctively related to dangerous criminality. As these are listed, it must be re-emphasized that no single factor is a necessary or sufficient cause of dangerous behavior. Prediction of dangerousness must ultimately be based upon an over-all subjective impression which is based upon an understanding of the interrelatedness of many factors.

A previous history of use of physical force to resolve conflicts is commonly found in those who ultimately commit a dangerous crime. This is true even when assaultive behavior has not previously led to a criminal charge or harm to the victim, and it is especially true when such behavior has occurred more than once. Careful evaluation is also warranted when a person has a history of periodic temper tantrums, especially when such eruptions are inappropriate, prolonged or associated with physical attacks upon others. In one study of the previous records of violent offenders in Great Britain, F. H. McClintock noted that roughly 20 percent of those who committed violent crimes had previously been convicted of similar offenses.[11] Of the remaining group of first offenders, 20 percent had been suspected of previous violence or had been described as having an unstable disposition.

There is at least one major type of exception to the above generalizations. Some violent crimes are committed by previously peaceful offenders who attack a loved one or a friend in a fit of jealousy or rage. Such offenders are not heavily predisposed toward criminality and are unlikely again to find themselves in the exact situation which precipitated their antisocial act. The criminal act itself and the subsequent remorse have such an enormous impact upon their personalities that recidivism is unlikely.

Most criminals do not commit dangerous acts. Criminality, however, implies a willingness to solve a problem of adaptation by breaking rules. A person who has some capacity to use this adaptive device is also more likely to behave in a dangerous manner when he confronts a situation in which attacking others will temporarily solve his problem. Many offenders who commit dangerous acts have previously demonstrated some other form of antisocial conduct. In a study of homicidal criminals, Marvin Wolfgang noted that nearly two-thirds had a previous arrest record.[12] Most of these arrests were for crimes against persons, but property offenses were also represented. In McClintock's studies almost one-half of convicted violent offenders had previously been convicted of other crimes.

Since dangerous behavior is likely to be unreasonable behavior, the dangerous offender will frequently be a person who has previously demonstrated unreasonable behavior that may have been defined as mental illness. In a study of murderers, S. Palmer noted a higher incidence of physical frustrations (physical illnesses and handicaps) and emotional frustrations as compared with their own siblings.[13] Other studies have described the important relationship between mental illness and crimes of homicide.[14, 15, 16, 17] Guttmacher reports that one-third of the murderers he has examined could be classified as psychotic, and of this group one-third had previously been institutionalized because of mental illness.[18] While most studies suggest that the hospitalized mentally ill are no more inclined to commit criminal acts than the rest of the population, there are also indications that those defined as mentally ill do tend to have a higher arrest rate for some crimes such as robbery and rape.[19, 20]

Although we have argued that motivation does not fully explain crime, it is still an important factor in any criminal act. The psychiatrist recognizes that motivations to harm others are probably universal, but he has also learned that some types of aggressive fantasies are warning signals. The man who plots vengeance is more likely to hurt someone than the man who never thinks of it, and the man who is preoccupied with sadistic fantasies toward women is more likely to be sexually assaultive than the man whose inclinations are conventional.[21] Of course, neither of these individuals may ever hurt anyone. The psychiatrist must, however, listen and evaluate fantasies of violence, particularly when such thoughts are expressed in the form of threats or fears of losing control. In detecting such motivations, the psychiatrist uses every available communication, including the patient's verbalizations, his dream life, his use of metaphors and his responses to psychological tests.

In the course of interviewing offenders, the psychiatrist frequently encounters some who have great difficulty in identifying themselves with others. These men are emotionally cold, and although they may give lip service to conventional attitudes and sentiments, they are capable of behaving in a cruel manner, with little concern for their victims.[22] In an interview such individuals often fail to respond appropriately to emotionally charged questions or situations. Their coldness can often be traced to early deprivations of love and affection. Sometimes there is a history of violent behavior and brutal punishment within the offender's own family. Men exposed to violence during childhood will be more prone to violence in later life.[23, 24] Their phenomenological world is somewhat analogous to that of soldiers who have been involved in a cruel war for a long period of time. They have seen so much malice and have been subjected to so much cruelty that they can hardly understand why others get upset when they behave in a cruel manner. It is likely that violence arises more frequently among men who have learned the techniques of brutality and actual warfare. A diminished respect for the sanctity of life and a facility with weapons increase the likelihood of dangerous behavior. It might also be noted in this regard that other more immediate variables such as the offender's subculture might play an important role in crimes of violence. Wolfgang has postulated the existence of a "subculture of violence" which constantly exerts pressure upon its members to behave as if everyday living called for the aggressive behaviors of the battlefield.[25]

An ominous indicator of potential dangerousness is the presence of violent motivations which are deeply repressed or denied. The person who is distant from his own feelings, who does not recognize when he is angry and who denies all unpleasant impulses is more of a threat than the person who is troubled by conscious aggressive thoughts. The individual who is conscious of aggressive motivations at least has the opportunity to seek alternative means of adaptation. If one denies that all antisocial tendencies exist in himself, he has little room to maneuver when he is confronted with a stress situation in which denial cannot be maintained. Repressed motivations toward dangerous behavior can be detected through analysis of affect, dream life and history. Projective tests are often useful. A person who seems to be bland, friendly and passive may offer responses on the Rorschach test which suggest explosiveness and violence.

The individual who utilizes projective mechanisms to a point where his assessment of reality regularly and markedly differs from what is objectively observable is likely to be dangerous. Whenever a person sees his difficulties as emanating from outside of himself there is always the possibility that he will take arms against those agents which he perceives as causing his suffering. The projective mechanism also allows him to disavow responsibility for his actions. The most violent and cruel crimes are aften committed in response to bizarre paranoid delusions. When examined, sensational murderers are usually found to have been harboring bizarre and totally unrealistic fears or animosities which were projected onto the external world.

Men who have serious doubts as to their masculinity and a need to constantly reassure themselves or others are more prone to violent behavior. We have previously discussed how homosexual panic can lead to violent acts, and we have noted the importance of masculine-proving behavior in certain types of aggressive adolescent delinquents. A person who is driven to prove his masculinity is more likely to ignore the consequences of his actions, whether these are harmful to himself or to his victim.

While most individuals with acute or chronic brain disease do not commit criminal acts, the presence of confusion is sometimes conducive to expression of destructive impulses which are ordinarily restrained. Organic brain disease eventually leads to a deterioration of the individual's ability to maintain conventional patterns of behavior. Some types of disorders such as the "6 and 14 syndrome" may have a direct influence upon aggressivity. The brain-damaged person is also far more sensitive to alcohol. It impairs his judgment more quickly and more drastically than it does with the normal person.

We have previously emphasized the important relationship of alcohol to crime. Since drinking is a social function, many of the criminal activities which are facilitated by intoxication will result in actions against other persons.[26] The psychiatrist is especially concerned with behavioral trends during the intoxicated state. A history of repeated belligerency, argumentativeness or deep depression is often ominous. Generalizations as to potential violence cannot be made for the drug addict. Addiction to drugs such as heroin is not usually correlated with aggressive criminality. On the other hand, excessive usage of other drugs such as amphetamines is more likely to lead to aggressive behavior.

Many crimes of violence occur in situations where the offender is unable to control the behavior of a loved one or friend, and the threat of separation looms as an overpowering blow to his omnipotence.[27, 28] The person who cannot abandon control of others and who is enraged when they desert him is usually thought of as someone who is likely to become despondent or suicidally depressed. Behavioral scientists have learned, however, that violence directed toward oneself and violence directed toward others are closely linked and that it is sometimes impossible to determine which direction aggression will take.[29, 30] In general, any person who is suicidally depressed must be looked upon as an individual who is also capable of doing harm to others.

Ultimately, the occurrence of a dangerous act is dependent upon the patient's immediate social situation. Even the most predisposed person will not act aggressively if others avoid actions that will elicit this response. And under certain extremely stressful situations even the most benign person is capable of violent eruption. The evaluator, therefore, must make an effort to define those situations or environmental variables which increase the probability that a given person will harm others. A statement such as "This man continues to have a strong tendency to molest little children" is far less meaningful than a statement such as "This man begins to drink heavily when he feels that his wife is not gratifying his needs or when he feels that his employers do not appreciate him. When he is drinking and in contact with little girls, he usually makes sexual overtures." The latter statement suggests four procedures which might minimize dangerous potentialities; namely, helping the patient's wife, finding an understanding employer, making efforts to control the patient's drinking or reducing his opportunities to be near female children.

## *Chapter 21*

# PSYCHOTHERAPY

PSYCHOTHERAPY is the major therapeutic tool available to the psychiatrist. Roughly defined, it is a form of treatment in which a trained person deliberately establishes a professional relationship with an emotionally troubled person in order to help him find a more comfortable and effective adaptation.* Through a series of mainly verbal interactions the troubled person is helped to understand the nature of the oppressive stresses within his life, and he is encouraged to use all his capacities for dealing with them. Psychotherapy deals with all types of oppressive stress, but it is especially concerned with unrealistic stress, that is, stress which does not emanate directly from the immediate environment but which is created by a distorted interpretation of that environment. Psychotherapy is frequently the most effective treatment for changing the unreasonable behavioral patterns of people who are responding to unrealistic stress. In our present state of knowledge it is the most humane treatment for changing the behavior of unreasonable lawbreakers.

Throughout this chapter we will consider some of the theoretical and technical aspects of psychotherapy which are of special importance in psychiatric criminology.

### The Contractual Basis

Psychotherapy is the one activity of the correctional psychiatrist which is not invariably clouded with doubt as to when the needs of society must

* This is a broad definition of a process which is difficult to define with precision. See Wolberg[1] or Watkins[2] for other definitions.

take precedence over the needs of the individual. Psychotherapy is deeply rooted in medical tradition as a form of treatment which serves the individual. Many forms of psychotherapy do not even seek to influence the direction of behavior but have a major goal of providing self-understanding. The therapist assumes that the patient who understands himself will probably feel better and will behave more effectively. In other types of psychotherapy the therapist may have certain goals in mind which will encourage direct efforts to change the patient's belief system. In these cases the therapist assumes that he is in a better position to know what the patient must learn if he is to improve. Still, all forms of genuine psychotherapy are ultimately concerned with providing a service for the patient. Psychotherapy must, explicitly or implicitly, be a contractual arrangement for a type of service, an arrangement which can be terminated by either party at any time.

It could be argued that in the correctional setting psychotherapy is neither contractual nor voluntary. Many offenders would never seek treatment unless faced with the threat of continued punishment. Some, in fact, are faced with the choice of psychotherapy or prison. Yet in many ways the offender's situation is not different from that of most other people who seek psychiatric help. Few patients are ever eager to see a psychiatrist. A person seeks psychotherapy when he is desperate and unable to ward off the oppressive onslaughts of other people or his own conscience. In the case of the offender, it is sometimes the threat of oppression by society (imprisonment) which drives him to psychotherapy. He chooses treatment in order to avoid or shorten the duration of the psychological pain of imprisonment, just as the neurotic chooses treatment in order to ward of more covert sources of psychological pain. Both the offender and the neurotic approach therapy with considerable ambivalence. Although the pressures upon the offender may be more urgent than those upon the neurotic, both can elect not to participate.

## Symptom Removal vs. Psychotherapy

Because psychotherapy is a technique for changing adaptations in a manner compatible with the patient's own interests, it can be distinguished from many other forms of treatment. Crime is commonly looked upon as a symptom, and most correctional treatments seek only to remove the "antisocial symptom." In the United States, for example, our correctional system tries to produce greater internal control and to extinguish a tendency toward antisocial responses by punishing the symptom of "bad" behavior and by rewarding "good" behaviors. Recently more sophisticated methods for altering behavioral responses have been developed by psychologists and psychiatrists.[3, 4, 5] A group of techniques (usually referred to as behavior therapies) based on scientific exploitation of the effects of reward and punishment have had some effectiveness in relieving certain symptoms of mental illness. Predictably, behavioral therapies have been suggested as potential means of eliminating tendencies to criminal behaviors.[6] It is important to distinguish carefully between behavioral therapy (or any other treatment which seeks only to alleviate symptoms) and more traditional forms of psychotherapy. Traditional psychotherapy is concerned with relieving symptoms, but it is also concerned with much more.

The limitations of any therapy which seeks only to relieve symptoms can be more clearly understood if we consider the question, "Is it really in the patient's best interest to extinguish a maladaptive behavior if nothing is done to alleviate the other stresses of his existence?" If only physical illnesses are considered, the answer to this question is usually affirmative. A physical symptom is likely to be painful or irritating. The patient complains and requests relief. Removal of the symptom usually means a more favorable adaptation and the patient is able to feel and function better. Even in medical practice which deals only with physical illnesses, however, there are exceptions. Sudden removal of a long-standing physical symptom such as an ulcer sometimes results in psychotic behavior. Following some surgical procedures, the patient may find that the handicaps incurred by surgery are more distressing than his original symptoms.

If mental-illness behaviors are looked upon as symptoms, the situation becomes much more complicated. Mental illness is determined by a complex interaction of biological, psychological and social stresses. Removing a specific behavioral pattern without examining the patient's total situation could have undesirable consequences. Let us suppose that a woman married to a cruel and insensitive man suddenly develops a fear of leaving the house. Her phobic reaction leads to greater solicitousness upon her husband's part. He must spend more time with her and has to abandon other activities which she resented. In such a case the phobic symptom is at least in part an effort to neutralize the oppressive nature of the marital relationship. Now let us assume that there are techniques available which could cure our patient of her phobia. If the symptom were removed and nothing else were done, the benefits to the patient would be questionable. She might temporarily feel better, but she would either have to accommodate herself to her husband's continued oppressive onslaughts or find a new adaptation. There is no assurance that the new adaptation would be less painful or more effective than the initial phobia.

Symptomatic treatment implies that the symptom is an affliction that has descended upon one individual. It ignores the fact that maladaptive behavior develops within an interpersonal network and that it is a means of influencing that network. If our phobic patient were treated with psychotherapy, efforts would still be made to alleviate her suffering, but detailed attention would also be paid to the nature of her marital relationship. Hopefully, she would learn to understand what goes on between her and her husband, and would be in a better position to deal with his neglect. She would learn about her own vulnerabilities and would be encouraged to seek new and better means of dealing wiith stressful relationships. Perhaps even the husband would be brought in as an active participant in the therapeutic process.

There are even greater problems with any treatment approach which looks upon crime as a symptom and attempts to treat it without paying attention to the interpersonal and social context. Crime may have valuable social purposes. If selected behaviors are defined as crimes, other, more desirable behaviors which are not so defined are strengthened. Crime is also a means of fulfilling social needs that cannot be satisfied through legitimate channels. Perhaps an outstanding example in current American life is the civil rights movement. In this instance, a group of dedicated people have had to violate laws deliberately in order to produce a social change. Most of us applaud such activity as noble and righteous. But consider what would happen if behavior which was based on a desire for social change were treated as a symptom. Its value as a form of protest would be eliminated.

The trouble with efforts at symptom removal which are based on analogies with physical medicine is that such efforts are based on the assumption that the social structure has an inherent perfection and that any deviation from the norms is a symptom of imperfection. If the phobic wife is treated without considering the adverse influence of her husband, he (by inference) is defined as a healthy and moral man. If the criminal's behavior is looked upon as something which must be extinguished without examining its social causes, we must believe that every single law is correct and moral. Eysenck has suggested that criminals are people who do not condition easily, who could be retrained to be more conforming through behavioral therapies.[7] If he is correct, I would feel that indiscriminate utilization of such techniques would be disastrous. Civil rights demonstrators may be "poor conditioners," but our society has many reasons to be thankful that they are.

Some would agree that crimes arising from political dissent may have a useful purpose but would argue that destructive crimes such as stealing are never of any value to the society. I would still disagree. All crimes are purposive, and to the extent that they are responses to realistic and perceivable oppression they may be socially useful. Poverty-stricken adolescents who steal have not been entirely ineffective in influencing their environment. Much of our recent rediscovery of poverty stems from a concern with rising rates of juvenile delinquency. Even the child who steals to draw his parents' attention to a serious conflict within the family may accomplish something useful. Often it is only after one of its members commits a crime that some families begin to examine and try to change inequities and injustices within their own group.

To the extent that a person's criminal behavior is influenced by feelings of oppression that is unreal it is less likely to influence favorably the family or the social order. In these instances treating crime as a symptom is easier to justify. One of the obligations of the person who treats the offender is to clarify the nature of the oppressive stress to which he is responding, in order to determine which stresses are realistic and which are unrealistic. Once such clarification has been obtained, there could be few rational objections to using conditioning techniques to eradicate behaviors that serve neither the offender nor society. But the indications for symptom removal cannot be determined unless the individual has first been exposed to a thorough evaluation. Often it is not clear which symptoms the patient could do without until he has had some psychotherapy.

Although every symptom of deviant behavior has some initial adaptive value, it is incorrect to assume that *every* symptom, even a chronic one, had such an urgent adaptive purpose that its indiscriminate removal might result in a new symptom or severe personality disintegration. Over a period of time some symptomatic behaviors become learned habits which continue to appear even when they no longer have adaptive value. The phobic woman of our earlier example might continue to be phobic even after her husband had changed and even if she were certain that he would not go back to his old ways if she lost her symptom. The fetishist who has been stealing women's undergarments for years might have sufficiently resolved the initial problems which engendered his deviation but may find himself driven to repeat a behavior that brings him nothing but anguish. For these individuals, behavioral therapies could be the treatments of choice or a useful adjunct to traditional psychotherapies.

## Crucial Factors in Psychotherapy*

We have previously noted that criminals have great difficulty in distinguishing external oppression from that which arises from within them-

* Much of the material of this section is based upon classical psychiatric and psychoanalytic models of psychotherapy. The reader is referred to the writings of Alexander,[8] Fromm-Reichmann[9] and Menninger[10] as especially useful.

selves. The man who has been mistreated by his own father may, for example, come to see all authority figures, even benign ones, as oppressors. One of the therapist's tasks is to help such an offender learn that all authority figures are not malevolent. The offender, unfortunately, is not easily convinced that his perceptions are incorrect, and clarification of what is real and what is unreal is not an easy job.

The therapist is unlikely to succeed in clarifying the offender's perception of reality unless he is able to accept certain realities himself. To begin with, he must appreciate how very difficult it is for a middle-class person like himself to comprehend the unpleasant aspects of lower-class life.[11] Therapists who are not familiar with the severity of stresses imposed upon criminals tend to diagnose too much paranoia. Unless the therapist can come to appreciate fully the harsh realities of his patient's life and communicate this appreciation, the offender will never be in a position to examine that part of himself that is reacting to internal conflict. A therapist who insists that every antisocial attitude or action is neurotic simply cannot be taken seriously by the offender.

Having shown some capacity to understand the realistic stress in the patient's life, the therapist can begin to question the unreasonable aspects of his patient's behavior. As he asks such questions as "What were you looking for?" and "Did your behavior accomplish this goal?" the offender may slowly come to realize that he is either completely ineffective as a criminal or that his motivations are unreasonable. Encouraging the patient to examine repeatedly every aspect of his antisocial behavior eventually clarifies the fact that such behavior cannot be explained in terms of his realistic needs. As he begins to ask himself, "Why did I do that?" and to answer, "That isn't what I wanted," he approaches a state of mind in which he is more susceptible to useful personality change.

By remaining on the side of the patient and by thinking in terms of the adaptive value of the criminal act, the therapist is usually able to arrive at a therapeutic position in which he looks down upon antisocial conduct but does not condemn it. He does not have to say, "What you are doing is bad and you must stop it." He can say, "Your behavior does not seem to be bringing you what you are looking for, and since it results in loss of liberty it is probably a source of great discomfort. I wonder why you continue to hurt yourself? Are there better ways of getting what you want?"

The therapist must have some ability to identify himself with the offender's world, to understand what criminality does for the patient and to communicate that understanding in an empathic manner. This is especially important in the beginning of therapy. If the offender does not believe that his therapist has some appreciation of the adaptive value of criminality, he is not likely to develop a meaningful relationship. It is difficult to trust someone who doesn't seem to understand how painful it is to give up old ways. It is even more difficult to change if one doesn't feel cared for and understood.

While all therapy is in a sense educative, the need for didactic efforts on the part of the therapist is more apparent in work with offenders. Cultural limitations and emotional immaturity have often deprived the offender of knowledge that is more readily available to the middle or upper classes. The therapist may have to spend considerable time explaining elementary concepts of interpersonal relationships. Sometimes even more basic information must be provided. Many offenders have little understanding of the problems of their spouses. Some do not know how to keep a budget. The sex offender is often ignorant of certain basic anatomical and physiological facts. Much of his educative work can be done in didactic group sessions which supplement formal psychotherapy. In the Wisconsin Sex Crimes Program, for example, classroom presentation of basic facts about sex and marriage has been found to be a useful adjunct to psychotherapy. Such information is not only reassuring, but it also helps the offender to clarify for himself how much of his deviant behavior was determined by normal motivations, how much by ignorance and how much by his personality disturbance.

Perhaps the most esteemed goal in traditional psychotherapy is insight. The patient who understands himself, and particularly the patient who has gained a knowledge of his unconscious motivations, is believed to have been significantly helped. In the early days of psychoanalysis some believed that insight, particularly that insight which the patient derived for himself, would be sufficient to alleviate symptoms and facilitate personality change. Today's psychotherapists are more skeptical. They have learned that much insight, even that which the patient derives for himself, may not lead to any real change in behavioral patterns. Sometimes insight even helps the offender to sustain his criminality since he uses his knowledge to justify his behavior. Statements like "Now I know why I behaved as I did, and with my background who can blame me when I do bad things?" are evidence of the possibility that psychiatric knowledge can be used for corrupt as well as for useful goals.

It is important to emphasize the limitations of insight because so many therapists become discouraged when they discover that insight can be so superficial or so intellectualized that it has little or no impact upon the personality Yet it must also be noted that insight can be deep as well as superficial, can be experienced as well as intellectualized and can have a profound effect upon a person's behavior. As an offender discovers the motivations underlying his antisociality, he may come to feel that they are no longer important. Bringing emotions out into the open often detoxifies the guilt or shame that accompanies them and allows the patient to perceive the absurdity of the maladaptive behavior which such affects engender. Insight brings greater control since it is easier to deal with what one knows, and because self-awareness facilitates the discovery of the existence of alternative adaptations.

Sometimes even insight that appears to be superficial and intellectualized is beneficial. The writer has had an opportunity to follow the course of a number of men who were exposed to a form of psychotherapy which consisted largely of dogmatic explanations of their problems couched in the jargon of Freudian psychology. After treatment they would come up with such discouraging statements as "I know now why I like to molest little boys. It is because I really want to sleep with my mother and fear castration if I approach a woman. Now that I know that, I am cured." While the author was initially inclined to look upon such insights as new and singularly unfavorable defenses, his experience has suggested that this is not always so. Most of these men seemed to be more comfortable after their therapy experience, and many of them managed to do quite well upon leaving the institution. Of course, other factors may have been responsible for this improvement (particularly the relationship with the therapist), but it is possible that even gross caricatures of Freudian psychology contain enough truth so that the offender can use them to provide mechanistic explanations of his behavior. Having an explanatory model (however naïve) upon which one can lean during times of stress is comforting and could bolster efforts to find noncriminal adaptations.

The most crucial factor in psychotherapy is the relationship that develops between patient and therapist. Personality is shaped by interpersonal events and is most likely to change under the influence of an intense interpersonal encounter. Psychotherapy is such an encounter. As the patient shares his innermost secrets with the therapist, he develops strong feelings toward that person and may come to believe that his destiny is in his therapist's hands. The helping person is seen as a powerful person, and his conduct within the therapeutic interaction will have a profound impact upon the patient.

At the very least, the therapist's efforts to be interested, emphatic, intimate and incorruptible will have a supportive effect. If the offender does nothing more than lean on the relationship for a safe kind of nuturance, he is likely to feel better. When therapy is discontinued he may carry with him an internalized model of what a comfortable relationship can be like and this may increase his capacity to seek support in other relationships. Sometimes the offender learns to like and even trust the therapist and may incorporate some of the latter's values. These may bolster him when stressful situations make antisociality loom as a seductive adaptation.

The hope of the therapist is that the therapeutic relationship will provide much more than support. It is assumed that the offender will bring certain fixed attitudinal and behavioral patterns to the relationship which are largely molded by past interpersonal experience. Frequently, the patient reacts to the therapist as if he were a reincarnation of a parental or sibling figure. These reactions, which are called transference, can be used to clarify the irrational basis of much of the offender's antisocial conduct. Interpretations of transference will provide the patient with insight, but, even more importantly, the therapist's response to the unreasonable responses of his patient will provide what psychoanalysts call a corrective emotional experience. If the patient expresses thoughts which he perceives as shameful and is not shamed, if he expresses aggression and is not punished, or if he expresses affection and is not rejected, such new experiences may lead him to re-examine and modify his entire belief system.

The offender-therapist relationship is the most powerful technique available for influencing behavioral patterns such as masochism or paranoia. If the patient with intense psychopathic tendencies can be kept in therapy, he eventually comes to acknowledge an involvement with the therapist. A climate of warmth, trust and safety threatens the very basis of the psychopathic defense.* There is less need to seek a painless freedom from object relations when the relations themselves do not appear to be painful. In a climate in which rejection or retaliation seems unlikely the psychopathic offender may be capable of experiencing his need, or at least his wish, for closeness.

Trust in a relationship also diminishes the need for masochistic or paranoid defenses. Masochism implies an omnipotent wish to control the timing and extent of one's suffering by bringing it upon oneself or by enticing others into bringing it upon oneself. It is a denial of closeness and a moving away from what is perceived as a painful quality in any uncontrolled relationship. As the patient experiences needs toward the therapist, and learns that it is safe and even beneficial to communicate these needs,

* Techniques for gaining the trust of the psychopathic offender are complex and can rarely be mastered without considerable experience or inherent skill. See Aichorn[12] and Redl[13] for more detailed descriptions of effective therapeutic interactions.

his intense drives to control all relationships is diminished. He learns to "take his chances" in an open and freer interaction.

We have noted earlier the close linkage of masochism and paranoia. The criminal usually denies that he has brought his difficulties upon himself and tries to convice himself that his problems are brought upon him from the outside. Again, real trust and closeness decrease the need to externalize problems. When the patient feels that it is safe to "take his chances" in relationships, he does not need to structure his belief system so it appears that the world is persecuting him.

The kind of relationship we are describing here does not come easily. Offenders have few reasons for trusting the therapist, and defense mechanisms which have been sustaining to him are not abandoned without a struggle. An assumption that a trusting relationship can be developed with a "psychopathic" offender in less than six months of intensive work is both naïve and dangerous. The therapist who has some need to prove that he can gain trust quickly is in a position to be manipulated and scorned by his patient. If he generalizes his inevitable disappointment to all disturbed offenders, he develops a pessimistic attitude which is neither justified nor useful.

## Some Troubling Questions in the Psychotherapy of Offenders

Do criminals have to become more emotionally disturbed before they can change? Ever since August Aichorn began to describe his work with delinquents it has been generally agreed that many criminals, especially those with psychopathic tendencies, cannot be successfully treated unless they first become anxious. This proposition is generally stated in the form, "The delinquent must first become a neurotic," and it is founded on the belief that offenders experience little emotional anguish before they enter therapy. Of course, this assumption is not always true. The unreasonable offender is likely to be far more anxious than the average person. Whether this is a result of imprisonment or fear of imprisonment is almost irrelevant. The fact is that the unabashed, "in command of the situation" offender is not easy to find. Still, the offender does give up a great deal when he abandons the belief systems and behaviors of the criminal adaptation. As psychotherapy helps him realize that much of his behavior does not make sense, he experiences considerable uneasiness. When he later discovers that his maneuvers with the therapist do not elicit anticipated reactions, he may feel anger. When he finally begins to appreciate the depths of his need for the therapist and others, his experience may be one of despair. At this point, many of the behaviors associated with mental illness begin to appear in the form of anxiety attacks, phobias, hypochondriasis and psychosomatic upheavals.

While the manifestations of despair seen in the psychotherapy of offenders may be especially intense and dramatic, they are not qualitatively different from those seen in the treatment of neurotics. Patients treated by psychoanalysis in a private-practice setting also experience considerable anguish during their treatment. Most psychotherapy in our day and age deals with character problems, and it is hard to see how anyone could change his character structure without experiencing psychic pain. In fact, psychoanalysts privately concede that an analysis is not really successful unless the patient has experienced occasional desperate moments. The criminal, like any other patient, may show an increase in mental-illness behaviors during the course of psychotherapy.

How much confidentiality can the psychiatrist promise the offender? How much is desirable? Communications made in a private medical setting are not usually shared with others. Although such communications are not given quite the same degree of sanctity as the Catholic confessional nor the same privileged status as that of communications to an attorney, the psychiatrist is entrusted with a considerable ethical obligation to protect the confidences of his patients. Ordinarily he discusses case material with no one but his colleagues. Psychotherapy with offenders does not take place in a private setting but is usually administered by agencies. The community-employed therapist will therefore be under far greater pressure to share his patient's communications with others. Agency workers request progress reports and seek other types of information. The therapist is especially tempted to report findings that would reflect favorably upon his client. In any case, confidentiality, one of the cornerstones of psychotherapy, is seriously threatened.

Actually, the only realistic need for sharing information arises when antisocial behavior is threatened or is impending. The manner in which this problem is usually handled in correctional institutions is for the therapist to inform his patient at the beginning of their relationship that any material which threatens harm to individuals or to the institutional structure must be reported. It is difficult for the therapist to avoid doing otherwise. He is, after all, an employee of the community, and while he may primarily intend to serve the patient, he has some obligation to those who pay his salary. This does not mean that he need report every threat of antisociality that he hears. He must rather evaluate such communications carefully, and act when he is convinced that harm cannot otherwise be avoided. In each instance he is obligated to tell his patient of his intention to inform. This in itself may prevent the act from taking place, and could help to preserve at least a modicum of trust.

The answer to the question, "How much confidentiality is desirable in treating offenders?" has to be, given the exceptions noted, "As much as possible." Otherwise the writer can see no need for the therapist ever revealing his patient's communications unless there is a need for consultation with another professional. This attitude is often a source of irritation to other correctional workers. They fail to realize that it does not imply any distrust but is simply a necessary condition of treatment. It is often useful to clarify that such confidentiality applies only to therapy and not to evaluation. The reader may wonder why this inflexible attitude is necessary. Offenders may have committed quite shameful acts, which are described in detail in legal records. Their most intimate secrets are often public knowledge. It could legitimately be asked, "What more could be revealed in therapy that is more damaging or shameful than what is already known?" The writer feels that it is this very intense previous exposure to public scrutiny that makes later confidentiality so necessary. What shreds of dignity the offender still retains can only be preserved if he is treated in a respectful manner and afforded the same protection given to any other patient. Even though the offender's secrets may not be earth-shattering, he is much more likely to communicate honestly in an atmosphere which respects his needs and rights.

Are countertransference problems with offenders different from those met with in other patients? The patient is not the only one who brings unconscious attitudes and unrealistic expectations to therapy. The therapist also tends to project onto the patient attitudes and expectations derived from past interpersonal experiences. Countertransference in the therapist is a natural part of the treatment process, which either helps to clarify relationships or becomes a stumbling block to progress. Criminals probably elicit more profound countertransference reactions than other patients. The openness of their aggressivity, sexuality and dependency must eventually touch some feeling in the therapist. Feelings of anger or revulsion, which the therapist easily controls or utilizes to gain better understanding in ordinary therapeutic interactions, sometimes become serious impediments in the treatment of the offender. It is one thing to hear fantasies of a gory murder; it is another to know that what is described actually took place. Listening to patients' fantasies of incest may not threaten the therapist, but trying to help a person work through his feelings about an actual incestual experience is more likely to rekindle the therapist's own Oedipal problems.

One factor that tends to neutralize intense countertransference feelings is the great amount of external control that is put on an offender who is institutionalized or subjected to probationary status. The therapist is not alone with his patient. He may have less personal involvement in the patient's antisociality since he knows that other people will quickly move in to control any aberrant behavior.

The rigid controls put upon the patient also have a direct influence on the therapist's reactions. He may be sufficiently impressed by the retribution imposed upon his patient so that he feels the need to repress vigorously any antisocial fantasies of his own. This means that much countertransference material will be repressed. Therapy with offenders is usually less interesting and vital than therapy with free citizens. In an ideal therapeutic climate the offender should be free to experiment with provocative behaviors, and the therapist should be free to experience and constructively utilize the emotions which such behaviors generate in himself.

Can therapy be effective in a correctional institution? The impact of excessive external control on countertransference reactions is only one of the impediments to therapy in the correctional setting. Correctional institutions have other built-in tendencies which undermine therapeutic progress. Their excessively restrictive environments are antagonistic to therapeutic change even when the offender is ready to adopt new patterns of behavior. The patient may say, "I think I am ready to change," and he may be right, but there is no way for him to prove it in a milieu which will not allow them to test out new behaviors. His behavior in the prison is not predictive of what he will do in the free world. His verbal protestations of change may be even more meaningless.

Therapy is difficult in any institutional setting, correctional or otherwise. The institutional world is simply not real enough nor rich enough to allow for the kinds of new experience that make for psychological growth. Therapeutic interactions for both patient and therapist tend to be stereotyped. There are few shared moments of mastery and even fewer surprises. Therapy is most fruitful when there is opportunity for contact with relatives and members of the opposite sex, opportunity for limited periods of freedom (passes, leaves) and opportunity to take responsibility for making decisions. When these outlets are lacking, psychotherapy becomes more arduous for the therapist and less rewarding for the patient. None of this should be taken to mean that psychotherapy is impossible in a correctional institution. It is true that it is more difficult, but man's capacity to change is such that effective psychotherapy is possible even in the most restrictive environment.

Is therapy facilitated or hindered when the offender is subjected to an indeterminate commitment? We have previously described the potential dangers and advantages of indeterminate sentencing. Indeterminacy seems to provide an especially supportive background to psychotherapeutic efforts since the offender's motivation would be increased in a situation where release was dependent upon psychological improvement. Unfortunately, there are some perplexing side effects to psychotherapy programs for men committed indeterminately. The patient can become so concerned with gaining his freedom that he forgets about everything else. He may focus all his efforts on trying to convince the therapist that he is improved or well. This makes it very difficult for him to experience the kind of therapeutic interactions that are essential for psychological growth.

The therapist, too, is in an awkward position. He feels the urgency of his patient's needs to obtain freedom and loses the degree of professional detachment which is sorely needed. If therapy does not go well, he may feel responsible for the offender's continued commitment. These problems are magnified in settings where the therapist is required to report on his patient's progress. In such situations the therapist may actually have the power to release or continue to restrain the patient. Such power is hardly compatible with therapeutic rapport. Human beings simply do not communicate information which reflects unfavorably upon themselves unless they are desperate.

Faced with such issues, some therapists despair of working with indeterminate patients and begin to yearn for the certainty of fixed commitments. Fixed sentences enable the therapist to detach himself from release decisions and to establish a relationship more similiar to private practice models. The therapist can say to his patient, "I have nothing to do with what happens to you here. I can only help you to understand yourself so you are better equipped to deal with your environment. Therapy may help you get along better, it may even help you to get out sooner, but this would be because you have changed or because other circumstances have changed and not because I have had any power over your environment." Such a working situation has its merits. It removes most of the conflicts as to whose agent the therapist is and provides a relatively "clean" model.

It does seem that therapy is somewhat more difficult with indeterminate patients. Yet there are many other advantages to indeterminacy. One way of keeping problems to a minimum would be to set up programs in which the therapist is given no control over the release date of his indeterminate patient. This would require that release decisions be turned over to those whom the patient never sees in a formal therapeutic relationship. Such individuals might be other psychiatrists or, preferably, independent parole boards composed of representatives of a number of disciplines. The function of the releasing agency would be simply to determine who is sufficiently rehabilitated to return to the community. If a current assessment of the offender's psychological status were needed, a psychiatrist who was not that man's therapist could do the evaluation.

Can psychotherapy make the offender a better criminal? If the stand of the therapist is "Why do you continue to engage in criminal acts which do not serve your needs?" the response of the offender need not be, "Very well, I will give up antisocial behavior," but could be, "I will have to become a better criminal so that my actions will serve my interests." Increased criminal behavior following psychotherapy is in theory always a possibility. The offender might develop better controls and a more integrated personality, which could be used to further a criminal career.

The author doubts, however, that psychotherapy encourages many offenders to continue in their criminal ways. The number of offenders who are able to make a successful career out of crime is quite limited. Unreasonable offenders (who are most likely to receive therapy) usually lack the temperament, the training and the "connections" that are needed for successful criminality. If treatment is helpful, they ultimately realize that the risks of apprehension and punishment outweigh their abilities to obtain an adequate income as criminals. Therapy also helps the offender to find other adaptations which, although less immediately gratifying, are also less risky.

Which offenders should receive psychotherapy? Not all offenders can be offered psychotherapy, and not all offenders should receive it. Where there is a chronic scarcity of trained therapists, some judgment has to be exercised in directing help to those who are in greatest need and who are most likely to benefit. Therapy is most necessary and most useful when the patient is aware of the unreasonableness of his criminal behavior, and when he wants to do something about it. Where staff resources are limited, efforts to treat the unmotivated offender are difficult to justify unless there is clear evidence of dangerousness. The evaluation of a person's motivation to receive help or change must ultimately reflect highly subjective judgments by the therapists. In the author's opinion, the therapist in the correctional setting is ordinarily too inclined to minimize the patient's motivation. Generally, a patient who asks for therapy is a troubled person (even when it appears that he may also wish to manipulate the therapist), and a great majority of offenders are usually eager to seek or to accept help once they are convinced that the therapist's offer is sincere.

## Group Therapy

Group therapy has been used in correctional institutions since World War II.[14] It has been widely heralded as effective as or even more effective than individual therapy. One problem in evaluating group therapy is that it is so diversified.[15,16,17] The omnibus term "group therapy" describes a great variety of techniques often based on divergent philosophies. There is little resemblance, for example, between a group in which the therapist exhorts his patients to change and one in which he is practically non-directive. Without attempting to define the goals or philosophies of the many varieties of group therapy, we could note several reasons why this form of treatment could be especially useful for offenders.

Group therapy allows offenders to realize that other people are "in the same boat." This may have a great impact upon those offenders who are inclined to be especially isolated because of shame or remorse.

Communication problems related to socioeconomic class differences are somewhat attentuated in a group setting, where there are several patients who can assist each other and the therapist in correcting misperceptions.

The group provides a greater number of possible relationships, some of which may come to be especially meaningful.

The group may be the only place in a correctional setting where offenders are able to express affection and anger toward one another.

In group therapy the offender must take more responsibility for his own treatment. He also has some obligation to help others. Anything that increases the offenders sense of social responsibility is helpful.

To the extent that criminality may be modified by attitude change the group would appear to be the most attractive vehicle for such change. Attitudes are largely formed in association with peers, and if the group develops more conventional attitudes, so must its individual members.

Perhaps the majority of group-psychotherapy techniques used by psychiatrists in a correctional setting are based on psychoanalytic principles. These do not radically differ from group analytic techniques used with the mentally ill and will not be discussed here. A different set of techniques developed primarily by sociologists for the specific purpose of treating offenders will be briefly considered. These are referred to as guided group interactions or group counseling and are based on the premise that talking about problems with a trained person will help the group to change its values and attitudes in a socially acceptable direction.[18,19,20] It is assumed that changes in peer-group values will have a direct impact upon the individual's susceptibility to crime. The goal of such treatment is termination of antisocial behavior. No effort is made to deal explicitly with unconscious motivation, and it is assumed that a noncriminal adaptation will always be in the offender's own interest. The offender is not considered a "sick person," and words such as "therapy" and "patient" are deliberately avoided. Since the problem is one of changing group attitudes, more stress is put upon the therapist's moral values and personality than upon his training or experience.

Guided group interaction and group counseling (particularly when done by guards or by others who are closer to the inmates' socioeconomic group) do seem to help prison inmates to adjust in a more conforming manner. Whether they have much of an impact upon subsequent criminality is another question. Claims of success have so far been confined to programs which use this technique as part of over-all treatment of juvenile delinquents.[21] Long-term favorable results with adult offenders have not been reported. We could anticipate that adolescents would be more likely to respond to this technique since their antisociality does seem to be largely influenced by the immediate social environment. Criminality in adults, however, is determined by far more than exposure to delinquent value systems, and it would be less likely to be influenced by techniques which focused only on attitude change. The guided-interaction approach seems to be deficient on at least two scores. It tends to ignore that criminality which is a response to unrealistic oppression, and it denies the adaptive value of crime for the individual.* Insofar as it assumes that individual behavior is determined by the group and that society's interests are always compatible with individual interests, it has undertones of a grim collectivism which some would find abhorrent.

The author has made only brief comments upon selected aspects of group therapy in the correctional setting and has not done justice to the rich literature in this area. Group therapy or group counseling is looked upon by some as the ultimate rehabilitative technique for the offender. Whether this enthusiasm is justified is questionable. There is little doubt that group therapy is an economical means of reaching large groups of offenders. The understaffed institution may seize upon it as a practical answer to almost any problem. Therein lies a danger that its value may be

* This criticism is directed more toward theory than practice. The author has had the opportunity to observe a number of group counselors at work. Some of the more skillful counselors, while completely denying psychoanalytic theory, actually conduct their groups in much the same manner as psychiatrists. Transference, resistance and other defense mechanisms are interpreted much as in conventional therapy. The rationale for such techniques, however, is always presented in terms of a different theoretical model.

overestimated. The attractiveness of group therapy may reside more in its economy than in its effectiveness.

### The Potential Use of Family Therapy

The role of the family in the etiology of mental illness is becoming increasingly clear.[22, 23] Today's psychiatrists recognize that disturbed behaviors do not arise in a vacuum. If a child is having serious difficulty, the chances are that there is a serious conflict within the family. If a husband is emotionally disturbed, it is likely that his marital relationship is also disturbed. We have previously noted that stress within the family may be expressed through the behavioral disturbance of only one of its members. If that member is isolated and treated as the sole embodiment of that family's total illness, the possibilities of therapeutic effectiveness are limited. Many new techniques have therefore been developed to incorporate principles of family dynamics into the treatment process.

In some clinics a married person will not be accepted as a patient unless his spouse is also treated. Some therapists see couples or whole families together at the same time, and others have tried to work with groups of couples or families. All these techniques have advantages. The dynamics of the maladaptive behavior of each person quickly become more apparent and understandable. When families or couples are seen together, their individual members begin to communicate with one another. They come to appreciate each other's needs and are less inclined to utilize symptoms to indirectly influence oppressive situations. A healthier family can more effectively band together to combat shared oppression as a unit, and in so doing the individual members experience a new sense of closeness and purpose.

Family therapy as of this date is just beginning to be utilized in a correctional setting. Its usefulness in criminology is therefore unproven. It would appear, however, that disturbed family relationships would play as great a role in the genesis of crime as in the genesis of mental illness. The parent who unconsciously encourages his child to be antisocial or the wife of the sex deviate who subtly depreciates her husband's masculinity are deeply involved in setting the stage for a criminal act. Family disturbances not only exert an immediate situational influence, but they also create and help to strengthen personality traits which make an individual more predisposed to criminality. Whenever the criminal still has strong emotional links to his family, there would appear to be considerable logic in having his treatment include efforts to work with the entire family group.

One of the possible drawbacks to family therapy with offenders is that defensive reactions to feelings of guilt or shame could interfere with real cooperation from the noncriminal members. When a family is told that one of its members is mentally ill, it is common to see a great deal of vacillation between attitudes of self-blame and an angry denial of any involvement in the problems of the patient. Relatives of the mentally ill are relieved when external causes or defects can be invoked, since they need no longer examine their own influence upon the disturbed member of their family. It is likely that the criminal's family is even more defensive, since any tendency toward self-blame is exaggerated by the accusations of society. The natural tendency is to express concern for the deviant member, to moralize or to blame "bad companions," and most families would find it easier to take this route rather than become active participants in a treatment process. Bringing the family into the therapeutic picture, therefore, requires great skill and repeated assurance that their involvement in the offender's behavior does not make them responsible for what he has done.

Frequently heard statements such as "the parents are to blame" or "the parents are the ones who should really be punished" have a kernel of moralistic truth. They invariably, however, do more harm than good. The offender is encouraged to deny responsibility for his behavior, and the family is frightened away from any meaningful involvement. A society dominated by democratic principles cannot afford to assign legal blame to anyone but the person who has committed an illegal act. This does not mean that others should not have a moral obligation to assist in therapeutic efforts to resolve what they have helped to create. Another way of putting this is that the family should be held responsible for its own behavior (which may have encouraged social deviancy), but it is not responsible for the offender's behavior.

Even when the family is willing to participate in the treatment process, there are many formidable obstacles to family therapy of the offender. The institutionalized offender is a special problem. Since he is geographically isolated from his kin, bringing his family together on even a once-a-week basis requires financial resources which usually are unavailable to the lower classes. Custody regulations in the prison are opposed to family interaction, and the therapist is sometimes hard put to schedule meetings or even to find a private room for meetings. If the group is able to meet, family therapy still cannot be conducted in the same manner as in the outside world. Many of the affects generated in a family therapy session must be worked on by the participants outside of the hour. This is almost impossible when one of the family members is institutionalized. Another unfortunate side effect of the institutional setting is a fear of openness. An offender who expresses anger toward his wife during the therapy session may have reason to fear that she will not return the next week. There is no way in which he can persuade her to continue her attendance if she decides to leave. In some clinical settings this obstacle is met by bringing families in to live with the disturbed patient. Such a solution is obviously not possible in our current correctional structure.

If family therapy is to be used with offenders, new techniques and modifications in our correctional system will be needed. Treating the family away from the patient might be one way of having a useful impact. It has been noted that alcoholic patients do much better when their wives participate in individual or group therapy.[24] It would seem that therapy for the wives of offenders would be equally useful. If families are to be treated together, however, more radical changes in correctional practices which allow for easy access of the criminal to his family will be needed.

## Does Psychotherapy Work?

In spite of the enormous effort that has gone into treatment of the mentally ill, there is no scientific proof of the effectiveness of psychotherapy. This should not be surprising. The goals of the therapist or patient may encompass so many variables that it is often difficult to measure which patient has benefited and which has not. Some therapists define successful treatment as symptom removal. Still others seek only personality change and insight. The patient may seek an endless variety of goals, not all of which are realistically possible. Not infrequently, therapy fails to accomplish what the patient wanted it to do but helps materially in some unexpected way. An anxious patient may, for example, still be subject to anxiety after therapy but finds that he is working better and enjoying his family more. The few studies that have attempted to evaluate psychotherapy have either failed to specify which goals were sought or have been overly restrictive in evaluating only a limited number of goals. Given our present knowledge, any optimism that psychotherapy is helpful must reside in the admittedly subjective impressions of therapists and patients. Nevertheless, it is a rare patient who does not feel helped by the therapeutic experience and an even rarer psychiatrist who does not feel that psychotherapy helps the majority of his patients.

Skepticism of psychiatry has been exceptionally high in the correctional setting, where it is often argued that psychotherapy may be useful for the neurotic or psychotic but that it has little impact on the offender. It must be admitted that there are even less objective data to prove the effectiveness of psychotherapy with offenders than there are with the mentally ill.

The problem with evaluating psychotherapy in the correctional setting is not only a lack of precison in defining what changes we are looking for but also an unjustified carelessness in deciding what is to be called psychotherapy. There is an unfortunate tendency to label any conversation which takes place between a professional and an offender as psychotherapy. We can hardly expect the offender who receives five to fifty hours of therapy with an untrained psychiatric resident or social worker to respond in the same way as a wealthy neurotic who receives 500 to a thousand hours of therapy from a highly skilled psychoanalyst. There is simply no way of determining how large groups of offenders would respond to intensive psychotherapy since no one has ever offered this service. In the author's experience, offender patients have done as well as or better than other patients (in terms of goals of greater comfort plus abstention from criminality) exposed to similar kinds of therapy. He, as well as most other psychiatric criminologists, adheres to the admittedly unscientific hope that really intensive psychotherapy would help the great majority of unreasonable criminals.

# Chapter 22

# HUMANE AND RATIONAL CRIMINOLOGY

CORRECTIONAL practices in America are neither rational nor humane. The uses made of psychiatry, while sometimes beneficial, are frequently inefficient and potentially threatening to the rights of offenders. In this final chapter changes will be recommended which might improve our current efforts to control and reform the apprehended criminal. These recommendations are not offered as a panacea and certainly would not eradicate crime. If put into practice, however, they might establish a system of social control and a method of utilization of psychiatric skills which could bring criminology away from its archaic preoccupation with the protocol of revenge and toward rational and humane practices.

Some of the following recommendations are concerned only with the practice of psychiatric criminology. Others are related to the entire system of correctional justice. Specifically, an enlightened criminology would adhere to the following practices:

*It would abolish the death penalty and the nonparolable life sentence.* The presence of the death penalty is a malignant influence which holds back progress throughout our entire correctional system. It creates chaos in the courtroom, where it encourages the psychiatric profession to disavow its own teachings in order to facilitate a social ritual. It creates despair in the prison, where its pernicious effects set the tone for a punitive rather than a rehabilitative approach. The death penalty is more detested by prison workers than by so-called "bleeding hearts" or humanitarians. Wardens and guards realize that this gross symbol of society's vindictiveness eventually permeates every aspect of correctional practice. The physical presence of offenders who are about to be executed necessitates extraordinary emphasis on custody and leads other offenders to distrust the intentions of society. Such a state of affairs is not conducive to an enlightened criminology. Even if we ignore the humanistic arguments (it is not easy to create a nonviolent society when the government itself is willing to kill) and the practical arguments (there is no evidence whatsoever that invoking the death penalty reduces the number of crimes of violence) against this procedure, the amount of damage it does in the correctional setting is a sufficient reason for its abolishment.

The death penalty is not only a blight upon our correctional system, but it is also a blight upon our democratic society. The social rituals which have become part of our efforts to determine whether we are to spare an offender or destroy him are incredibly cruel and sadistic. One need merely examine the history of a given case such as that of Caryl Chessman to appreciate that the ghastly business of delays, appeals, further delays and final execution represents about as sadistic a "cat and mouse" game as society can play. It is a kind of mass perversion, a perversion which is sanctimoniously rationalized as a form of justice.

Similar considerations apply to life-sentencing without the possibility of parole. When the society sentences a man to life imprisonment, it abandons all hope of his reformation. The very presence of life prisoners in a correctional institution symbolizes an attitude of grim fatalism, an attitude which is inevitably carried over to other offenders. The desperation created by life-sentencing means that there must be greater emphasis on maximum custodial care, that stone fortresses must be built which invariably will be used to house lesser offenders who neither pose escape risks nor are dangerous.

*It would abolish or modify the insanity plea.* Some of the abuses of our correctional system would be partially rectified if we simply agreed to designate as criminals any persons who were proven to have committed a criminal act (except where there is no evil intent because of self-defense or accident). An offender should not be released from his responsibilities to society just because he is mentally ill. This does not mean that he should be treated harshly; it does mean that he must be treated like a mature and respected member of a democratic society who is accountable to his community even when he is gravely disturbed. The writer's conviction is that such a policy would foster a greater sense of responsibility throughout our society, would eventually be helpful to offenders and would free psychiatrists to devote more time to the actual treatment of offenders.

The overwhelming majority of offenders currently diagnosed as incompetent to stand trial could be rehabilitated and returned to court. Under a system which saw all proven offenders as responsible these men would be found guilty. Those few suspected offenders who would be incapable of recovering sufficiently to participate in their own defense could be civilly committed if they were judged dangerous to themselves or others, and released if they were not.

If we are unwilling to make such radical changes and if we insist on finding selected offenders nonresponsible, we should at least abolish the current rules of responsibility and allow psychiatrists to testify just like any other expert witness. This would mean that psychiatrists would merely present all their knowledge of a given case to the court, and would not have to act as an apologist for a society intent upon excusing selected criminals.

Another moderate change that would improve our current system of correctional justice would be to abolish the practice of routine civil commitment for every offender found not guilty by reason of insanity. If a man is truly believed to be nonresponsible, he should not be institutionalized unless he is likely to harm others. Under a more rational system many nondangerous offenders who currently languish in our hospitals for the criminally insane would be released.

*It would designate no individual a criminal or delinquent unless he had been found guilty of committing a crime in a judicial proceeding.* Insisting that a person is in need of treatment and then calling him a criminal or delinquent without proof of his having committed a criminal act is an abuse of constitutionally guaranteed civil liberties. This procedure is rarely invoked against adults; the grossest abuses currently occur with adolescents. Many injustices are perpetrated against adolescents under the guise of treatment, injustices which may well increase the adolescent's rebelliousness and diminish his sense of responsibility. Although the delinquent is given a civil commitment by a juvenile court, he is subjected to correctional procedures which are discouragingly similar to those used with adult criminals. The end result is that many adolescents are permanently damaged by confinement to punitive training schools, a confinement that never would have taken place if the child were provided with due process.

This situation could be improved if we committed only those adolescents who were proven to have violated laws. Our communities would then be obligated to face their own responsibilities, and it is not inconceivable that many adolescents would behave more conventionally. Adolescents who needed institutional care because they had been neglected or because they were emotionally disturbed would not be labeled delinquents but would be sent to nonpunitive institutions which were equipped to care for their needs. The author is not recommending that we coddle delinquents, only that we treat them consistently. If they commit crimes, they are criminals; if there is no proof of criminality, there is no justification for correctional treatment.

*It would impose civil commitments only when the probability of the patient's harming himself or others was great.* The question of civil commitments is only tangentially related to the central thesis of this book, but since civil commitments is so often recommended for emotionally disturbed offenders, the issue cannot be ignored in a comprehensive outline of psychiatric criminology. Civil commitments have recently received a great deal of critical scrutiny, and at least one prominent psychiatrist has recommended that they be abolished.[1] The writer believes that civil commitments are invoked too frequently and too often on shaky grounds, but also believes that a stable society must at times restrain some emotionally disturbed people even when they have not violated laws. There are times when it is obvious to the psychiatrist that some people will hurt others unless restrained. The community then has a right to use the psychiatrist as a protector. There are times when it is obvious to the psychiatrist that some people plan to hurt themselves. Again, a stable society must take an ethical position against any of its citizens engaging in self-destruction. The writer recognizes that the question of suicide is a complex one and that there are alternative ethical positions which argue for allowing the patient the liberty to do away with himself. The physician, however, whose guiding ethic is the preservation of life, would be untrue to himself and his profession if he did not do everything in his power to prevent suicide or serious self-harm. (The incompetent patient who is so disorganized that he is unable to care for himself and who has no one else to care for him must sometimes be involuntarily hospitalized. The author is assuming that such a patient could not survive without hospital care and that continued freedom would lead to eventual self-destruction.) Although the psychiatrist will sometimes make mistakes and hospitalize some people who do not need institutionalization, most injustices could be prevented if psychiatrists made maximum use of their diagnostic and therapeutic skills. Judges, attorneys and psychiatrists would do well to remind themselves that civil commitment of individuals who are dangerous neither to themselves nor to others is rarely justified. Civil commitment to institutions which are more like prisons than hospitals is totally inhumane.

*It would make sentencing more flexible.* The argument that fixed sentence leads to equal justice ignores the existence of individual differences in personality and social situation. Even if our primary concern is punishment, trying to make the punishment fit the crime rather than the individual does not make sense. All men may be equal before the law in terms of their guilt, but no two men respond the same way to punishment. Some men would find thirty days in prison as agonizing as others would find thirty months. Many first offenders are so ashamed and humiliated after they are apprehended and legally designated as criminals that further punishment is often superfluous. For other minor offenders the probationary status represents a sufficient punitive stress in itself. Both of these groups would be deterred from future criminality by minor punishment. For other, more disturbed criminals, however, even prolonged incarceration is no guarantee against recidivism. An enlightened system of correctional justice would recognize that while some punishment may be necessary for all offenders, indiscriminate use of lengthy institutionalization often represents extreme and unnecessary punishment which interferes with rehabilitation.

The Model Sentencing Act proposed by the Advisory Council of the Judges of the National Council on Crime and Delinquency would be a step in the right direction.[2] This act proposes to sentence selected offenders for a period of no more than thirty years if they have committed a dangerous crime and are believed to have a severe personality disorder indicating a propensity toward continued criminal activity. The only exceptions are defendants convicted of first-degree murder, who can be sentenced for life, and confirmed racketeers, who can be sentenced for a period up to thirty years even in the absence of proof of a personality disorder. Dangerous crimes are carefully defined as illegal actions which inflict serious bodily harm or endanger the life or safety of others. The determination of the seriousness of the personality disorder of the dangerous offender is left up to the psychiatrist. All nondangerous offenders who have committed a felony are sentenced for a period not exceeding five years. Probation, suspended sentence, fine or a reduced sentence are also utilized when appropriate. The offender can be paroled at any time under either the five-year or the thirty-year sentence.

In effect, the Model Sentencing Act provides for a type of indeterminate sentencing for almost all offenders. Limits are provided mainly at the maximum level, and the act is founded upon the assumption that true indeterminacy at the minimum level and adequate treatment facilities will be available. Under such a system specialized sentencing for sex offenders would be unnecessary. Dangerous sex offenders would receive a thirty-year maximum sentence and would have the opportunity to seek treatment and an early release. Nondangerous sex offenders could not be sentenced for more than five years.

It appears that the philosophies underlying the Model Sentencing Act are those of minimum punishment consistent with preservation of law and order and protection of the public. This law is based upon a deep concern with rehabilitating the criminal and protecting his rights. Sol Rubin points out that the Model Sentencing Act also solves many of the problems of the psychiatrist, since it allows him to use his skills to influence the sentencing process rather than to determine the question of guilt or innocence.[3] This writer is in substantial agreement with most of the premises of the Model Sentencing Act but would hope that psychiatric resources could eventually be used for a larger group of offenders than those who are suspected of dangerousness. Both diagnosis and treatment should be available for all felons, not only those who have committed dangerous crimes.

*It would make correctional institutions less punitive.* It is generally true that for most men any deprivation of freedom, even for a short period of time, is a formidable punishment. The ingenious degradations devised by so many of our penal institutions are a cruel and unusual punishment. There is no reason why our correctional institutions have be so punitive. Few offenders can be classified as "escape risks," and the overwhelming number of men confined to maximum-security institutions (particularly check forgers, nonsupporters and petty burglars), do not have to be there. The great majority of criminals are not "troublemakers" and would not suddenly riot or raise havoc if they were allowed some of the dignity and rights available to other citizens. If maximum-security institutions were built only to house "escape risks" and "troublemakers" (such an institution in a state with a four million population such as Wisconsin would barely be required to have more than one to two hundred beds), all but a few prisoners could be housed in a more open and therapeutic environment.

In current penology every effort is made to isolate the offender from his community. This is about as destructive a policy as could be devised and goes against every conceivable principle of rehabilitation. In many ways our current prisons are not too different from old-fashioned mental hospitals. They are located in remote areas and are isolated from professional and community contacts which could help to prevent the stifling aura of regimentation and hopelessness which is generated within their walls. If we are to learn from what has happened in our mental hospitals, we must realize that the community must become more involved with our prisons and our prisoners must have some opportunity to become involved with the community. Social agencies and "watchdog groups" should have the same easy access to our correctional institutions as they do to our mental hospitals.

If there is to be any real hope of reformation, the offender must also have more access to his family. Present-day restrictions on visiting do nothing but isolate the prisoner from legitimate sources of comfort and hope. The correctional system would do well to borrow the concept of halfway hospitals from the mental hygiene movement and institute halfway prisons. Many nondangerous offenders could be allowed to spend weekends at home or allowed to work in the community. Spending five days a week or the greater part of the evening and night in a prison would be sufficient punishment for the majority of offenders. The remaining time could well be spent learning to live with their families and their communities.

*It would expand treatment facilities in correctional institutions.* We do not have to decide that prisoners are mentally ill to treat them rationally and humanely. Principles of rehabilitation can be applied as effectively in a correctional setting as in a hospital setting. Perhaps the most crucial change needed to create a favorable climate would be doing away with our ridiculously oversized penitentiaries. Maximum-security units (of no more than one-to-two-hundred-bed capacity) may be needed for selected offenders. All other offenders, however, could be safely housed in small minimum-security institutions. The mental hygiene movement has learned that rehabilitation becomes progressively more difficult as the populations of institutions become greater. Prisons, just like hospitals, should be small. Any institution which exceeds a five-hundred bed capacity becomes too entangled in administrative problems to do a proper job of treatment.

Of course, prisons (particularly if the insanity plea were abolished) would be entrusted with the care of a high percentage of emotionally disturbed offenders. If prisons were truly rehabilitative institutions, however, most offenders could get along quite well without specialized care. The few inmates who could not adjust would need to be housed in institutions more similar to hospitals, but these units would remain a part of the correctional system. Under such a system there would be little need for hospitals for the criminally insane. The emotionally disturbed prisoner would be cared for in hospital-type units within the prison system, and the incompetent offender or the dangerous nonoffender would be cared for in an ordinary mental hospital.

Treatment in a correctional institution should provide all the modalities that are available in our better mental hospitals. Of particular importance is the creation of a therapeutic milieu, which is characterized by a belief in man's capacity to change. This milieu must bear some resemblance to that of the outside world. The offender, for example, must have some opportunity to come into contact with women during his institutional stay. The current practices of barring female nurses and other employees from social contact with the offender does nothing but alienate him further from society. To those who would argue that there would be a possibility of danger to women employees, the author would reply that this is practically never a problem in mental hospitals, where the percentage of emotionally disturbed and "uncontrollable" patients is much greater.

Of equal urgency is the need to provide prisoners with useful work and realistic incentives. Prison industries must become competitive and the prisoner must receive training that will enable him to find employment in the real world. It is particularly important for the prisoner to learn to assume responsibility for his work. This means that he must be given some opportunity to involve himself in the administrative as well as the menial functions of the prison industry.

An increase in the availability of individual psychotherapy, group psychotherapy and family psychotherapy is essential to an enlightened criminology. The goals of such therapies must recognize the needs of the individual and be directed toward helping him to find a better adaptation. There is not much social value or moral justification in controlling a man's antisocial behavior, only to have him end up as a helpless hollow shell of a man or a mental patient. Those who have never been in a prison will have difficulty in appreciating the dehumanized "zombie-like" quality which characterizes many prisoners. In fact, many current-day prisoners look just like mental patients used to look ten to fifteen years ago.

It is unfortunately not easy to find skilled therapists who are willing to work with offenders. However, this problem is not insurmountable. There will never be enough psychiatrists to treat all our offenders who could benefit (or for that matter, there will never be enough to treat the mentally ill), but there are enough psychiatrists, psychologists, social workers, educators, pastors and other professionals who could be trained to make a significant contribution.

A large part of the problem of chronic shortages of therapists is an outgrowth of professional biases and rivalries. Psychiatrists must learn that they do not have any monopoly on helping relationships, whether these are defined as psychotherapy or counseling. Other professional groups must swallow their pride and come to realize that if they really wish to do psychotherapy with offenders they should learn something about it. The average psychologist, sociologist or social worker who is just out of graduate school is poorly equipped to treat anyone and is especially inept with the offender.

This is not his fault. He is simply untrained and inexperienced. Too often the recent graduate begins unsupervised therapy, gets into trouble, blames his client and assumes that psychotherapy will never help offenders. The only remedy for this grandiosity is training and experience. It takes from one to three years of training and experience to become a competent psychotherapist. If nonpsychiatric professionals could begin realistic training in psychotherapy from the moment they began working in correctional institutions (and before professional defensiveness and a desperate withdrawal to administration and bureaucracy could develop), they would constitute a sufficient resource to meet the therapy needs of most offenders.

*It would scientifically study dangerous behavior.* Unfortunately, practically none of the money now being spent in criminological research is being used to study the most important problem, namely, the prediction and control of dangerous behavior. In earlier chapters, pessimism was expressed as to the possibility or advisability of doing away with crime. Neither of these considerations applies to the dangerous offender. Violent behavior is rarely a response to realistic stress, and it rarely serves a useful social purpose. Theoretically, it should be possible to create a relatively nonviolent society. So far we have made insignificant progress in understanding the problem of dangerousness. Our criteria for predicting who will commit a dangerous act are totally inadequate, and our efforts at treatment are pitiful. If more money is to be spent on crime research, the question of how to detect and treat dangerousness should receive first priority.

## A Concluding Note

Because our society cannot afford to redefine crime as illness, criminology will not and should not become a subspeciality of psychiatry. Still, the suffering of the criminal and the havoc he creates throughout the community will often call for the services of the psychiatric profession. Psychiatric resources thus far have been spent in wrong directions. Efforts to redefine criminals as patients are socially damaging and wasteful. The usefulness of the psychiatric criminologist will ultimately depend upon his ability to find a rational means of integrating his individual-oriented philosophies and practices into a correctional system that is rarely sympathetic to individual needs. He must begin by helping his community to understand the unreasonable aspect of deviant behavior, and by demonstrating that techniques which help the mentally ill may also help the criminal. This is neither an easy nor a glamorous task.

The usefulness of any helping profession is severely impaired if the community is uninterested in humane and rational treatment of offenders. Unfortunately, even in the 1960's, when crime has become one of America's major problems, our society seems to show little enthusiasm for rehabilitating criminals. New government programs in crime prevention and detection have created interest in the total problem of crime, but this interest seems to terminate abruptly once the offender is apprehended. The apprehended offender is still exposed to a system of correctional justice that is inconsistent, cruel and irrational. Society errs when it attempts to fight crime while failing to treat the criminal.

Even if a rational and humane criminology would not rehabilitate a majority of offenders, there are still important reasons for trying to create such a system. There should be a system of correctional justice in which each citizen is considered a responsible person and in which the community would treat its deviant citizens with compassion. The values of personal responsibility and compassion for others have always characterized that which is special about our nation. If we sacrifice either value, if we insist on being cruel to those who are responsible or if we insist that we can be compassionate only toward those who are nonresponsible, we will lose a great deal. A society can be judged by the manner in which it treats its deviant citizens. If it treats them as lesser beings who are to be systematically degraded and abused, it is not a great society. It is not even a decent society.

# NOTES

## Chapter 1. Problems in Explaining Criminal Behavior

1. W. L. Marshall and W. L. Clark, "The Legal Definition of Crime and Criminals," in *A Treatise on the Law of Crimes,* Chicago: Callaghan, Callaghan, 1952, p. 1.
2. T. Sellin, *Culture, Conflict and Crime,* New York: Social Science Research Council, Bulletin 41, 1938.
3. K. Eissler (ed.), *Searchlights on Delinquency,* New York: International Universities Press, 1948.
4. P. W. Tappan, "Who Is the Criminal?," *American Sociological Review,* 12 (February, 1947), 96–102.
5. W. Healy, *The Individual Delinquent,* Boston: Little Brown, 1915.
6. C. Burt, *The Young Delinquent,* London: University of London Press, 1944.
7. A Cohen, "Juvenile Deliquency and the Social Structure," Ph.D. Thesis, Harvard University, 1951.
8. G. Vold, *Theoretical Criminology,* New York: Oxford University Press, 1958.
9. M. E. Wolfgang, L. Savitz and N. Johnson, *The Sociology of Crime and Delinquency,* New York: John Wiley & Sons, 1962.
10. E. M. Lemert, "An Isolation and Closure Theory of Naïve Check Forgery," *Journal of Criminal Law, Criminology and Police Science,* 44:3 (1953), 296–307.
11. D. C. Gibbons, *Changing the Lawbreaker,* Englewood Cliffs, New Jersey: Prentice-Hall, 1965.
12. B. C. Glueck, Jr., "Psychodynamic Patterns in the Homosexual Sex Offender," *American Journal of Psychiatry,* 112 (February, 1956), 584–590.
13. W. Bromberg, *The Mold of Murder,* New York: Grune & Stratton, 1961.
14. D. C. Gibbons, *op. cit.*

## Chapter 2. Biological Theories

1. A. E. Fink, *Causes of Crime,* New York: A. S. Barnes, Perpetua Edition, 1962.
2. C. Lombroso, *Crime, Its Causes and Remedies,* translated by H. P. Horton, Boston: Little Brown, 1911.
3. C. Goring, *The English Convict,* London: His Majesty's Stationery Office, 1913.
4. E. A. Hooton, *Crime and the Man,* Cambridge: Harvard University Press, 1939.

5. G. Vold, *Theoretical Criminology,* New York: Oxford University Press, 1958.
6. W. H. Sheldon, *Varieties of Delinquent Youth,* New York: Harper & Brothers, 1949.
7. E. Kretschmer, *Physique and Character,* translated by W. J. H. Spratt, London: K. Paul, Trench, Trubner, 1925.
8. S. Glueck and E. Glueck, *Physique and Delinquency,* New York: Harper & Brothers, 1956.
9. A. Montagu, "The Biologist Looks at Crime," *Annals of the American Academy of Political and Social Science,* 217 (September, 1951), 53.
10. R. R. Korn and L. W. McKorkle, *Criminology and Penology,* New York: Henry Holt, 1959.
11. H. H. Goddard, *Proceedings of the American Prison Association,* 1912, p. 355.
12. V. V. Anderson, "Mental Disease and Delinquency," *Mental Hygiene,* 3 (1919), 177–198.
13. W. Fernald, "A State Program for the Care of the Mentally Defective," *Mental Hygiene,* 3 (1919), 556–574.
14. M. G. Schlapp and E. H. Smith, *The New Criminology,* New York: Liveright, 1928.
15. L. Berman, "Crime and the Endocrine Glands," *American Journal of Psychiatry,* 12 (1932), 215–235.
16. E. Podolsky, "The Chemical Brew of Criminal Behavior," *Journal of Criminal Law, Criminology and Police Science,* 45 (March-April, 1955), 675–678.
17. M. Molitch, "Endocrine Disturbance in Behavior Problems," *American Journal of Psychiatry,* 93 (March, 1937), 1175–1179.
18. D. Hill and D. A. Pond, "Reflections on 100 Capitol Cases Submitted to EEG," *Journal of Mental Science,* 98 (1952), 23–43.
19. D. Hill and D. Watterson, "Electroencephalographic Studies of Psychopathic Personalities," *Journal of Neurology and Psychiatry,* 5 (1952), 47.
20. M. Ostow and M. Ostow, "Bilaterally Synchronous Paroxysmal Slow Activity in the Electroencephalogram of Non-Epileptics," *Journal of Nervous and Mental Diseases,* 103 (1946), 346–358.
21. F. A. Gibbs, B. K. Bagchi and W. Bloomberg, "Electroencephalographic Study of Criminals," *American Journal of Psychiatry,* 102 (1945), 294–300.
22. G. N. Thompson, *The Psychopathic Delinquent and Criminal,* Springfield: Charles C. Thomas, 1953.
23. D. Stott, "Evidence for a Congenital Factor in Maladjustment and Delinquency," *American Journal of Psychiatry,* 119 (1962), 781–793.
24. J. V. Larsen, "Physical Characteristics of Disturbed Adolescents," *Archives of General Psychiatry,* 10 (1964), 55–61.
25. H. J. Eysenck, *Crime and Personality,* Boston: Houghton Mifflin, 1964.
26. G. E. McLearan, "Genetics and Behavioral Development," in M. L. Hoffman and L. N. W. Hoffman (eds.), *Review of Child Development Research,* New York: Russell Sage Foundation, 1964, p. 433.

## Chapter 3. Sociological Theories

1. E. Sutherland, *White Collar Crime,* New York: Dryden Press, 1949.
2. F. Hartung, "Methodological Assumption in a Social-Psychological Theory of Criminality," *Journal of Criminal Law and Criminology,* 45 (1955), 652–661.
3. É. Durkheim, "The Normal and the Pathological," in E. G. George (ed.), *The Rules of Sociological Method,* eighth edition, Glencoe: Free Press, 1950, p. 65.
4. E. Sutherland and D. Cressey, *Principles of Criminology,* sixth edition, New York: Lippincott, 1960.
5. S. Glueck, "Theory and Fact in Criminology," *British Journal of Delinquency,* 7 (October, 1956), 92–98.
6. G. Caldwell, *Criminology,* New York: Ronald Press, 1956.
7. G. M. Sykes and D. Matza, "Techniques of Neutralization: A Theory of Delinquency," *American Sociological Review,* 22 (1957), 664–670.
8. W. C. Reckless, S. Dinitz and E. Murray, "Self Concept as an Insulator Against Delinquency," *American Sociological Review,* 21 (1956), 744–746.
9. D. Glaser, "Criminality Theories and Behavioral Images," *American Journal of Sociology,* 61 (1956), 433–445.
10. D. Abrahamsen, *Who Are the Guilty?,* New York: Rinehart, 1952.
11. E. H. Erikson, *The Syndrome of Identity Diffusion in Adolescents and Young Adults in Discussions in Child Development, World Health Organization,* Vol. 3, New York: International Universities Press, 1958.
12. T. Sellin, *The Conflict of Conduct Norms, Culture Conflict and Crime,* New York: Social Science Research Council, 1938, pp. 63–70.
13. R. Merton, "Social Structure and Anomie," *American Sociological Review,* 3 (October, 1938), 672–682.
14. R. A. Cloward and L. E. Ohlin, "Illegitimate Means and Delinquent Subcultures," in *Delinquency and Opportunity,* Glencoe: Free Press, pp. 145–152.
15. A. K. Cohen, *Delinquent Boys,* New York: Free Press, 1955.
16. P. Goodman, *Growing Up Absurd,* New York: Viking Press, 1962.
17. E. W. Burgess, "The Natural Area as the Unit for Social Work in the Large City," *Proceedings of the National Conference of Social Work,* 1926.
18. C. R. Shaw, G. H. Zorbaugh, H. D. McKay and L. S. Cottrece, *Delinquency Areas,* Chicago: University of Chicago Press, 1929.
19. D. Abrahamsen, *The Psychology of Crime,* New York: Columbia University Press, 1960.
20. W. McCord, J. McCord and I. Zola, *Origins of Crime,* New York: Columbia University Press, 1959.
21. W. Healy and A. Bronner, *Delinquents and Criminals,* New York: Macmillan, 1925.
22. T. P. Monahan, "Family Status and Delinquency: A Re-appraisal of Some New Findings," *Social Forces,* 35 (March, 1957), 250.

23. C. R. Shaw and H. D. McKay, "Are Broken Homes a Causative Factor in Delinquency?," *Social Forces,* 10 (1932), 514–524.
24. J. Toby, "The Differential Impact of Family Disorganization," *American Sociological Review,* 22 (October, 1957), 505.
25. R. W. Korn and L. W. McKorkle, *Criminology and Penology,* New York: Henry Holt, 1959, p. 327.
26. M. Hakeem, "A Critique of Psychiatric Approaches to Crime and Correction," *Law and Contemporary Problems,* Duke University, 23 (Autumn, 1958), 650–682.
27. F. Hartung, "A Critique of Sociologic Approaches to Crime and Correction," *Law and Contemporary Problems,* Duke University, 23 (Autumn, 1958), 703–734.
28. F. Hartung, *Crime, Law and Society,* Detroit: Wayne University Press, 1965.
29. D. J. Bordua, "Delinquent Subcultures: A Critique of Sociological Interpretations of Gang Delinquency," *Annals of American Academy of Political and Social Science,* 338 (1961), 120–136.
30. H. A. Bloch, "Crime Causation: Research and Its Applications," *Federal Probation,* 21 (1957), 19.
31. M. B. Clinard, "Criminological Research," in R. Merton, L. Broom and L. Cottrell (eds.), *Sociology Today,* New York: Basic Books, 1959, p. 521.
32. D. C. Gibbons and D. L. Garrity, "Some Suggestions for the Development of Treatment Theory in Criminology," *Social Forces,* 38 (1959), 51–58.

## Chapter 4. Mental Illness and Crime

1. S. L. Halleck, "American Psychiatry and the Criminal: A Historical Review," *American Journal of Psychiatry,* 121 (Supplement, 1965), pp. I–XXI.
2. K. A. Menninger, *The Vital Balance,* New York: Viking Press, 1963.
3. R. Roessler and N. S. Greenfield (eds.), *Physiological Correlates of Psychological Disorder,* Madison: University of Wisconsin Press, 1962.
4. N. S. Greenfield and W. C. Lewis (eds.), *Psychoanalysis and Current Biological Thought,* Madison: University of Wisconsin Press, 1965.
5. M. Guttmacher, "A Psychiatric Approach to Crime and Corrections," *Law and Contemporary Problems,* School of Law, Duke University, 23 (Autumn, 1958), 633–649.
6. W. Overholser, "The Briggs Law of Massachusetts: A Review and an Appraisal," *Journal of Criminal Law and Criminology,* 25 (1935), 859–866.
7. B. Karpman, "Criminal Psychodynamics: A Platform," *Journal of Criminal Psychodynamics,* 1 (1955), 1–96.
8. D. Abrahamsen, *Who Are the Guilty?,* New York: Rinehart, 1952.
9. A. Fortas, "Implications of Durham's Case," *American Journal of Psychiatry,* 113:7 (January, 1957), 577–582.
10. A. Watson, "Durham Plus Five Years: Development of the Law of Criminal Responsibility in the District of Columbia," *American Journal of Psychiatry,* 116:3 (September, 1959), 289–297.

## Chapter 5. Concepts of Adaptation

1. C. Bernard, *An Introduction to the Study of Experimental Medicine* (1865), New York: Macmillan, 1927.
2. W. Cannon, *The Wisdom of the Body,* New York: W. W. Norton, 1939.
3. G. L. Freeman, *The Energetics of Human Behavior,* Ithaca: Cornell University Press, 1948.
4. E. W. Dempsey, "Homeostasis," in S. S. Stevens (ed.), *Handbook of Experimental Psychology,* New York: John Wiley & Sons, 1951, p. 232.
5. K. Menninger, *The Vital Balance,* New York: Viking Press, 1963.
6. R. A. Spitz, "Hospitalism: An Inquiry into the Genesis of Psychiatric Conditions in Early Childhood," *Psychoanalytic Study of the Child,* 1 (1945), 53–74.
7. H. Harlow, "Social Deprivation in Monkeys," *Scientific American,* November, 1962, pp. 1–11.
8. E. Goffman, *The Presentation of Self in Everyday Life,* Garden City: Doubleday Anchor, 1959.
9. A. Freud, *The Ego and the Mechanisms of Defense* (1936), New York: International Universities Press, 1946.
10. H. F. Ellenberger, "Psychiatric Phenomenology and Existential Analysis," in R. May, E. Angel and H. F. Ellenberger (eds.), *Existence,* New York: Basic Books, 1958, p. 96.
11. L. Berkowitz, *Aggression: A Social Psychological Analysis,* New York: McGraw-Hill, 1962.
12. S. Freud, "Instincts and Their Vicissitudes," in J. Strachey (ed.), *The Standard Edition of the Complete Psychological Works of Sigmund Freud,* Vol. 4, London: Hogarth Press, 1959.
13. O. Fenichel, *The Psychoanalytic Theory of Neurosis,* New York: W. W. Norton, 1945.
14. H. Hartmann, E. Kris and R. M. Loewenstein, "Notes on the Theory of Aggression," in *Psychoanalytic Study of The Child,* Vols. 3-4, New York: International Universities Press, 1949.
15. S. Freud, "Inhibition, Symptoms and Anxiety," in J. Strachey (ed.), *The Standard Edition of the Complete Psychological Works of Sigmund Freud,* Vol. 20, London: Hogarth Press, 1959.

## Chapter 6. The Adaptive Value of Crime

1. Discussed in W. Reich, *Character Analysis,* New York: Orgone Institute Press, 1949, p. 159.
2. F. Alexander, "The Neurotic Character," *International Journal of Psychoanalysis,* 11 (1930), 292–311.
3. E. Fromm, *The Sane Society,* New York: Rinehart, 1955.
4. T. Szasz, *Law, Liberty and Psychiatry,* New York: Macmillan, 1963.
5. S. Freud, "Inhibitions, Symptoms and Anxiety," in J. Strachey (ed.), *Standard Edition of the Complete Psychological Works of Sigmund Freud,* Vol. 20, London: Hogarth Press, 1959.

6. K. Marx, *The German Ideology*, New York: International Publishers, 1939.
7. M. Weber, *Essays in Sociology*, H. Gerth and C. W. Mills (eds.), New York: Oxford University Press, 1946.
8. C. W. Mills, *White Collar*, New York: Oxford University Press, 1957.
9. T. Szasz, The Myth of Mental Illness, New York, Hoeber-Harper, 1961.
10. G. Engel, "Guilt, Pain and Success," *Psychosomatic Medicine*, 24:37–48, 1962.
11. S. Halleck, "The Criminal's Problem with Psychiatry," *Psychiatry*, 23:4 (1959), 409–412.
12. See F. M. Thrasher, *The Gang*, Chicago: University of Chicago Press, 1927.

## Chapter 7. Early Stresses and Predisposition to Crime

1. S. Glueck and E. Glueck, *Predicting Delinquency and Crime*, Cambridge: Harvard University Press, 1959.
2. R. A. Spitz, "Anaclitic Depression: An Inquiry into the Genesis of Psychiatric Conditions in Early Childhood," *Psychoanalytic Study of the Child*, 1 (1945), 313–342.
3. J. Bowlby, *Maternal Care and Mental Health*, Monograph Series No. 2, Geneva: World Health Organization, 1951.
4. L. J. Yarrow, "Separation from Parents in Early Childhood," in M. L. Hoffman and L. N. W. Hoffman (eds.), *Child Development Research*, Vol. 1, New York: Russell Sage Foundation, 1964.
5. L. Bender, "Psychopathic Disorders in Children," in R. M. Lindner (ed.), *Handbook of Correctional Psychology*, New York: Philosophical Library, 1947, p. 360.
6. L. J. Yarrow *op. cit.*
7. R. A. Spitz and K. Wolf "Autoerotism," *Psychoanalytic Study of the Child*, 3–4 (1949), 85–120.
8. I. Kauffman, E. S. MacKay and J. Zilbach, "The Impact of Adolescence on Girls with Delinquent Character Formation," *American Journal of Orthopsychiatry*, 29 (January, 1959), 130–143.
9. A. Bandura and R. H. Walters, "Dependency Conflicts in Aggressive Delinquents," *Journal of Social Issues*, 14:3 (1958), 52–65.
10. W. C. Becker, "Consequences of Different Kinds of Parental Discipline," in Hoffman and Hoffman (eds.), *op. cit.*
11. C. H. Kemp, "The Battered Child Syndrome," *Journal of the American Medical Association*, 181 (1962), 17.
12. C. Burt, *The Young Delinquent*, New York: Appleton, 1929.
13. S. Glueck and E. T. Glueck, *Unraveling Juvenile Delinquency*, Cambridge: Harvard University Press, 1950.
14. W. McCord, J. McCord and I. K. Zola, *Origins of Crime*, New York: Columbia University Press, 1959.
15. A. Bandura and R. H. Walters, *Adolescent Aggression*, New York: Ronald Press, 1959.
16. J. Haley, *Strategies of Psychotherapy*, New York: Grune & Stratton, 1963.
17. G. Bateson, D. Jackson, J. Haley and J. Weakland, "Toward a Theory of Schizophrenia," Behavioral Sciences, 1 (1956), 251–264.

18. W. McCord, J. McCord and A. Howard, "Familial Correlates of Aggression in Non-delinquent Male Children," *Journal of Abnormal and Social Psychology,* 62 (1961), 79–93.
19. A. Johnson and S. A. Szurek, "The Genesis of Antisocial Acting Out in Children and Adults," *Psychoanalytic Quarterly,* 21 (1952), 323–343.
20. J. Haley, *op. cit.*
21. M. Molitch, "Chronic Post Encephalitic Behavioral Problems," *American Journal of Psychiatry,* 91 (1935), 843–861.
22. M. Harrington, *The Other America,* New York: Macmillan, 1963.
23. E. May, *The Wasted Americans,* New York: Harper & Row, 1964.
24. D. Gottlieb, "Goal Aspirations and Goal Fulfillments," *American Journal of Orthopsychiatry,* 34:5 (1964), 934–941.
25. T. F. Pettigrew, *A Profile of the American Negro,* Princeton: D. Van Nostrand, 1964.
26. A. Aichorn, *Wayward Youth,* New York: Viking Press, 1935.
27. K. Friedlander, *Psychoanalytic Approach to Juvenile Delinquency,* New York: International Universities Press, 1947.
28. K. Eissler, "Ego-Psychological Implications of the Psychoanalytic Treatment of Delinquents," *Psychoanalytic Study of the Child,* 5 (1950), 97–121.
29. E. Glover, *Roots of Crime,* New York: International Universities Press, 1960.
30. A. M. Johnson, "Juvenile Delinquency," in S. Arieti (ed.), *American Handbook of Psychiatry,* Vol. 1, New York: Basic Books, 1959.
31. F. Alexander and H. Staub, *The Criminal, the Judge and the Public,* Glencoe: Free Press, 1956.
32. K. Friedlander, *op. cit.*
33. K. Friedlander, "Formation of the Antisocial Character," *Psychoanalytic Study of the Child,* 1 (1945), 189–204.
34. J. Lampl-DeGroot, "Neurotics, Delinquents and Ideal Formation," in K. Eissler (ed.), *Searchlights on Delinquency,* New York: International Universities Press, 1949.
35. A. Bandura and R. H. Walters, *op. cit.*
36. L. Berkowitz, *Aggression: A Social Psychological Analysis,* New York: McGraw-Hill, 1962.

## Chapter 8. Psychopathy and Related Traits

1. J. C. Prichard, *A Treatise on Insanity,* Philadelphia: Haswell, Barrington & Haswell, 1855.
2. W. McCord and J. McCord, *Psychopathy and Delinquency,* New York: Grune & Stratton, 1956.
3. F. Alexander, "The Neurotic Character," *International Journal of Psychoanalysis,* 11 (1930), 292–311.
4. W. McCord and J. McCord, *op. cit.*
5. *Diagnostic and Statistical Manual—Mental Disorders,* Washington, D.C.: American Psychiatric Association, 1952.
6. D. Henderson, *Psychopathic States,* New York: W. W. Norton, 1939.
7. F. Alexander, *op. cit.*

8. B. Karpman, "On the Need of Separating Psychopathy into Two Distinct Clinical Types: The Symptomatic and the Idiopathic," *Journal of Criminal Psychopathology*, 3 (1947), 112–137.
9 M. Miller, "Time and the Character Disorder," *Journal of Nervous and Mental Diseases*, 138 (1964), 535–540.
10. A. Wheelis, *The Seeker*, New York: Random House, 1960.
11. H. M. Cleckley, *The Mask of Sanity*, third edition, St. Louis: C. V. Mosby, 1955.
12. B. Karpman, *Case Studies in the Psychopathology of Crime*, Washington, D.C.,: Medical Science Press, 1933.
13. T. Reik, *Masochism in Modern Man*, New York: Farrar, Straus, 1941.
14. M. Brenman, "On Teasing and Being Teased: and the Problem of Moral Masochism," *Psychoanalytic Study of the Child*, 7 (1952), 264–285.
15. E. Bergler, *The Basic Neurosis: Oral Regression and Psychic Masochism*, New York: Grune & Stratton, 1949.
16. S. Freud, "Some Character Types Met with in Psychoanalytic Work, the Criminal out of a Sense of Guilt," in *Collected Papers*, Vol. 4, London: Hogarth Press, 1959.
17. E. Bergler, "Crime and Punishment: Why Punishment Fails to Prevent Crime," *Psychiatric Quarterly Supplement*, 21 (1947), 263–303.
18. B. Karpman, "Criminality, the Super-Ego and the Sense of Guilt," *Psychoanalytic Review*, 17 (1930), 280–296.

## Chapter 9. The Stress of Adolescence

1. A. Cohen, *Delinquent Boys: The Culture of the Gang*, Glencoe: Free Press, 1955.
2. A. Freud, "Adolescence," *Psychoanalytic Study of the Child*, 13 (1958), 255–278.
3. E. H. Erikson, "Identity and the Life Cycle," *Psychological Issues*, Vol. I, New York: International Universities Press, 1959.
4. P. Blos, *On Adolescence: A Psychoanalytic Interpretation*, Glencoe, Free Press, 1962.
5. A. Kardiner and L. Ovesey, *The Mark of Oppression: Psychosocial Study of the American Negro*, New York: W. W. Norton, 1951.
6. D. Matza, *Delinquency and Drift*, New York: John Wiley & Sons, 1965.
7. P. Goodman, *Growing Up Absurd*, New York: Vintage Books, 1962.
8. J. H. Scharr, "Violence in Juvenile Gangs," *American Journal of Orthopsychiatry*, 33:1 (1963), 29–37.
9. F. Solomon, *et al.* "Civil Rights Activity and Reduction in Crime Among Negroes," *Archives of General Psychiatry*, 12 (1965), 227–236.

## Chapter 10. Crucial Issues in Juvenile Delinquency

1. G. Geis, *Juvenile Gangs*, President's Committee on Juvenile Delinquency and Youth Crime, Washington, D.C.: June, 1965.
2. F. M. Thrasher, *The Gang*, Chicago: University of Chicago Press, 1927.

3. W. F. Whyte, *Street Corner Society*, Chicago: University of Chicago Press, 1943.
4. R. Jenkins, "Adaptive and Maladaptive Delinquency," *The Nervous Child*, 11 (1955), 9–11.
5. D. Abrahamsen, *The Psychology of Crime*, New York: Columbia University Press, 1960.
6. E. Sutherland, *The Professional Thief*, Chicago: University of Chicago Press, 1937.
7. E. M. Lemert, "The Behavior of the Systematic Check Forger," *Social Problems*, 6 (1958), 141–149.
8. F. Redl and D. Wineman, *The Aggressive Child*, New York: Free Press, 1957.
9. P. Chodoff and H. Lyons, "Hysteria, the Hysterical Personality and 'Hysterical' Conversion," *American Journal of Psychiatry*, 114 (1958), 734–740.
10. B. Karpman, *The Sexual Offender and His Offenses*, New York: Julian Press, 1954.
11. R. E. Masters, *Patterns of Incest*, New York: Julian Press, 1963.
12. S. L. Halleck, "Victims of Sex Offenders," *Journal of the American Medical Association*, 180:4 (1962), 273–278.

## Chapter 11. The Stresses of Adulthood

1. W. Reckless, S. Dinitz and B. Kay, "Self Component in Potential Delinquency and Non-Delinquency," *American Sociological Review*, 22 (1957), 666–670.
2. V. Riccio, *All the Way Down*, New York: Simon & Schuster, 1962.
3. World Health Organization, Technical Report Series, *Alcoholism*, No. 19, 1950.
4. W. McCord and J. McCord, *Origins of Alcoholism*, Stanford, Stanford University Press, 1960.
5. R. Rubington, "The Alcohol Offender and His Treatment," in H. H. Toch (ed.), *Legal and Criminal Psychology*, New York: Holt, Rinehart & Winston, 1961, pp. 381–399.
6. R. E. Banay, "Alcoholism and Crime," *Quarterly Journal of Studies on Alcohol*, 2 (1942), 686–716.
7. J. McDonald, *The Murderer and His Victim*, Springfield: Charles C. Thomas, 1961.
8. L. M. Shupe, "Alcohol and Crime," *Journal of Criminal Law and Criminology*, 44 (1954), 661–664.
9. I. Chein, *et. al. The Road to H*, New York: Basic Books, 1964.
10. R. McGee, *Social Disorganization in America*, San Francisco: Chandler, 1962.
11. H. S. Becker, "Becoming a Marijuana User," *American Journal of Sociology*, 59 (1953), 235–242.
12. R. H. Felix, "An Appraisal of the Personality Type of the Addict," *American Journal of Psychiatry*, 100 (1944), 462–467.

13. A. Wikler, *Opiate Addiction,* Springfield: Charles C Thomas, 1953.
14. C. Winick, "The Drug Addict and His Treatment, in Toch (ed.), *Legal and Criminal Psychology, op. cit.,* pp. 357–380.
15. I. Chein, *et al. op cit.*
16. E. Goffman, *Asylums,* Garden City: Doubleday, 1961.
17. I. Bellknap, *Human Problems of a State Mental Hospital,* New York: McGraw-Hill, 1961.
18. W. A. Lunden, *Facts on Crimes and Criminals,* Ames, Iowa: Art Press, p. 101.
19. B. M. Carmiet, *et al.* "Criminal Process and Emotional Growth," in D. E. Cameron (ed.), *International Psychiatry Clinics, Forensic Psychiatry and Child Psychiatry,* Vol. 2, Boston: Little Brown, 1965, pp. 3–41.
20. Sir N. W. East, *Society and the Criminal,* Springfield: Charles C Thomas, 1951.

## Chapter 12. Crime as Reaction

1. A. Noyes, *Modern Clinical Psychiatry,* Philadelphia: Saunders, 6th Edition, 1963.
2. D. Abrahamsen, *The Psychology of Crime,* New York: Columbia University Press, 1960.
3. P. L. Pinel, *A Treatise on Insanity,* translated by D. D. Davis, London: W. Todd, 1806.
4. C. Lombroso, *The Man of Genius,* London: Walter Scott, 1891.
5. W. G. Lennox, *Epilepsy and Related Disorders,* Vol. 2, Boston: Little Brown, 1960.
6. C. H. Alstrom, *A Study of Epilepsy in Its Clinical, Social and Genetic Aspects,* Copenhagen: Munksgaard, 1950.
7. A. O. Kellog, "Epilepsy and Its Relation to Insanity," *Journal of Psychological Medicine,* 6 (1872), 651–664.
8. E. A. Walker, "Murder or Epilepsy," *Journal of Nervous and Mental Diseases,* 133:5 (1961), 430–437.
9. *Ibid.*
10. E. D. Schwade and S. Geiger, "Abnormal Electroencephalographic Findings in Severe Behavior Diseases," *Diseases of the Nervous System,* 17 (1956), 307.
11. F. A. Gibbs and E. L. Gibbs, "Thalamic and Hypothalamic Epilepsy," in *Atlas of Electroencephalography,* Vol. 2, *Epilepsy,* Cambridge: Addison-Wesley Press, 1952.
12. S. Woods, "Adolescent Violence and Homicide," *Archives of General Psychiatry,* 5 (1961), 528–534.
13. G.. H. Glaser, *EEG and Behavior,* New York: Basic Books, 1963, p. 327.
14. O. Diethelm, "Panic," *Archives of Neurology and Psychiatry,* 28 (1932), 1153–1168.
15 . J. F. Bateman, "The Manic State as an Emergency Defense Reaction," *Journal of Nervous and Mental Diseases,* 119 (1954), 349–357.
16. J. R. Ewalt and D. L. Farnsworth, *Textbook of Psychiatry,* New York: McGraw-Hill, 1963.

17. A. E. Fireman, "The Pre-Acute Crime Milieu," *Archives of Criminal Psychodynamics,* 4 (1961), 269–284.
18. K. A. Menninger, *Man Against Himself,* New York: Harcourt, Brace, 1938.
19. J. M. MacDonald, "Suicide and Homicide by Automobile," *American Journal of Psychiatry,* 121 (1964), 366–370.

## Chapter 13. Sex Crimes and Deviation

1. A. J. Bachrach, "Some Applications of Operant Conditioning to Behavior Therapy," in J. Wolpe *et al.* (eds.), *The Conditioning Therapies,* New York: Holt, Rinehart & Winston, 1964.
2. S. L. Halleck, "Emotional Effects of Victimization," in R. Slovenko (ed.), *Sexual Behavior and the Law,* Springfield: Charles C. Thomas, 1965, pp. 673–686.
3. B. Karman, *The Sexual Offender and His Offenses,* New York: Julian Press, 1954.
4. I. Bieber, *et al.,* Homosexuality, New York: Basic Books, 1962.
5. R. Fine, "Psychoanalytic Theory of Sexuality," in R. Slovenko (ed.), *Sexual Behavior and the Law, op. cit.,* pp. 147–167.
6. M. Boss, "The Case History of a Sadistic Pervert," in *Psychoanalysis and Daseinsanalysis,* New York: Basic Books, 1963.
7. Discussed in M. Boss, *Meaning and Content of Sexual Perversions,* New York: Grune & Stratton, 1949.
8. J. Genêt, *Our Lady of the Flowers,* New York: Bantam Books, 1964.
9. O. Fenichel, *Psychoanalytic Theory of the Neuroses,* New York: W. W. Norton, 1945.
10. A. C. Kinsey *et al., Sexual Behavior in the Human Male,* Philadelphia: Saunders, 1948.
11. P. H. Gebhard *et al., Sex Offenders,* New York: Hoeber-Harper, 1965.
12. B. Karpman, *op. cit.*
13. M. S. Guttmacher, *Sex Offenses: The Problem, Cause and Prevention,* New York: W. W. Norton, 1961.
14. G. W. Henry, *Sex Variants,* New York: Hoeber-Harper, 1948.
15. I. Bieber, *et al., op. cit.*
16. J. Rechy, *City of Night,* New York: Grove Press, 1963.
17. A. Aldrich, *We Walk Alone,* New York: Fawcett Publication, 1959.
18. J. Genêt, *A Thief's Diary,* New York: Bantam Books, 1964.
19. J. Money, "Hermaphroditism, Gender and Precocity in Hyper Adrenocorticism," *Bulletin of the Johns Hopkins Hospital,* 97 (1955), 253–273.
20. E. Knight, "Overt Male Homosexuality," in R. Slovenko (ed.), *Sexual Behavior and the Law, op. cit.,* pp. 434–461.
21. I. Bieber, *et al., op. cit.*
22. E. Bergler, *Homosexuality, Disease or Way of Life,* New York: Hill & Wang, 1956.
23. M. L. Enelow, "Exhibitionism, Voyeurism and Transvestism, in R. Slovenko (ed.), *Sexual Behavior and the Law, op. cit.,* pp. 478–486.
24. B. C. Glueck, Jr., "Pedophilia," in *ibid.,* pp. 539–562.

25. J. T. Landis, "Experience of 500 Children with Adult Sexual Deviation," *Psychiatric Quarterly,* Suppplement 30 (1956), 91–109.
26. A. W. Epstein, "Fetichism," in R. Slovenko (ed.), *Sexual Behavior and the Law, op cit.,* pp. 515–520.
27. S. Freud, "Three Contributions to the Theory of Sex," A. A. Brill (ed.), *The Collected Writings of Sigmund Freud,* New York: Modern Library, 1938.
28. Gebhard, *et al., op cit.*
29. *Ibid* and M. L. Enlow, *op. cit.*
30. E. Bergler, *The Basic Neurosis,* New York: Grune & Stratton, 1948.
31. B. Karpman, "The Psychopathology of Exhibitionism," *Psychoanalytic Review,* 13 (1926), 63–97.
32. N. D. C. Lewis, "Pathological Fire Setting and Sexual Motivation," in R. Slovenko (ed.), *Sexual Behavior and the Law, op. cit.,* pp. 627–642.

## Chapter 14. The Choice of Crime

1. H. J. Eysenck, *Crime and Personality,* Boston: Houghton Mifflin, 1954.
2. K. Friedlander, "Formation of the Antisocial Character," *Psychoanalytic Study of the Child,* 1 (1945), 189–204.
3. A. Aichorn, *Wayward Youth,* New York: Viking Press, 1935.
4. J. Bowlby, *Maternal Care and Mental Health,* Monograph Series, No. 2, Geneva, World Health Organization, 1951.
5. A. Bandura and R. H. Walters, *Adolescent Aggression,* New York: Ronald Press, 1959.
6. L. Berkowitz, *Aggression: A Social Psychological Analysis,* New York: McGraw-Hill, 1962.
7. E. Sutherland and D. Cressey, *Principles of Criminology,* sixth edition, New York, Lippincott, 1960.
8. R. Korn and L. McKorkle, *Criminology and Penology,* New York: Henry Holt, 1959.
9. H. von Hentig, *The Criminal and His Victim,* New Haven: Yale University Press, 1948.
10. W. Reckless, *The Crime Problem,* New York: Appleton-Century-Crofts, 1950.
11. D. R. Cressey, *Other People's Money,* New York: Free Press, 1953.

## Chapter 15. The Psychiatrist and the Legal Process

1. *Holloway* vs. *U.S.,* 148 F. 2d 665 (D.C. Cir. 1945), p. 666.
2. S. Rubin, *Psychiatry and Criminal Law,* Dobbs Ferry, New York: Oceana Publications, 1965.
3. J. Biggs, *The Guilty Mind,* New York: Harcourt Brace, 1955.
4. H. J. Eysenck, *Crime and Personality,* Boston: Houghton Mifflin, 1964.
5. R. Waelder, "Psychic Determinism and the Possibility of Prediction," *Psychoanalytic Quarterly,* 32 (1963), 15–42.
6. G. Zilboorg and G. W. Henry, *History of Medical Psychology,* New York: W. W. Norton, 1941.

7. T. Szasz, "Criminal Responsibility and Psychiatry," in H. Toch (ed.), *Legal and Criminal Psychology,* New York: Holt, Rinehart & Winston, 1961, pp. 146–168.
8. G. Williams, *The Criminal Law,* London: Stevens & Sons, 1950.
9. N. Reider, "The Demonology of Modern Psychiatry," *American Journal of Psychiatry,* 111 (1955), 851–856.
10. G. Zilboorg, *The Psychology of the Criminal Act and Punishment,* New York, Harcourt Brace, 1954
11. F. Alexander and H. Staub, *The Criminal, the Judge and the Public,* New York: Free Press, 1956.
12. E. Glover, *The Roots of Crime,* New York: International Universities Press, 1960.
13. S. Freud, "Moral Responsibility for the Content of Dreams," in *19 Complete Psychological Works of Sigmund Freud,* 19, p. 131 (Stanford ed., 1961).
14. C. Rogers, "Client Centered Therapy," *Scientific American,* 187 (1952), 66–74.
15. M. Boss, *Psychoanalysis and Daseinsanalysis,* New York: Basic Books, 1963.
16. Daniel M'Naghton's Case, 10 Cloth and Fin., 200, 210, 8, Eng. Rep. 718, 722, 1843.
17. D. Abrahamsen, *Crime and the Human Mind,* New York: Columbia University Press, 1944.
18. E. Glover, "Notes on the M'Naghton Rules," *British Journal of Delinquency,* 1 (1951), 276–282.
19. D. W. Louisell and B. L. Diamond, "Law & Psychiatry: Détente, Entente or Concomitance?," *Cornell Law Quarterly,* 50 (1965), 217–234.
20. S. Glueck, *Mental Disorder and the Criminal Law,* Boston: Little Brown, 1925.
21. W. Overholser, "Major Principles of Forensic Psychiatry," in S. Arieti, *et al.* (eds.), *American Handbook of Psychiatry,* Vol. 2, New York: Basic Books, 1959.
22. B. L. Diamond, "Criminal Responsibility of the Mentally Ill., *Stanford Law Review,* 14 (1961), 60–61.
23. *Durham* vs. *U.S.,* 214 F. 2d 862 (D.C. Cir. 1954).
24. J. Hall, "Mental Disease and Criminal Responsibility, M'Naghton vs. Durham," *Indiana Law Journal,* 33 (1958), 212–225.
25. E. De Grazia, "The Distinction of Being Mad," *University of Chicago Law Review,* 22 (1955), 339–355.
26. T. S. Szasz, "Psychiatry, Ethics and the Criminal Law," *Columbia Law Review,* 58 (1958), 183–198.
27. C. Savage, "Discussion of Watson's Article, 'Durham Plus Five Years,'" *American Journal of Psychiatry,* 116 (1959), 295–297.
28. S. Rubin, *op. cit.*
29. S. L. Halleck, "Juvenile Delinquents; "Sick" or "Bad"?", *Social Work,* 7 (1962), 58–61.
30. S. Rubin, *op. cit.*

31. J. Hall, "The Scientific and Humane Study of Criminal Law," *Boston University Law Review* 42 (1962), 267–280.
32. T. S. Szasz, *Law, Liberty and Psychiatry*, New York: Macmillan, 1963.
33. See S. Rubin, *op. cit.*, for review of these alternative proposals.
34. *State* vs. *Esser*, 16 Wis. 2d. 567, 115 N.W. 2d. 505 (1962).
35. R. Waelder, "Psychiatry and the Problem of Criminal Responsibility," *University of Pennsylvania Law Review*, 101 (1952), 378–390.
36. E. De Grazia, *op. cit.*
37. J. Hall, "The Scientific and Humane Study of Criminal Law," *op. cit.*
38. M. Hakeem, "A Critique of the Psychiatric Approach to Crime and Correction," *Law and Contemporary Problems*, 23 (1958), 650–682.
39. T. Szasz, "Psychiatric Expert Testimony, Its Covert Meaning and Social Function," *Psychiatry*, 20 (1957), 313–316.
40. K. A. Menninger, "Verdict Guilty, Now What?," *Harper's Magazine*, August, 1959.
41. P. Roche, *The Criminal Mind*, New York: Farrar, Straus & Cudahy, 1958.
42. W. Haines, "The Future of Court Psychiatry," in R. W. Nice (ed.), *Criminal Psychology*, New York: Philosophical Library, 1962, pp. 268–282.
43. D. C. Cameron, "Did He Do It? If So, How Should He Be Managed?," *Proceedings of Midwest Governors' Conference Workshop on the Mentallly Disordered Offender*, 1964.
44. J. Biggs, "Procedures for Handling the Mentally Ill Offender in Some European Countries," *Temple Law Quarterly*, 29 (1956), 254–263.
45. J. H. Hess and H. E. Thomas "Incompentency to Stand Trial, Procedures, Results and Problems," *American Journal of Psychiatry*, 119 (1963), 713–720.
46. T. S. Szasz, *Law, Liberty and Psychiatry*, *op. cit.*
47. S. Rubin, *op. cit.*

## Chapter 16. Control and Treatment

1. F. Wertham, "Psychoauthoritarianism and the Law," *University of Chicago Law Review*, 22 (1955), 336–338.
2. A. Auerbach, "The Anti-Mental Health Movement," *American Journal of Psychiatry*, 120 (1963), 105–111.
3. T. S. Szasz, "Psychiatry's Threat to Civil Liberties," *National Review*, 14: 1963.
4. T. S. Szasz, "Politics and Mental Health," *American Journal of Psychiatry*, 115 (1958), 508–511.
5. S. De Grazia, *Errors in Psychotherapy*, Garden City, New York: Doubleday, 1952.
6. E. De Grazia, "The Distinction of Being Mad," *University of Chicago Law Review*, 22 (1955) 339–355.

## Chapter 17. Nonpenological Roles

1. A. E. Fink, *Causes of Crime*, New York: A. S. Barnes, Perpetua Edition, 1938.

2. M. S. Guttmacher and H. Weihofen, *Psychiatry and the Law,* New York: W. W. Norton, 1952.
3. M. S. Guttmacher, *The Mind of the Murderer,* New York: Farrar, Straus & Cudahy, 1960.
4. M. S. Guttmacher, "Adult Court Psychiatry Clinics," *American Journal of Psychiatry,* 106 (1950), 881–888.
5. S. L. Halleck and M. H. Miller, "The Psychiatric Consultation," *American Journal of Psychiatry,* 120 (1963), 164–169.
6. D. H. Russel, "Division of Legal Medicine, Massachusetts Court Clinic Program," *Annual Report, Journal of Offender Therapy.* 8 (1964), 14–17.
7. H. Weihofen, "Institutional Treatment of Persons Acquitted by Reason of Insanity," *Texas Law Review,* 38 (1960), 849–869.
8. D. W. Stearns, "Concepts of Limited Responsibility," *Federal Probation,* 18 (1954), 20–25.
9. B. L. Diamond, "Criminal Responsibility of the Mentally Ill," *Stanford Law Review,* 14 (1961), 88.
10. M. Jones, *The Therapeutic Community,* New York: Basic Books, 1953.
11. A. E. Elliott, "A Group Treatment Program for Mentally Ill Offenders," *Crime and Delinquency,* 12 (1966), 29–37.
12. S. Rubin, *Psychiatry and Criminal Law,* Dobbs Ferry, New York: Oceana Publications, 1965, pp. 37–39.
13. R. J. Thurrell, S. L. Halleck and A. F. Johnson, "Psychosis in Prison," *Journal of Criminal Law, Criminology and Police Science,* 56 (1965), 271–276.
14. S. L. Halleck and A. R. Pacht, "Current Status of the Wisconsin State Sex Crimes Law," *Wisconsin Bar Bulletin,* December, 1960.
15. E. Sutherland, "The Diffusion of Sexual Psychopath Laws," *American Journal of Sociology,* 56 (1950), 142.
16. Report No. 9, *Psychiatrically Deviated Sex Offenders,* New York: Group for the Advancement of Psychiatry, 1949, revised, February, 1950.
17. A. Ellis, and R. Brancale, *The Psychology of Sex Offenders,* Springfield: Charles C. Thomas, 1956.
18. A. Ellis, "The Sex Offender and His Treatment," in H. Toch (ed.), *Legal and Criminal Psychology,* New York: Holt, Rinehart & Winston, 1961, pp. 400–416.
19. *Wisconsin's First Eleven Years of Experience with Its Sex Crimes Law,* Statistical Bulletin, Wisconsin Department of Public Welfare, April, 1965.
20. M. Coogan, "Wisconsin's Experience in Treating Psychiatrically Deviated Sex Offenders," *Journal of Social Therapy,* 3 (1955), 6.
21. A. Pacht, S. Halleck and J. Ehrmann, "Diagnosis and Treatment of the Sex Offender, A Nine Year Study," *American Journal of Psychiatry,* 118 (1962), 802–808.
22. N. Showstack, "Preliminary Report on Psychiatric Treatment of Prisoners at the California Medical Facility," *American Journal of Psychiatry,* 112 (1956), 821–824.
23. F. H. Ernst and W. C. Keating, "Psychiatric Treatment of the California Felon," *American Journal of Psychiatry,* 120 (1964), 974–979.

24. H. M. Boslow and W. Kohlmeyer, "The Maryland Defective Delinquency Law," *American Journal of Psychiatry,* 120 (1963), 118–124.
25. H. Boslow and S. Manne, "Mental Health in Action," *Crime and Delinquency,* 12 (1956), 22–28.
26. Commission to Study and Re-evaluate the Patuxent Institution. *Report to Legislative Council of the General Assembly of Maryland,* January 25, 1961.
27. A. R. Lindesmith, "The British System of Narcotics Control," *Law and Contemporary Problems,* 22 (1957), 138–154.
28. H. J. Anslinger and W. F. Tompkins, *The Traffic in Narcotics,* New York: Funk & Wagnalls, 1953.
29. Discussed in C. Winick, "The Drug Addict and His Treatment," in H. Toch (ed.), *Legal and Criminal Psychology,* New York: Holt, Rinehart & Winston, p. 371; and in S. Rubin, *Psychiatry and Criminal Law,* Dobbs Ferry, New York: Oceana Publications, 1965, p. 119.
30. D. C. Cameron, "Addiction—Current Issues," *American Journal of Psychiatry,* 120 (1963), 313–319.
31. K. Menninger, "Are Policemen Supermen?," in *A Psychiatrist's World,* New York: Viking Press, 1959, pp. 749–756.

## Chapter 18. Psychiatry and the Juvenile Delinquent

1. E. Davidoff and E. S. Joetzel, *The Child Guidance Approach to Juvenile Delinquency,* New York: Child Care Publications, 1951.
2. W. W. Wattenberg, "Psychologists and Juvenile Delinquency," in H. Toch (ed.), *Legal and Criminal Psychology,* New York: Holt, Rinehart & Winston, 1961, pp. 243–270.
3. R. W. Alexander, "Of Juvenile Court Justice and Judges," in *1947 Yearbook of the National Probation and Parole Association,* New York, 1948, p. 189.
4. P. Tappan, *Juvenile Delinquency,* New York: McGraw-Hill, 1949.
5. O. W. Ketcham, "The Unfulfilled Promise of the Juvenile Court," *Crime and Delinquency,* 7 (1961), 97–130.
6. L. Diana, "The Rights of Juvenile Delinquents; An Appraisal of Juvenile Court Procedures," *Journal of Criminal Law, Criminology and Police Science,* 47 (1957), 561–569.
7. D. Matza, "Delinquency and Drift," New York: John Wiley & Sons, 1964.
8. S. L. Halleck, "The Impact of Professional Dishonesty on Behavior of Disturbed Adolescents," *Social Work,* 8 (1963), 48–53.
9. S. L. Halleck, "The Criminal's Problem with Psychiatry," *Psychiatry,* 23:4 (November, 1960), 409–412.
10. J. Bowlby, "A Note on Mother-Child Separation as a Mental Health Hazard," *British Journal of Medical Psychology,* 31 (1958), 247–248.
11. G. Engel, F. Reichsman and H. Segal, "A Study of an Infant with Gastric Fistula in Behavior and the Rate of Total Hydrochloric Acid Secretion," *Psychosomatic Medicine,* 18 (October, 1956), 374–398.
12. H. Harlow, "The Nature of Love," *American Psychologist,* 13 (1958), 673–685.

13. I. Kaufman, "The Psychiatrist in the Institution," *Crime and Delinquency,* 12 (1966), 12–21.
14. S. L. Halleck, "A Role of the Psychiatrist in Residential Treatment of the Delinquent," *Journal of Social Therapy,* 4 (1958), 1–6.
15. M. C. Greco and S. C. Wright, "The Correctional Institution in the Etiology of Chronic Homosexuality," *American Journal of Orthopsychiatry,* 14 (1944), 295–307.
16. S. L. Halleck and M. Hersko, "Homosexual Behavior in a Correctional Institution for Adolescent Girls," *American Journal of Orthopsychiatry,* 32 (1962), 911–917.

## Chapter 19. Psychiatric Service in Prison

1. D. C. Gibbons, "Who Knows About Corrections?" *Crime and Delinquency,* 9 (1963), 137–144.
2. H. E. Barnes and N. K. Tecter, *New Horizons in Criminology,* New York: Prentice-Hall, 1952.
3. A. C. Schnur, "Current Practices in Correction, a Critique," in H. Toch (ed.), *Legal and Criminal Psychology,* New York: Holt, Rinehart & Winston, 1961.
4. K. Menninger, 'What's Wrong with Our Prisons," *Plain Talk* 7 (1930), 175–182.
5. H. Powelson and A. Bendix, "Psychiatry in Prison," *Psychiatry,* 14 (February, 1951), 73–86.
6. J. B. Martin, *Break Down the Walls,* New York: Ballantine Books, 1954.
7. G. M. Sykes, *The Society of Captives,* Princeton: Princeton University Press, 1958.
8. D. Cressey, "Limitation on the Organization of Treatment in the Modern Prison," in *Theoretical Studies of Social Organization of the Prison,* New York Social Science Research Council, 1960, pp. 78–110.
9. B. Cormier, *et al.,* "Criminal Process and Emotional Growth," in E. Cameron (ed.), *International Psychiatric Clinics,* Boston: Little Brown, 1965, pp. 3–41.
10. R. J. Thurrel, S. L. Halleck and A. F. Johnson, "Psychosis in Prison," *Journal of Criminal Law, Criminology and Police Science,* 56 (1965), 271–276.
11. P. Solomon, *et al.* (eds.), *Sensory Deprivation,* Cambridge: Harvard University Press, 1961.
12. A. Pacht and S. Halleck, "Mental Health Programs in Correction," *Crime and Delinquency,* 12 (1966), 1–8.
13. L. N. Shapiro, "Psychiatry in the Correctional Process," *Crime and Delinquency,* 12 (1966), 9–16.
14. G. M. Sykes, *op. cit.*
15. C. R. Keith and R. A. Stamm, "The Use of the Prison Code as a Defense," *Bulletin of the Menninger Clinic,* 28 (1964), 251–259.
16. N. Graff, "Experiences in a Prison Hospital," *Bulletin of the Menninger Clinic,* 20 (1956), 85–92.

## Chapter 20. Evaluating the Offender


1. A. Ludwig, *The Importance of Lying,* Springfield: Charles C. Thomas, 1965.
2. J. Haley, *Strategies of Psychotherapy,* New York: Grune & Stratton, 1963.
3. J. M. MacDonald, *Psychiatry and the Criminal,* Springfield: Charles C. Thomas, 1958.
4. K. Eissler, "Malingering," in G. Wilbur and W. Muensterberger (eds.), *Psychoanalysis and Culture,* New York: International Universities Press, 1951, pp. 218–253.
5. J. M. MacDonald, *The Murderer and His Victim,* Springfield: Charles C. Thomas, 1961.
6. H. A. Davidson, *Forensic Psychiatry,* New York: Ronald Press, 1952.
7. D. C. Gibbons, *Changing the Law Breaker,* New York: Prentice-Hall, 1965.
8. A. Ludwig, *op. cit.*
9. S. L. Halleck, "The Initial Interview with the Offender," *Federal Probation,* 25 (1961), 23–27.
10. V. E. Mazzanti and H. Bessell, "Communication Through the Latent Language," *American Journal of Psychotherapy,* 10 (1956), 250–260.
11. F. H. McClintock, *Crimes of Violence, an Enquiry by the Cambridge Institute of Criminology,* London: Macmillan, 1963.
12. M. Wolfgang, "A Sociological Analysis of Criminal Homicide," *Federal Probation,* 25 (1961), 48–55.
13. S. Palmer, *A Study of Murder,* New York: Thomas Crowell, 1960.
14. G. M. Woddis, "Depression and Crime," *British Journal of Delinquency,* 8 (1957), 85–94.
15. J. Lankron, "Murder and Insanity: A Survey," *American Journal of Psychiatry,* 119 (1963), 756–758.
16. W. Bromberg, *The Mold of Murder,* New York: Grune & Stratton, 1961.
17. W. L. Neustatter, *The Mind of the Murderer,* New York: Philosophical Library, 1957.
18. M. S. Guttmacher, *The Mind of the Murderer,* New York: Farrar, Straus & Cudahy, 1960.
19. J. J. Brennan, "Mentally Ill Aggressiveness, Popular Delusion or Reality," *American Journal of Psychiatry,* 120 (1964), 1181–1184.
20. J. E. Rappeport and G. Lassen, "Dangerousness—Arrest Rate Comparisons of Discharged Patients and the General Population," *American Journal of Psychiatry,* 121 (1965), 776–781.
21. J. M. MacDonald, "The Threat to Kill," *American Journal of Psychiatry* 120 (1963), 125–130.
22. J. Satten *et al.,* "Murder Without Apparent Motive: A Study in Personality Disorganization," *American Journal of Psychiatry,* 116 (1960), 48–53.
23. G. C. Curtis, "Violence Breeds Violence? Perhaps," *American Journal of Psychiatry,* 120 (1963), 386–387.
24. G. M. Duncan *et al.,* Etiological Factors in First Degree Murder," *Journal of the American Medical Association,* 168 (1958), 1755–1758.

25. M. E. Wolfgang, *Patterns in Criminal Homicide,* Philadelphia: University of Pennsylvania, 1958.
26. M. E. Wolfgang and R. Strohm, "The Relationship Between Alcohol and Criminal Homicide," *Quarterly Journal of Studies on Alcohol,* 17 (1956), 411–425.
27. B. M. Cormier, "Psychodynamics of Homicide Committed in a Marital Relationship," *Journal of Social Therapy,* 8 (1962), 187–194.
28. N. Blackman, J. Weiss and J. Lamberti, "The Sudden Murderer, III, Clues to Preventive Interaction," *Archives of General Psychiatry,* 8 (1963), 289–294.
29. A. F. Henry and J. F. Short, *Suicide and Homicide,* New York: Free Press, 1964.
30. O. Fenichel, *The Psychoanalytic Theory of Neurosis,* New York: W. W. Norton, 1945.

## Chapter 21. Psychotherapy

1. L. R. Wolberg, *The Techniques of Psychotherapy,* New York: Grune & Stratton, 1954.
2. J. G. Watkins, "Psychotherapeutic Methods," in B. Wolman (ed.), *Handbook of Clinical Psychology,* New York: McGraw-Hill, 1965, pp. 1143–1167.
3. H. S. Eysenck, *Behavior Therapy and the Neuroses,* New York: Pergamon Press, 1960.
4. J. Wolpe, A. Salter and L. J. Reyna, (eds.), *The Conditioning Therapies,* New York: Holt, Rinehart & Winston, 1964.
5. H. I. Kalish, "Behavior Therapy," in B. Wolman, *op. cit.,* pp. 1230–1253.
6. H. J. Eysenck, *Crime and Personality,* Boston: Houghton Mifflin, 1964.
7. *Ibid.*
8. F. Alexander and T. M. French, *Psychoanalytic Therapy,* New York: Ronald Press, 1946.
9. F. Fromm-Reichmann, *Principles of Intensive Psychotherapy,* Chicago: University of Chicago Press, 1950.
10. K. A. Menninger, *Theory of Psychoanalytic Technique,* New York: Basic Books, 1955.
11. C. Harari and J. Chwast "Class Bias in Psychodiagnosis of Delinquents," *Crime and Delinquency,* 10 (1964), 145–156.
12. A. Aichorn, *Wayward Youth,* New York: Viking Press, 1938.
13. F. Redl and D. Wineman, *The Aggressive Child,* New York: Free Press, 1957.
14. L. W. McCorkle, "The Present Status of Group Therapy in United States Correctional Institutions," *International Journal of Group Psychotherapy,* 3 (1953), 85.
15. S. R. Slavson, *A Textbook in Analytic Group Psychotherapy,* New York: International Universities Press, 1964.
16. J. A. Johnson, *Group Therapy, a Practical Approach,* New York: McGraw-Hill, 1963.

17. M. Rosenbaum, "Group Psychotherapy and Psychodrama," in B. Wolman, *op. cit.*, pp. 1254–1273.
18. R. Korn and L. W. McCorkle, *Criminology and Penology*, New York: Henry Holt, 1959, p. 569.
19. N. Fenton, "The Prison as a Therapeutic Community," *Federal Probation*, 20 (1956), 26–29.
20. N. Fenton, *An Introduction to Group Counseling in State Correctional Service*, New York: The American Correctional Association, 1958.
21. L. W. McCorkle, A. Elias and F. L. Bixby, *The Highfields Story*, New York: Henry Holt, 1957.
22. N. W. Ackerman, *The Psychodynamics of Family Life*, New York: Basic Books, 1958.
23. I. Boszormenyi-Nagy and J. L. Framo (eds.), *Intensive Family Therapy*, New York: Hoeber-Harper, 1965.
24. L. H. Gliedman *et al.*, "Group Therapy of Alcoholics with Concurrent Group Meetings of Their Wives," *Quarterly Journal of Studies on Alcohol*, 17 (1956), 655–670.

## Chapter 22. Humane and Rational Criminology

1. T. Szasz, *Law, Liberty and Psychiatry*, New York: Macmillan, 1963.
2. The Model Sentencing Act, Advisory Council of Judges of the National Council on Crime and Delinquency, New York, 1963.
3. S. Rubin, *Psychiatry and Criminal Law*, Dobbs Ferry, New York: Oceana Publications, 1965.

# INDEX